CONTENTS

DINNER

MEAT 116

SPECIAL RECIPES **185**

INTRODUCTION

Diabetes is a disease that affects many people, and there are those of us who have to deal with it daily. Having diabetes can be difficult for a number of reasons. For one, you have to constantly watch what you eat, and that can get very tedious. As a matter of fact, you have to be very careful with the amount of carbohydrates you eat as well. It can take a toll on your health if you are not careful, and it can also alter your moods, which is never good. In order to control diabetes and its many side effects, you have to make sure you have a healthy diet plan that is easy to follow.

Oral Rehydration Solution-Orals (ORS) is a solution used to avoid dehydration in the patient. In many cases, dehydration happens as a result of vomiting and diarrhea. Diabetics may notice dehydration only when their urine becomes darker in color.

One thing that affects the blood sugar level of diabetic patients is their diet. People who have diabetes should stay away from foods that are high glycemic index (g.i.) foods such as those that are corn, wheat, and rice based because these foods can raise blood sugar levels quickly. Low glycemic index foods include all fruits which means that you can eat them without your blood sugar levels going up quickly. Foods such as Greek yogurt tend to have lower g.i. rating so if you are diabetic and have to avoid high g.i. foods, Greek yogurt can be your best friend.

There are many different ways that people can treat diabetes, however the one thing that could be done to help most with diabetes would be to lower it through diet and exercise. Both of these things will work with the other to help lower your blood sugar level. In order to lower your blood sugar level as far as possible, a look at your diet is important because what you eat greatly affects how your blood sugar levels work out. The way in which you maintain your weight also plays an important role in how well your diabetes works and could have a positive effect on it as well.

Whatever the connotations of diet and diabetes, it is important to understand that there are not many things that you can do to treat the disease. What you can do is try to manage it as best as possible with a healthy diet, and then get plenty of exercise. Not only should you deal with your diabetes through treatment, but you should also make sure that it does not cause other health problems such as high cholesterol levels or risk for heart disease.

There are many different ways to treat diabetes, however the one thing that could be done to help most with diabetes would be to lower it through diet and exercise. Both of these things will work with the other to help lower your blood sugar level. In order to lower your blood sugar level as far as possible, a look at your diet is important because what you eat greatly affects how your blood sugar levels work out. The way in which you maintain your weight also plays an important role in how well your diabetes works and could have a positive effect on it as well.

Because diabetes is mainly caused by lifestyle factors, it is essential to manage the disease through proper diet and exercise. Diet and exercise together can ensure that you have a healthy weight which will help prevent the high blood glucose levels that come with diabetes. Your physician will be able to tell you more about the appropriate diet for yourself, but here are some general guidelines:

1. If you are overweight, you should lose weight. If you are not overweight but have excess fat, you should avoid gaining weight or maintain your current weight. This can be done through portion control and choosing healthy foods. An additional way to lose weight is through exercise.

2. For the main part, a healthy balanced diet can help with diabetes. A healthy mix of carbohydrates, proteins and fats is usually recommended for people with diabetes. Many people have found that eating foods that contain a lot of fiber lowers their blood glucose levels substantially which is partially why many diabetic diets focus on foods such as whole grain breads and cereals.

3. It is important to not avoid sugar completely when you are trying to treat diabetes. While sugar can be part of a diet that is healthy for people with diabetes, it should be used in moderation. Baked goods made with whole grains and low on the glycemic scale are fine, as are fruits and fresh vegetables which contain natural sugars.

4. Continue to maintain your weight, if you are overweight or obese. Exercising regularly while watching what you eat will help you stay at a healthy weight and will also help your blood sugar levels stay under control since the food that you eat will remain in a normal ranges instead of going high or low.

5. Take your medications on time as instructed by your physician. Sometimes, people need to take extra insulin in order to help keep blood sugar levels controlled. If you are not taking your medication on time, this could cause your blood glucose levels to go up.

Regardless of how you choose to manage diabetes, it is important that you know how to keep yourself healthy and eat a balanced diet while also exercising regularly. By eating healthy and exercising regularly, you can ensure that your diabetes will work effectively and do not have any other unexpected side effects such as high cholesterol and heart disease.

BREAKFAST

Scallion Sandwich

Preparation Time: 10 minutes
Cooking Time: 10 minutes
Servings: 1
Ingredients:
- 2 slices of wheat bread
- 2 teaspoons butter, low fat
- 2 scallions, sliced thinly
- 1 tablespoon of parmesan cheese, grated
- 3/4 cup of cheddar cheese, reduced-fat, grated

Directions:
1. Preheat the Air fryer to 356 degrees.
2. Spread butter on a slice of bread. Place inside the cooking basket with the butter side facing down.
3. Place cheese and scallions on top. Spread the rest of the butter on the other slice of bread Put it on top of the sandwich and sprinkle with parmesan cheese.
4. Cook for 10 minutes.

Nutrition: Calorie: 154 Carbohydrate: 9g Fat: 2.5g Protein: 8.6g Fiber: 2.4g

Lean Lamb and Turkey Meatballs with Yogurt

Preparation Time: 10 minutes
Cooking Time: 10 minutes
Servings: 4
Ingredients:
- 1 egg white
- 4 ounces ground lean turkey
- 1 pound of lean ground lamb
- 1 teaspoon both of cayenne pepper, ground coriander, red chili pastes, salt, and ground cumin
- 2 garlic cloves, minced
- 1 1/2 tablespoons parsley, chopped
- 1 tablespoon mint, chopped
- 1/4 cup of olive oil
- For the yogurt

- 2 tablespoons of buttermilk
- 1 garlic clove, minced
- 1/4 cup mint, chopped
- 1/2 cup of Greek yogurt, non-fat
- Salt to taste

Directions:
1. Set the Air Fryer to 390 degrees.
2. Blend all the ingredients for the meatballs in a bowl. Roll and mound them into golf-size round pieces. Arrange in the cooking basket.
3. Cook for 8 minutes.
4. While waiting, syndicate all the ingredients for the mint yogurt in a bowl. Mix well.
5. Serve the meatballs with the mint yogurt. Top with olives and fresh mint.

Nutrition: Calorie: 154 Carbohydrate: 9g Fat: 2.5g Protein: 8.6g Fiber: 2.4g

Air Fried Eggs

Preparation Time: 15 minutes
Cooking Time: 10 minutes
Servings: 4
Ingredients:
- 4 eggs
- 2 cups of baby spinach, rinsed
- 1 tablespoon of extra-virgin olive oil
- 1/2 cup of cheddar cheese, reduced-fat, shredded, divided
- Pinch of salt
- Pinch of pepper

Directions:
1. Preheat the Air Fryer to 350 degrees.
2. Warmth oil in a pan over medium-high flame. Cook the spinach until wilted. Drain the excess liquid. Put the cooked spinach into 4 greased ramekins.
3. Add a slice of bacon to each ramekin, crack an egg, and put cheese on top.
4. Season with salt and pepper.

5.   Put the ramekins inside the cooking basket of the Air Fryer.

6.   Cook for 15 minutes.

Nutrition Facts: Calorie: 106 Carbohydrate: 10g Fat: 3.2g Protein: 9.0g Fiber: 1.2g

Cinnamon Pancake

Preparation Time: 15 minutes

Cooking Time: 10 minutes

Servings: 4

Ingredients:

- 2 eggs
- 2 cups of cream cheese, reduced-fat
- ½ teaspoon cinnamon
- 1 pack Stevia

Directions:

1.   Preheat Air Fryer to 330 degrees F.

2.   Combine cream cheese, cinnamon, eggs, and stevia in a blender.

3.   Pour ¼ of the mixture in the Air fryer basket.

4.   Cook for 2 minutes on each side.

5.   Recap the process with the rest of the mixture. Serve.

Nutrition: Calorie: 106 Carbohydrate: 10g Fat: 3.2g Protein: 9.0g Fiber: 1.2g

Spinach and Mushrooms Omelet

Preparation Time: 15 minutes

Cooking Time: 10 minutes

Servings: 4

Ingredients:

- ½ cup spinach leaves
- 1 cup mushrooms
- 3 green onions
- 1 cup of water
- ½ teaspoon turmeric
- 1/2 red bell pepper
- 2 tablespoons butter, low fat
- 1 cup of almond flour
- ½ teaspoon onion powder
- ½ teaspoon garlic powder
- ½ teaspoon fresh ground black pepper
- ¼ teaspoon ground thyme
- 2 tablespoons extra virgin olive oil
- 1 teaspoon black salt
- Salsa, store-bought

Directions:

1.   Preheat the Air Fryer to 300 degrees.

2.   Rinse spinach leaves over tap water. Set aside.

3.   In a mixing bowl, combine green onions, onion powder, garlic powder, red bell pepper, mushrooms, turmeric, thyme, olive oil, salt, and pepper. Mix well.

4.   In another bowl, combine water and flour to form a smooth paste.

5.   In a pan, heat olive oil. Sauté peppers and mushrooms for 3 minutes. Tip in spinach and cook for 3 minutes. Set aside.

6.   In the affrayer basket, our Omelette batter. Cook for 3 minutes before flipping. Place vegetables on top. Season with salt. Serve with salsa on the side.

Nutrition: Calorie: 110 Carbohydrate: 9g Fat: 1.3g Protein: 5.4g Fiber: 1.0g

All Berries Pancakes

Preparation Time: 15 minutes

Cooking Time: 10 minutes

Servings: 4

Ingredients:

- ½ cup frozen blueberries, thawed
- ½ cup frozen cranberries, thawed
- 1 cup of coconut milk
- 2 Tbsp. coconut oil, for greasing
- 2 Tbsp. stevia
- 1 cup whole wheat flour, finely milled
- 1 Tbsp. baking powder
- 1 tsp. vanilla extract
- ¼ tsp. salt

Directions:

1.   Preheat Air Fryer to 330 degrees F.

2.   In a collaborating bowl, combine coconut oil, coconut milk, flour, stevia, baking powder, vanilla extract and salt. Gently fold in berries.

3.   Divide batter into equal portions. Pour into the Air fryer basket. Flip once the edges are set. Do not press down on pancakes.

4. Transfer to a plate. Sprinkle palm sugar. Serve.
Nutrition: Calorie: 57 Carbohydrate: 14g Fat: 0.3g
Protein: 0.7g
Fiber: 2.4g

Cinnamon Overnight Oats

Preparation Time: 5 minutes, plus overnight to refrigerate
Cooking Time: 0 minutes
Servings: 2
Ingredients:
- 2/3 cup unsweetened almond milk
- 2/3 cup rolled oats
- 1/2 apple, cored and finely chopped
- 2 tablespoons chopped walnuts
- 1 teaspoon cinnamon
- Pinch sea salt

Directions:
1. In a single-serving container or Mason jar, combine all of the ingredients and mix well.
2. Cover and refrigerate overnight.
Nutrition: Calories: 242 kcal Total Fat: 12g Saturated Fat: 1g Sodium: 97mg Carbohydrates: 30g Fiber: 6g Protein: 6g

Ham and Cheese English muffin Melt

Preparation Time: 10 minutes
Cooking Time: 5 minutes
Servings: 2
Ingredients:
- 1 whole-grain English muffin, split and toasted
- 2 teaspoons Dijon mustard
- 2 slices tomato
- 4 thin slices deli ham
- 1/2 cup shredded Cheddar cheese
- 2 large eggs, fried (optional)

Directions:
1. Preheat the oven broiler on high.
2. Spreads each toasted English muffin half with 1 teaspoon of mustard, and place them on a rimmed baking sheet, cut-side up.
3. Top each with a tomato slice and 2 slices of ham. Sprinkle each with half of the cheese.

4. Broil in the warmed oven until the cheese melts, 2 to 3 minutes.
5. Serve immediately, topped with a fried egg, if desired.
Nutrition: Calories: 234 kcal Total Fat: 13g Saturated Fat: 7g Sodium: 834mg Carbohydrates: 16g Fiber: 3g Protein: 16g

Asparagus Omelet

Preparation Time: 10 minutes
Cooking Time: 8 minutes
Servings: 2
Ingredients:
- 3 eggs
- 5 steamed asparagus tips
- 2 tablespoons of warm milk
- 1 tablespoon parmesan cheese, grated
- Salt and pepper to taste
- Non-stick cooking spray

Directions:
1. Mix in a large bowl, eggs, cheese, milk, salt and pepper then blend them. Spray a baking pan with non-stick cooking spray.
2. Relocation the egg mixture into the pan and add the asparagus, then place the pan inside the baking basket. Set air fryer to 320 Fahrenheit for 8-minutes. Serve warm.
Nutrition: Calories: 231 Total Fat: 9.2g Carbs: 8gProtein: 12.2g

Pumpkin Pie French toast

Preparation Time: 10 minutes
Cooking Time: 20 minutes
Servings: 4
Ingredients:
- 2 larges, beaten eggs
- 4 slices of cinnamon swirl bread
- ¼ cup milk
- ¼ cup pumpkin puree
- ¼ teaspoon pumpkin spices
- ¼ cup butter

Directions:

1. In a large mixing bowl, mix milk, eggs, pumpkin puree and pie spice. Whisk until mixture is smooth. In the egg mixture, dip the bread on both sides.

2. Place rack inside of air fryer's cooking basket. Place 2 slices of bread onto the rack. Set the temperature to 340 Fahrenheit for 10-minutes. Serve pumpkin pie toast with butter.

Nutrition: Calories: 212 Total Fat: 8.2g Carbs: 7g Protein: 11.3g

Breakfast Cheese Bread Cups

Preparation Time: 10 minutes
Cooking Time: 15 minutes
Servings: 2

Ingredients:
- 2 eggs
- 2 tablespoons cheddar cheese, grated
- Salt and pepper to taste
- 1 ham slice, cut into 2 pieces
- 4 bread slices, flatten with rolling pin

Directions:
1. Spray the inside of 2 ramekins with cooking spray. Place 2 flat pieces of bread into each ramekin. Add the ham slice pieces into each ramekin.

2. Crack an egg in each ramekin, then sprinkle with cheese. Season with salt and pepper. Place the ramekins into air fryer at 300 Fahrenheit for 15-minutes. Serve warm.

Nutrition: Calories: 162 Total Fat: 8g Carbs: 10g Protein: 11g

Breakfast Cod Nuggets

Preparation Time: 10 minutes
Cooking Time: 10 minutes
Servings: 4

Ingredients:
- 1 lb. Of cod
For breading:
- 2 eggs, beaten
- 2 tablespoons olive oil
- 1 cup almond flour
- ¾ cup breadcrumbs
- 1 teaspoon dried parsley

- Pinch of sea salt
- ½ teaspoon black pepper

Directions:
1. Preheat the air fryer to 390 Fahrenheit. Cut the cod into strips about 1-inch by 2-inches. Blend breadcrumbs, olive oil, salt, parsley and pepper in a food processor.

2. In three separate bowls, add breadcrumbs, eggs, and flour. Place each piece of fish into flour, then the eggs, and the breadcrumbs. Add pieces of cod to air fryer basket and cook for 10-minutes. Serve warm.

Nutrition: Calories: 213 Total Fat: 12.6g Carbs: 9.2g Protein: 13.4g

Vegetable Egg Pancake

Preparation Time: 10 minutes
Cooking Time: 15 minutes
Servings: 2

Ingredients:
- 1 cup almond flour
- ½ cup milk
- 1 tablespoon parmesan cheese, grated
- 3 eggs
- 1 potato, grated
- 1 beet, peeled and grated
- 1 carrot, grated
- 1 zucchini, grated
- 1 tablespoon olive oil
- ¼ teaspoon nutmeg
- 1 teaspoon onion powder
- 1 teaspoon garlic powder
- ½ teaspoon black pepper

Directions:
1. Preheat your air fryer to 390 Fahrenheit. Mix the zucchini, potato, beet, carrot, eggs, milk, almond flour and parmesan in a bowl.

2. Place olive oil into an oven-safe dish. Form patties with vegetable mix and flatten to form patties. Place patties into an oven-safe dish and cook in the air fryer for 15-minutes. Serve with sliced tomatoes, sour cream, and toast.

Nutrition: Calories: 223 Total Fat: 11.2g Carbs: 10.3g Proteins: 13.4g

Oriental Omelet

Preparation Time: 10 minutes

Cooking Time: 12 minutes

Servings: 1

Ingredients:

- ½ cup fresh Shimeji mushrooms, sliced
- 2 eggs, whisked
- Salt and pepper to taste
- 1 clove of garlic, minced
- A handful of sliced tofu
- 2 tablespoons onion, finely chopped
- Cooking spray

Directions:

1. Spray baking dish with cooking spray. Add onions and garlic. Air fry in the preheated air fryer at 355 Fahrenheit for 4-minutes.

2. Place the tofu and mushrooms over the onions and add salt and pepper to taste. Whisk the eggs and pour them over tofu and mushrooms. Air fry again for 20-minutes. Serve warm.

Nutrition: Calories: 210 Total Fat: 11.2g Carbs: 8.6g Protein: 12.2g

Crispy Breakfast Avocado Fries

Preparation Time: 10 minutes

Cooking Time: 8 minutes

Servings: 2

Ingredients:

- 2 eggs, beaten
- 2 large avocados, peeled, pitted, cut into 8 slices each
- ¼ teaspoon pepper
- ½ teaspoon cayenne pepper
- Salt to taste
- Juice of ½ a lemon
- ½ cup of whole wheat flour
- 1 cup whole-wheat breadcrumbs
- Greek yogurt to serve

Directions:

1. Add flour, salt, pepper and cayenne pepper to bowl and mix. Add bread crumbs into another bowl. Beat eggs in a third bowl. First, dredge the avocado slices in the flour mixture. Next, dip them into the egg mixture and finally dredge them in the breadcrumbs. Place avocado fries into the air fryer basket.

2. Preheat the air fryer to 390 Fahrenheit. Place the air fryer basket into the air fryer and cook for 6-minutes. When Cooking Time is completed, transfer the avocado fries onto a serving platter. Sprinkle with lemon juice and serve with Greek yogurt.

Nutrition: Calories: 272 Total Fat: 13.4g Carbs: 11.2g Protein: 15.4g

Cheese & Egg Breakfast Sandwich

Preparation Time: 10 minutes

Cooking Time: 6 minutes

Servings: 1

Ingredients:

- 1-2 eggs
- 1-2 slices of cheddar or Swiss cheese
- A bit of butter
- 1 roll sliced in half (your choice, Kaiser Bun, English muffin, etc.

Directions:

1. Butter your sliced roll on both sides. Place the eggs in an oven-safe dish and whisk. Add seasoning if you wish such as dill, chives, oregano, and salt. Place the egg dish, roll and cheese into the air fryer.

2. Make assured the buttered sides of the roll are in front of upwards. Set the air fryer to 390 Fahrenheit with a Cooking Time of 6-minutes. Remove the ingredients when Cooking Time is completed by air fryer.

3. Place the egg and cheese between the pieces of roll and serve warm. You might like to try adding slices of avocado and tomatoes to this breakfast sandwich!

Nutrition: Calories: 212 Total Fat: 11.2g Carbs: 9.3g Protein: 12.4g

Baked Mini Quiche

Preparation Time: 10 minutes

Cooking Time: 15 minutes

Servings: 2

Ingredients:

- 2 eggs
- 1 large yellow onion, diced

- 1 ¾ cups whole wheat flour
- 1 ½ cups spinach, chopped
- ¾ cup cottage cheese
- Salt and black pepper to taste
- 2 tablespoons olive oil
- ¾ cup butter
- ¼ cup milk

Directions:

1. Preheat the air fryer to 355 Fahrenheit. Add the flour, butter, salt, and milk to the bowl and knead the dough until smooth and refrigerate for 15-minutes. Abode a frying pan over medium heat and add the oil to it. When the oil is heated, add the onions into the pan and sauté them. Improve spinach to pan and cook until it wilts.

2. Drain excess moisture from spinach. Whisk the eggs together and add cheese to bowl and mix. Proceeds the dough out of the fridge and divide into 8 equal parts. Roll the dough into a round that will fit into the bottom of quiche mound. Place the rolled dough into molds. Place the spinach filling over dough.

3. Place molds into air fryer basket and place basket inside of air fryer and cook for 15-minutes. Remove quiche from molds and serve warm or cold.

Nutrition: Calories: 262 Total Fat: 8.2g Carbs: 7.3g Protein: 9.5g

Peanut Butter & Banana Breakfast Sandwich

Preparation Time: 10 minutes
Cooking Time: 6 minutes
Servings: 1

Ingredients:

- 2 slices of whole wheat bread
- 1 teaspoon of sugar-free maple syrup
- 1 sliced banana
- 2 tablespoons of peanut butter

Directions:

1. Evenly coat both sides of the slices of bread with peanut butter. Add the sliced banana and drizzle with some sugar-free maple syrup.

2. Heat in the air fryer to 330 Fahrenheit for 6 minutes. Serve warm.

Nutrition: Calories: 211 Total Fat: 8.2g Carbs: 6.3g Protein: 11.2g

Eggs & Cocotte on Toast

Preparation Time: 10 minutes
Cooking Time: 15 minutes
Servings: 2

Ingredients:

- 1/8 teaspoon of black pepper
- ¼ teaspoon salt
- ½ teaspoon Italian seasoning
- ¼ teaspoon balsamic vinegar
- ¼ teaspoon sugar-free maple syrup
- 1 cup sausages, chopped into small pieces
- 2 eggs
- 2 slices of whole-wheat toast
- 3 tablespoons cheddar cheese, shredded
- 6-slices tomatoes
- Cooking spray
- A little mayonnaise to serve

Directions:

1. Spray baking dish with cooking spray. Abode the bread slices at the bottom of the dish. Sprinkle the sausages over bread. Lay the tomatoes over it. Sprinkle top with cheese. Beat the eggs and then pour over top of bread slices.

2. Drizzle vinegar and maple syrup over eggs. Flavor with Italian seasoning, salt, and pepper, then sprinkle some more cheese on top. Place the baking dish in the air fryer basket that should be preheated at 320 Fahrenheit and cooked for 10-minutes. Remove from air fryer and add a spot of mayonnaise and serve.

Nutrition: Calories: 232 Total Fat: 7.4g Carbs: 6.3g Protein: 14.2g

Egg and Avocado Breakfast Burrito

Preparation Time: 10 minutes
Cooking Time: 3 to 5 minutes
Servings: 4

Ingredients:
- 2 hard-boiled egg whites, chopped
- 1 hard-boiled egg, chopped
- 1 avocado, peeled, pitted, and chopped
- 1 red bell pepper, chopped
- 3 tablespoons low-sodium salsa, plus additional for serving (optional)
- 1 (1.2-ounce / 34-g) slice low-sodium, low-fat American cheese, torn into pieces
- 4 low-sodium whole-wheat flour tortillas

Directions:
1. In a medium bowl, thoroughly mix the egg whites, egg, avocado, red bell pepper, salsa, and cheese.
2. Place the tortillas on a work surface and evenly divide the filling among them. Fold in the edges and roll up. Secure the burritos with toothpicks if necessary.
3. Put the burritos in the air fryer basket. Air fry at 390ºF (199ºC) for 3 to 5 minutes, or until the burritos are light golden brown and crisp. Serve with more salsa (if using).

Nutrition: Calories: 205 Fat: 8g Protein: 9g Carbs: 27g Fiber: 3g Sugar: 1g Sodium: 109mg

Mixed Berry Dutch Pancake

Preparation Time: 10 minutes
Cooking Time: 12-16 minutes
Servings: 4

Ingredients:
- 2 egg whites
- 1 egg
- ½ cup whole-wheat pastry flour
- ½ cup 2% milk
- 1 teaspoon pure vanilla extract
- 1 tablespoon unsalted butter, melted
- 1 cup sliced fresh strawberries
- ½ cup fresh blueberries
- ½ cup fresh raspberries

Directions:

1. In a medium bowl, use an eggbeater or hand mixer to quickly mix the egg whites, egg, pastry flour, milk, and vanilla until well combined.
2. Use a pastry brush to grease the bottom of a baking pan with the melted butter. Immediately pour in the batter and put the baking pan in the fryer. Bake at 330ºF (166ºC) for 12 to 16 minutes, or until the pancake is puffed and golden brown.
3. Remove the pan from the air fryer; the pancake will fall. Top with the strawberries, blueberries, and raspberries. Serve immediately.

Nutrition: Calories: 155 Fat: 5g Protein: 7g Carbs: 21g Fiber: 4g Sugar: 6g Sodium: 59mg

Crunchy Fried French toast Sticks

Preparation Time: 6 minutes
Cooking Time: 10-14 minutes
Servings: 4

Ingredients:
- 3 slices low-sodium whole-wheat bread, each cut into 4 strips
- 1 tablespoon unsalted butter, melted
- 1 egg
- 1 egg white
- 1 tablespoon 2% milk
- 1 tablespoon honey
- 1 cup sliced fresh strawberries
- 1 tablespoon freshly squeezed lemon juice

Directions:
1. Place the bread strips on a plate and drizzle with the melted butter.
2. In a shallow bowl, beat the egg, egg white, milk, and honey.
3. Dip the bread into the egg mixture and place on a wire rack to let the batter drip off.
4. Air fry half of the bread strips at 380ºF (193ºC) for 5 to 7 minutes, turning the strips with tongs once during cooking, until golden brown. Repeat with the remaining strips.
5. In a small bowl, mash the strawberries and lemon juice with a fork or potato masher. Serve the strawberry sauce with the French toast sticks.

Nutrition: Calories: 145 Fat: 5g Protein: 7g Carbs: 18g Fiber: 3g Sugar: 7g Sodium: 120mg

Pumpkin Oatmeal with Raisins

Preparation Time: 10 minutes

Cooking Time: 10 minutes

Servings: 3

Ingredients:

- 1 cup rolled oats
- 2 tablespoons raisins
- ¼ teaspoon ground cinnamon
- Pinch of kosher salt
- ¼ cup pumpkin purée
- 2 tablespoons pure maple syrup
- 1 cup low-fat milk

Directions:

1. In a medium bowl, combine the rolled oats, raisins, ground cinnamon, and kosher salt, then stir in the pumpkin purée, maple syrup, and low-fat milk.

2. Spray a baking pan with nonstick cooking spray, then pour the oatmeal mixture into the pan and bake at 300°F (149°C) for 10 minutes.

3. Remove the oatmeal from the fryer and allow to cool in the pan on a wire rack for 5 minutes before serving.

Nutrition: Calories: 304 Fat: 4g Protein: 10g Carbs: 57g Fiber: 6g Sugar: 26g Sodium: 140mg

Mushroom and Black Bean Burrito

Preparation Time: 10 minutes

Cooking Time: 15 minutes

Servings: 1

Ingredients:

- 2 tablespoons canned black beans, rinsed and drained
- ¼ cup sliced baby portobello mushrooms
- 1 teaspoon olive oil
- Pinch of kosher salt
- 1 large egg
- 1 slice low-fat Cheddar cheese
- 1 (8-inch) whole grain flour tortilla
- Hot sauce (optional)

Directions:

1. Spray a baking pan with nonstick cooking spray, then place the black beans and baby portobello mushrooms in the pan, drizzle with the olive oil, and season with the kosher salt.

2. Bake at 360°F (182°C) for 5 minutes, then pause the fryer to crack the egg on top of the beans and mushrooms. Bake for 8 more minutes or until the egg is cooked as desired.

3. Pause the fryer again, top the egg with cheese, and bake for 1 more minute.

4. Remove the pan from the fryer, then use a spatula to place the bean mixture on the whole grain flour tortilla. Fold in the sides and roll from front to back. Serve warm with the hot sauce on the side (if using).

Nutrition: Calories: 276 Fat: 12g Protein: 16g Carbs: 26g Fiber: 6g Sugar: 2g Sodium: 306mg

Bacon and Egg Sandwiches

Preparation Time: 3 minutes

Cooking Time: 8 minutes

Servings: 2

Ingredients:

- 2 large eggs
- ¼ teaspoon kosher salt, divided
- ¼ teaspoon freshly ground black pepper, divided (plus extra for serving)
- 2 slices Canadian bacon
- 2 slices American cheese
- 2 whole grain English muffins, sliced in half

Directions:

1. Spray two 3-inch ramekins with nonstick cooking spray, then crack one egg into each ramekin and add half the kosher salt and half the black pepper to each egg.

2. Place the ramekins in the fryer basket and bake at 360°F (182°C) for 5 minutes.

3. Pause the fryer and top each partially cooked egg with a slice of Canadian bacon and a slice of American cheese.

4. Bake for 3 more minutes or until the cheese has melted and the egg yolk has just cooked through.

5. Remove the ramekins from the fryer and allow cooling on a wire rack for 2 to 3 minutes, then flipping the eggs, bacon, and cheese out onto English muffins and sprinkling some black pepper on top before serving.

Nutrition: Calories: 309 Fat: 13g Protein: 22g Carbs: 26g Fiber: 3g Sugar: 3g Sodium: 618mg

Almond Crunch Granola

Preparation Time: 5 minutes

Cooking Time: 8-10 minutes

Servings: 1

Ingredients:

- ²/3 cup rolled oats
- ¹/3 cup unsweetened shredded coconut
- ¹/3 cup sliced almonds
- 1 teaspoon canola oil
- 2 teaspoons honey
- ¼ teaspoon kosher salt

Directions:

1. In a medium bowl, combine the rolled oats, shredded coconut, sliced almonds, canola oil, honey, and kosher salt.

2. Place a small piece of parchment paper on the bottom of a baking pan, then pour the mixture into the pan and distribute it evenly. Bake at 360ºF (182ºC) for 5 minutes, pause the fryer to gently stir the granola, and bake for 3 more minutes.

3. Remove the granola from the fryer and allow cooling in the pan on a wire rack for 5 minutes, then transferring the granola to a serving plate to cool completely before serving. (It becomes crunchier as it cools. Store the granola in an airtight container for up to 2 weeks.)

Nutrition: Calories: 181 Fat: 9g Protein: 4g Carbs: 21g Fiber: 5g Sugar: 4g Sodium: 94mg

Yogurt Raspberry Cake

Preparation Time: 10 minutes

Cooking Time: 8 minutes

Servings: 4

Ingredients:

- ½ cup whole wheat pastry flour
- 1/8 teaspoon kosher salt
- ¼ teaspoon baking powder
- ½ cup whole milk vanilla yogurt
- 2 tablespoons canola oil
- 2 tablespoons pure maple syrup
- ¾ cup fresh raspberries

Directions:

1. In a large bowl, combine the whole wheat pastry flour, kosher salt, and baking powder, then stir in the whole milk vanilla yogurt, canola oil, and maple syrup and gently fold in the raspberries.

2. Spray a baking pan with nonstick cooking spray, then pour the cake batter into the pan and bake at 300ºF (149ºC) for 8 minutes.

3. Remove the cake from the fryer and allow to cool in the pan on a wire rack for 10 minutes before cutting and serving.

Nutrition: Calories: 168 Fat: 8g Protein: 3g Carbs: 21g Fiber: 3g Sugar: 8g Sodium: 82mg

Spinach and Tomato Egg Cup

Preparation Time: 5 minutes

Cooking Time: 10 minutes

Servings: 1

Ingredients:

- 2 egg whites, beaten
- 2 tablespoons chopped tomato
- 2 tablespoons chopped spinach
- Pinch of kosher salt
- Red pepper flakes (optional)

Directions:

1. Spray a 3-inch ramekin with nonstick cooking spray, then combine the egg whites, tomato, spinach, kosher salt, and red pepper flakes (if using) in the ramekin.

2. Place the ramekin in the air fryer basket and bake at 300ºF (149ºC) for 10 minutes or until the eggs have set.

3. Remove the ramekin from the fryer and allow to cool on a wire rack for 5 minutes before serving.

Nutrition: Calories: 32 Fat: 0g Protein: 7g Carbs: 1g Fiber: 1g Sugar: 1g Sodium: 184mg

Egg Muffins with Bell Pepper

Preparation Time: 5 minutes

Cooking Time: 10 minutes

Servings: 2

Ingredients:

- 4 large eggs
- ½ bell pepper, finely chopped
- 1 tablespoon finely chopped red onion
- ¼ teaspoon kosher salt

- ¼ teaspoon freshly ground black pepper, plus extra for serving
- 2 tablespoons shredded Cheddar cheese

Directions:

1. In a large bowl, whisk together the eggs, then stir in the bell pepper, red onion, kosher salt, and black pepper.

2. Spray two 3-inch ramekins with nonstick cooking spray, then pour half the egg mixture into each ramekin and place the ramekins in the fryer basket. Bake at 390°F (199°C) for 8 minutes.

3. Pause the fryer, sprinkle 1 tablespoon of shredded Cheddar cheese on top of each cup, and bake for 2 more minutes.

4. Remove the ramekins from the fryer and allow to cool on a wire rack for 5 minutes, then turn the omelet cups out on plates and sprinkle some black pepper on top before serving.

Nutrition: Calories: 172 Fat: 12g Protein: 14g Carbs: 2g Fiber: 0g Sugar: 1g Sodium: 333mg

Egg-in-a-Hole

Preparation Time: 5 minutes
Cooking Time: 5-7 minutes
Servings: 1

Ingredients:
- 1 slice whole grain bread
- 1 large egg
- 1/8 teaspoon kosher salt
- ¼ cup diced avocado
- ¼ cup diced tomato
- Pinch of freshly ground black pepper

Directions:

1. Spray a baking pan with nonstick cooking spray, then use a ring mold or a sharp knife to cut a 3-inch hole in the center of the whole grain bread. Place the bread slice and the circle in the pan.

2. Crack the egg into the hole, then season with the kosher salt. Bake at 360°F (182°C) for 5 to 7 minutes or until the egg is cooked as desired.

3. Remove the pan from the fryer and allow to cool on a wire rack for 5 minutes before transferring the toast

to a plate, then sprinkle the avocado, tomato, and black pepper on top before serving.

Nutrition: Calories: 220 Fat: 12g Protein: 10g Carbs: 18g Fiber: 5g Sugar: 4g Sodium: 406mg

Egg and Cheese Pockets

Preparation Time: 10 minutes
Cooking Time: 35 minutes
Servings: 4

Ingredients:
- 1 large egg, beaten
- Pinch of kosher salt
- ½ sheet puff pastry
- 1 slice Cheddar cheese, divided into 4 pieces

Directions:

1. Pour the egg into a baking pan, season with the kosher salt, and bake at 330°F (166°C) for 3 minutes. Pause the fryer, gently scramble the egg, and bake for 2 more minutes. Remove the egg from the fryer, keeping the fryer on, and set the egg aside to slightly cool.

2. Roll the puff pastry out flat and divide into 4 pieces.

3. Place a piece of Cheddar cheese and ¼ of the egg on one side of a piece of pastry, fold the pastry over the egg and cheese, and use a fork to press the edges closed. Repeat this process with the remaining pieces.

4. Place 2 pockets in the fryer and bake for 15 minutes or until golden brown. Repeat this process with the other 2 pockets.

5. Remove the pockets from the fryer and allow to cool on a wire rack for 5 minutes before serving.

Nutrition: Calories: 215 Fat: 15g Protein: 6g Carbs: 14g Fiber: 0g Sugar: 0g Sodium: 143mg

Huevos Rancheros

Preparation Time: 20 minutes
Cooking Time: 25 minutes
Servings: 4

Ingredients:

- 4 large eggs
- ¼ teaspoon kosher salt
- ¼ cup masa harina (corn flour)
- 1 teaspoon olive oil
- ¼ cup warm water
- ½ cup salsa
- ¼ cup crumbled queso fresco or feta cheese

Directions:

1. Crack the eggs into a baking pan, season with the kosher salt, and bake at 330ºF (166ºC) for 3 minutes. Pause the fryer, gently scramble the eggs, and bake for 2 more minutes. Remove the eggs from the fryer, keeping the fryer on, and set the eggs aside to slightly cool. (Clean the baking pan before making the tortillas.)
2. Increase the temperature to 390ºF (199ºC).
3. In a medium bowl, combine the masa harina, olive oil, and ¼ teaspoon of kosher salt by hand, then slowly pour in the water, stirring until a soft dough forms.
4. Divide the dough into 4 equal balls, then place each ball between 2 pieces of parchment paper and use a pie plate or a rolling pin to flatten the dough.
5. Spray the baking pan with nonstick cooking spray, then place one flattened tortilla in the pan and air fry for 5 minutes. Repeat this process with the remaining tortillas.
6. Remove the tortillas from the fryer and place on a serving plate, then top each tortilla with the scrambled eggs, salsa, and cheese before serving.

Nutrition: Calories: 136Fat: 8g Protein: 8g Carbs: 8g Fiber: 1g Sugar: 2g Sodium: 333mg

Jalapeño Potato Hash

Preparation Time: 10 minutes
Cooking Time: 19-20 minutes
Servings: 4

Ingredients:

- 2 large sweet potatoes
- ½ small red onion, cut into large chunks
- 1 green bell pepper, cut into large chunks
- 1 jalapeño pepper, seeded and sliced
- ½ teaspoon kosher salt
- ¼ teaspoon freshly ground black pepper, plus extra for serving
- 1 teaspoon olive oil
- 1 large egg, poached

Directions:

1. Cook the sweet potatoes on high in the microwave until softened but not completely cooked (3 to 4 minutes), then set aside to cool for 10 minutes.
2. Remove the skins from the sweet potatoes, then cut the sweet potatoes into large chunks.
3. In a large bowl, combine the sweet potatoes, red onion, green bell pepper, jalapeño pepper, kosher salt, black pepper, and olive oil, tossing gently.
4. Spray the air fryer basket with nonstick cooking spray, then pour the mixture into the basket and air fry at 360ºF (182ºC) for 8 minutes.
5. Pause the fryer to shake the basket, then air fry for 8 more minutes or until golden brown.
6. Remove the hash from the fryer, place on a plate lined with a paper towel, and allow to cool for 5 minutes, then add the poached egg, sprinkle black pepper on top, and serve.

Nutrition: Calories: 131 Fat: 3g Protein: 4g Carbs: 22g Fiber: 4g Sugar: 7g Sodium: 174mg

Asparagus Cheese Strata

Preparation Time: 12 minutes
Cooking Time: 17 minutes
Servings: 4

Ingredients:

- 6 asparagus spears, cut into 2-inch pieces
- 2 slices whole-wheat bread, cut into ½-inch cubes
- 4 eggs
- 3 tablespoons whole milk
- ½ cup grated Havarti or Swiss cheese
- 2 tablespoons chopped flat-leaf parsley
- Pinch salt
- Freshly ground black pepper, to taste

Directions:

1.   Place the asparagus spears and 1 tablespoon water in a baking pan and place in the air fryer basket. Bake at 330ºF (166ºC) for 3 to 5 minutes or until crisp and tender. Remove the asparagus from the pan and drain it. Spray the pan with nonstick cooking spray.

2.   Arrange the bread cubes and asparagus into the pan and set aside.

3.   In a medium bowl, beat the eggs with the milk until combined. Add the cheese, parsley, salt, and pepper. Pour into the baking pan.

4.   Bake for 11 to 14 minutes or until the eggs are set and the top starts to brown.

Nutrition: Calories: 167 Fat: 9g Protein: 12g Carbs: 9g Fiber: 2g Sugar: 1g Sodium: 200mg

Shrimp Rice Frittata

Preparation Time: 15 minutes
Cooking Time: 14-18 minutes
Servings: 4

Ingredients:

- 4 eggs
- Pinch salt
- ½ teaspoon dried basil
- Nonstick cooking spray
- ½ cup cooked rice
- ½ cup chopped cooked shrimp
- ½ cup baby spinach
- ½ cup grated Monterey Jack or Cojack cheese

Directions:

1.   In a small bowl, beat the eggs with the salt and basil until frothy. Spray a baking pan with nonstick cooking spray.

2.   Combine the rice, shrimp, and spinach in the prepared pan. Pour the eggs in and sprinkle with the cheese.

3.   Bake at 320ºF (160ºC) for 14 to 18 minutes or until the frittata is puffed and golden brown.

Nutrition: Calories: 227Fat: 9g Protein: 16g Carbs: 19g Fiber: 0g Sugar: 1g Sodium: 232mg

Vegetable Frittata

Preparation Time: 10 minutes

Cooking Time: 8-12 minutes
Servings: 4

Ingredients:

- ½ cup chopped red bell pepper
- 1/3 cup minced onion
- 1/3 cup grated carrot
- 1 teaspoon olive oil
- 6 egg whites
- 1 egg
- 1/3 cup 2% milk
- 1 tablespoon grated Parmesan cheese

Directions:

1.   In a baking pan, stir together the red bell pepper, onion, carrot, and olive oil. Put the pan into the air fryer. Bake at 350ºF (177ºC) for 4 to 6 minutes, shaking the basket once, until the vegetables are tender.

2.   Meanwhile, in a medium bowl, beat the egg whites, egg, and milk until combined.

3.   Pour the egg mixture over the vegetables in the pan. Sprinkle with the Parmesan cheese. Return the pan to the air fryer.

4.   Bake for 4 to 6 minutes more, or until the frittata is puffy and set.

5.   Cut into 4 wedges and serve.

Nutrition: Calories: 78 Fat: 3g Protein: 8g Carbs: 5g Fiber: 1g Sugar: 3g Sodium: 116mg

Avocado Toast with Tomato and Cottage Cheese

Preparation Time: 5 minutes
Cooking Time: 0 minutes
Servings: 2

Ingredients

- ½ cup cottage cheese
- ½ avocado, mashed
- 1 teaspoon Dijon mustard
- Dash hot sauce (optional)
- 2 slices whole-grain bread, toasted
- 2 slices tomato

Directions

1. In a small bowl, mix together the cottage cheese, avocado, mustard, and hot sauce, if using, until well mixed.
2. Spread the mixture on the toast.
3. Top each piece of toast with a tomato slice.

Nutrition Calories: 179 Fat: 8g: 327mg Carbohydrates: 17g Fiber: 4g Protein: 11g

Ginger Blackberry Bliss Smoothie Bowl

Preparation Time: 5 minutes
Cooking Time: 0 minutes
Servings: 2

Ingredients
- ½ cup frozen blackberries
- 1 cup plain Greek yogurt
- 1 cup baby spinach
- ½ cup unsweetened almond milk
- ½ teaspoon peeled and grated fresh ginger
- ¼ cup chopped pecans

Directions
1. In a blender or food processor, combine the blackberries, yogurt, spinach, almond milk, and ginger. Blend until smooth.
2. Spoon the mixture into two bowls.
3. Top each bowl with 2 tablespoons of chopped pecans and serve.

Nutrition Calories: 202 Fat: 15g Sodium: 104mg Carbohydrates: 15gFiber: 4g Protein: 7g

Heart-Healthy Yogurt Parfaits

Preparation Time: 10 minutes
Cooking Time: 5 minutes
Servings: 2

Ingredients
- 1 cup fresh pineapple chunks
- 1 cup plain Greek yogurt
- ¼ cup canned coconut milk
- ¼ cup flaxseed
- 2 tablespoons unsweetened toasted coconut flakes
- 2 tablespoons chopped macadamia nuts

Directions
1. Preheat the oven broiler on high.

2. Spread the pineapple chunks in a single layer on a rimmed baking sheet.
3. Broil until the pineapple begins to brown, 4 to 5 minutes.
4. In a small bowl, whisk together the yogurt, coconut milk, and flaxseed. Spoon the mixture into two bowls. Top with the pineapple chunks.
5. Serve with the coconut flakes and chopped macadamia nuts sprinkled over the top.

Nutrition Calories: 402 Fat: 31g Sodium: 71mg Carbohydrates: 26g Fiber: 9g Protein: 10g

Low-Carb Peanut Butter Pancakes

Preparation Time: 10 minutes
Cooking Time: 10 minutes
Servings: 2

Ingredients
- 1 cup almond flour
- ½ teaspoon baking soda
- Pinch sea salt
- 2 large eggs
- ¼ cup sparkling water (plain, unsweetened)
- 2 tablespoons canola oil, plus more for cooking
- 4 tablespoons peanut butter

Directions
1. Heat a nonstick griddle over medium-high heat.
2. In a small bowl, whisk together the almond flour, baking soda, and salt.
3. In a glass measuring cup, whisk together the eggs, water, and oil.
4. Pour the liquid ingredients into the dry ingredients, and mix gently until just combined.
5. Brush a small amount of canola oil onto the griddle.
6. Using all of the batter, spoon four pancakes onto the griddle.
7. Cook until set on one side, about 3 minutes. Flip with a spatula and continue cooking on the other side.
8. Before serving, spread each pancake with 1 tablespoon of the peanut butter.

Nutrition Calories: 454 Fat: 41g Sodium: 408mg Carbohydrates: 8g Fiber: 3g Protein: 17g

Toads in Holes

Preparation Time: 5 minutes
Cooking Time: 5 minutes
Servings: 2

Ingredients

- 2 tablespoons butter
- 2 slices whole-wheat bread
- 2 large eggs
- Sea salt
- Freshly ground black pepper

Directions

1. In a medium nonstick skillet over medium heat, heat the butter until it bubbles.
2. As the butter heats, cut a 3-inch hole in the middle of each piece of bread. Discard the centers.
3. Place the bread pieces in the butter in the pan. Carefully crack an egg into the hole of each piece of bread.
4. Cook until the bread crisps and the egg whites set, about 3 minutes.
5. Flip and cook just until the yolk is almost set, 1 to 2 minutes more.
6. Season to taste with the salt and pepper.

Nutrition Calories: 241 Fat: 17g Sodium: 307mg Carbohydrates: 12g Fiber: 2g Protein: 10g

Veggie and Egg White Scramble with Pepper Jack Cheese

Preparation Time: 5 minutes
Cooking Time: 10 minutes
Servings: 2

Ingredients

- 2 tablespoons extra-virgin olive oil
- ½ red onion, finely chopped
- 1 green bell pepper, seeded and finely chopped
- 8 large egg whites (or 4 whole large eggs), beaten
- ½ teaspoon sea salt
- 2 ounces grated pepper Jack cheese
- Salsa (optional, for serving)

Directions

1. In a medium nonstick skillet over medium-high heat, heat the olive oil until it shimmers.
2. Add the onion and bell pepper and cook, stirring occasionally, until the vegetables begin to brown, about 5 minutes.
3. Meanwhile, in a small bowl, whisk together the egg whites and salt.
4. Add the egg whites to the pan and cook, stirring, until the whites set, about 3 minutes. Add the cheese. Cook, stirring, 1 minute more.
5. Serve topped with salsa, if desired.

Nutrition Calories: 314Fat: 23gSodium: 977mgCarbohydrates: 6gFiber: 1gProtein: 22g

Tofu, Kale, and Mushroom Breakfast Scramble

Preparation Time: 5 minutes
Cooking Time: 10 minutes
Servings: 2

Ingredients

- 2 tablespoons extra-virgin olive oil
- ½ red onion, finely chopped
- 8 ounces mushrooms, sliced
- 1 cup chopped kale
- 8 ounces tofu, cut into pieces
- 2 garlic cloves, minced
- Pinch red pepper flakes
- ½ teaspoon sea salt
- 1/8 teaspoon freshly ground black pepper

Directions

1. In a medium nonstick skillet over medium-high heat, heat the olive oil until it shimmers.
2. Add the onion, mushrooms, and kale. Cook, stirring occasionally, until the vegetables begin to brown, about 5 minutes.
3. Add the tofu. Cook, stirring, until the tofu starts to brown, 3 to 4 minutes more.
4. Add the garlic, red pepper flakes, salt, and pepper. Cook, stirring constantly, for 30 seconds more.

Nutrition Calories: 234Fat: 16gSodium: 673mgCarbohydrates: 12gFiber: 2gProtein: 13g

Broccoli and Mushroom Frittata

Preparation Time: 5 minutes

Cooking Time: 10 minutes

Servings: 4

Ingredients

- 2 tablespoons extra-virgin olive oil
- ½ onion, finely chopped
- 1 cup broccoli florets
- 1 cup sliced shiitake mushrooms
- 1 garlic clove, minced
- 8 large eggs, beaten
- ½ teaspoon sea salt
- ½ cup grated Parmesan cheese

Directions

1.   Preheat the oven broiler on high.

2.   In a medium ovenproof skillet over medium-high heat, heat the olive oil until it shimmers.

3.   Add the onion, broccoli, and mushrooms, and cook, stirring occasionally, until the vegetables start to brown, about 5 minutes. Add the garlic and cook, stirring constantly, for 30 seconds. Arrange the vegetables in an even layer on the bottom of the pan.

4.   While the vegetables cook, in a small bowl, whisk together the eggs and salt. Carefully pour the eggs over the vegetables. Cook without stirring, allowing the eggs to set around the vegetables. As the eggs begin to set around the edges, use a spatula to pull the edges away from the sides of the pan. Tilt the pan and allow the uncooked eggs to run into the spaces. Cook 1 to 2 minutes more, until it sets around the edges. The eggs will still be runny on top.

5.   Sprinkle with the Parmesan and place the pan in the broiler. Broil until brown and puffy, about 3 minutes.

6.   Cut into wedges to serve.

Nutrition Calories: 280 Fat: 21g Sodium: 654mg Carbohydrates: 7g Fiber: 2g Protein: 19g

Canadian bacon and Egg Muffin Cups

Preparation Time: 5 minutes

Cooking Time: 20 minutes

Servings: 6

Ingredients

- Cooking spray (for greasing)
- 6 large slices Canadian bacon
- 12 large eggs, beaten
- 1 teaspoon Dijon mustard
- ½ teaspoon sea salt
- Dash hot sauce
- 1 cup shredded Swiss cheese

Directions

1.   Preheat the oven to 350°F. Spray 6 nonstick muffin cups with cooking spray.

2.   Line each cup with 1 slice of Canadian bacon.

3.   In a bowl, whisk together the eggs, mustard, salt, and hot sauce. Fold in the cheese. Spoon the mixture into the muffin cups.

4.   Bake until the eggs set, about 20 minutes.

Nutrition Calories: 259 Fat: 17g Sodium: 781mg Carbohydrates: 3g Fiber: 0g Protein: 24g

Sausage and Pepper Breakfast Burrito

Preparation Time: 10 minutes

Cooking Time: 15 minutes

Servings: 4

Ingredients

- 8 ounces bulk pork breakfast sausage
- ½ onion, chopped
- 1 green bell pepper, seeded and chopped
- 8 large eggs, beaten
- 4 (6-inch) low-carb tortillas
- 1 cup shredded pepper Jack cheese
- ½ cup sour cream (optional, for serving)
- ½ cup prepared salsa (optional, for serving)

Directions

1.   In a large nonstick skillet on medium-high heat, cook the sausage, crumbling it with a spoon, until browned, about 5 minutes. Add the onion and bell pepper. Cook, stirring, until the veggies are soft, about 3 minutes. Add the eggs and cook, stirring, until eggs are set, about 3 minutes more.

2.   Spoon the egg mixture onto the 4 tortillas. Top each with the cheese and fold into a burrito shape.

3.   Serve with sour cream and salsa, if desired.

Nutrition Calories: 486 Fat: 36g Sodium: 810mg Carbohydrates: 13g Fiber: 8g Protein: 32g

Pumpkin Walnut Smoothie Bowl

Preparation Time: 5 minutes

Cooking Time: 0 minutes

Servings: 2

Ingredients

- 1 cup plain Greek yogurt
- ½ cup canned pumpkin purée (not pumpkin pie mix)
- 1 teaspoon pumpkin pie spice
- 2 (1-gram) packets stevia
- ½ teaspoon vanilla extract
- Pinch sea salt
- ½ cup chopped walnuts

Directions

1. In a bowl, whisk together the yogurt, pumpkin purée, pumpkin pie spice, stevia, vanilla, and salt (or blend in a blender).
2. Spoon into two bowls. Serve topped with the chopped walnuts.

Nutrition Calories: 292Fat: 23g Sodium: 85mg Carbohydrates: 15g Fiber: 4g Protein: 9g

Melon sandwich

Preparation Time: 8 minutes

Cooking Time: 0 minutes

Servings: 2

Ingredients

- 4 slices of toast bread (50g)
- 6 slices of smoked ham
- 130 g net melon
- 4 tsp sour cream
- 4 leaves of lettuce

Directions

1. Toast. Remove the greasy edges from the ham slices.
2. Slice the melon. Cut the pulp into thin slices.
3. Brush one side of the toast with sour cream. Then cover the slices with the melon slice, ham and the salad.
4. Brush the second toast slice with sour cream and place it on the topped slice.

Nutrition: Calories 350 kcal Carbohydrates 31 g Protein 21 g Fat 10 g

Butter milk lentil

Preparation Time: 30 minutes

Cooking Time: 10 minutes

Servings: 2

Ingredients

- 2 eggs
- 60 g semolina
- 120 ml buttermilk
- Salt, lemon juice, sweetener (liquid)
- 4 tbsp low-fat quark
- 200 g strawberries
- 2 tsp nuts
- 3 teaspoons of oil

Directions

1. Separate egg yolks. Mix the egg yolks with the buttermilk, the semolina and two pinches of salt and leave to soak for about 10 minutes.
2. Season the quark with the lemon juice and the liquid sweetener. Wash the strawberries. Remove the stems. Halve the fruit.
3. Beat the egg whites with a whisk until stiff. Fold the mixture into the semolina.
4. Put some oil in a pan and heat it up. Use a ladle to pour the semolina into the hot pan and let it brown. Turn around with a dog. Fry about 4 pancakes in this way.
5. Fill the pancakes with the quark cream and add some strawberries. Serve on a plate.

Nutrition Calories330 kcal Carbohydrates 31 g Protein 22 g Fat 8 g

Pineapple omelette

Preparation Time: 20 minutes

Cooking Time: 10 minutes

Servings: 2

Ingredients

- 1 egg
- 16 g diabetic sweetness
- 20 g of flour
- 200 g cream cheese

- 70 g whipped cream
- 1 pineapple ring, sprinkles & lemon

Directions

1. Separate the egg. Beat the egg whites until stiff. Add the diabetic sweetness. Stir in the egg yolks.
2. Grate the lemon peel and add to the mixture. Add flour.
3. Preheat the oven.
4. Cover the baking sheet with parchment paper. With a tablespoon, spread the dough in a circle and bake in the oven for 10 minutes.
5. Remove the omelets, place them on plates and let them cool.
6. Mix the cream cheese with the cream. Beat the rest of the cream until stiff and stir in. Add sweetener and season to taste.

Nutrition Calories 376 kcal Carbohydrates 36 g Protein 26 g Fat 12g

Stracciatella omelette

Preparation Time: 30 minutes
Cooking Time: 15 minutes
Servings: 2

Ingredients

- 2 eggs
- 12 g diabetic sweetness
- 20 g of flour
- ½ cocoa powder
- 1 lemon
- 25 g dark chocolate
- 125 g whipped cream

Directions

1. Grate the lemon peel.
2. Separate the yolks from one egg. Beat egg white until stiff and slowly add diabetic sweetness. Stir in the egg yolk and lemon zest.
3. Preheat the oven.
4. Place parchment paper on a baking sheet. Spread the mixture with a spoon in two circles and bake in the oven for 10 minutes.
5. Remove the baking mixture from the baking paper, place on a plate and let cool down.

6. Grate the chocolate into grates. Whip the cream until stiff and stir in the chocolate. Put everything in a piping bag and apply to the omelets.
7. Dust the omelets with the cocoa and chill for a quarter of an hour.

Nutrition Calories 390 kcal Carbohydrates 22 g Protein 9 g Fat 30 g

Red grits slices

Preparation Time: 10 minutes
Cooking Time: 65 minutes
Servings: 2

Ingredients

- 75 g butter
- 200 ml of milk
- 1 cube of yeast
- 500g flour
- 2 eggs
- 108 g diabetic sweetness
- Salt, fat & 1 pack of red grass powder

Directions

1. Warm milk and dissolve the yeast in it.
2. Melt the butter and place in a bowl. Mix with the flour, eggs, diabetic sweetness and salt. Stir with the dough hook. Cover and let rise for about 40 minutes.
3. Knead the dough repeatedly. Grease the pan and roll out the dough. Let go about 20.
4. Mix red grits powder with 6 tablespoons of water, pour into a saucepan and briefly bring to the boil. Then take it off the stove and let it cool down.
5. Make hollows in the dough with a tablespoon and add the red jelly.
6. Let the dough rise for 10 minutes. Meanwhile preheat the oven. Bake the dough in the oven for 20 minutes.

Nutrition Calories160 kcal Carbohydrates 24 g Protein 5 g Fat 6 g

Raisin apple snails

Preparation Time: 10 minutes
Cooking Time: 40 minutes
Servings: 2

Ingredients

- 50 g apples
- 18 g diabetic sweetness
- 5 g raisins
- 10 almond sticks
- 20 g low-fat quark
- 1 tbsp oil, 40 g flour & 1/8 baking powder packet

Directions

1. Wash the apples, cut them open, remove the casing and put in small. Cut pieces.
2. Put the apple pieces in a saucepan. Add lemon juice and the diabetic sweetness. Steam everything for ten minutes. Add the raisins and almond slivers. Stir and let cool.
3. Mix the quark, diabetic sweetness, oil, flour and baking powder (about 1/8 packet). Sprinkle the work surface with flour and roll out the dough into a rectangle. Spread the apple pieces on top.
4. Preheat the oven.
5. Roll the dough. Cut the roll into even pieces, place on baking paper and bake in the bacon for 20 minutes.
6. Mix diabetic sweetness and lemon and spread on the snails.

Nutrition Calories 190 kcal Carbohydrates 27 g Protein 4 gFat 5 g

Plum muffins

Preparation time: 10 minutes
Cooking Time: 50 minutes
Servings: 2

Ingredients

- 25 g walnut kernels
- 85 g plums (pitted)
- 30 g butter
- 1 egg
- 12 g of sugar
- 30 ml of milk
- 60 grams of flour
- 15 g apricot jam
- Salt & baking powder

Directions

1. Roughly cut the nuts. Wash the plums, stone them if necessary and cut them into small pieces.
2. Mix egg and milk. Add flour, 1/2 teaspoon baking powder and a pinch of salt. Mix in the nuts and plums.
3. Put 4 - 6 paper sleeves into each other.
4. Preheat the oven.
5. The Mi Research fill in the Papier-mache tablets. The cuffs should be two thirds full.
6. Place the cuffs on a baking sheet and bake in the oven for 40 minutes.
7. Let the muffins cool down and then brush with the jam.

Nutrition Calories 250 kcal Carbohydrates 28 g Protein 7 g Fat 9 g

Italian bun

Preparation Time: 10 minutes
Cooking Time: 10 minutes
Servings: 2

Ingredients

- 60 g mozzarella
- 2 tomatoes
- 2 mini-Panelino rolls
- 2 teaspoons of garlic butter
- 2 slices of Italian mortadella (20 g)
- 2 lettuce leaves
- 3 olives
- Basil and colored pepper

Directions

1. Wash tomatoes, remove style and casing. Cut the mozzarella and tomatoes into strips.
2. Halve the bread roll and brush with garlic butter.
3. Preheat the oven.
4. Cover half of each with mortadella, tomato slices, mozzarella and basil. Grind pepper and sprinkle on top. Place the other half of the bun on top.

5. Put the rolls in the oven and brown for 3 minutes or brown on a grill for about 3 minutes.

6. Take out the rolls and serve on plates. Garnish with olives, lettuce and the remaining tomato slices.

NutritionCalories 320 kcalCarbohydrates 30 g Protein 13 g Fat 16 g

Strawberry-Ricotta Toast

Preparation Time: 5 minutes

Cooking Time: 0 minutes

Servings: 1

Ingredients:

- 2 slices whole-grain bread, toasted
- ½ cup ricotta cheese
- 2 cups diced strawberries
- 3 tablespoons toasted chopped hazelnuts
- 2 tablespoons chopped fresh mint (optional)

Directions:

1. Place the toast on your work surface and evenly divide the ricotta between the slices, spreading it out to cover the bread.

2. Top each slice with the strawberries, hazelnuts, and mint (if using), evenly distributing the ingredients on the cheese.

3. Serve immediately.

Nutrition Calories: 634 Fat: 30g Carbohydrates: 73g Fiber: 13g

Protein: 25g Calcium: 465mg

Easy Buckwheat Crêpes

Preparation Time: 5 minutes

Cooking Time: 15 minutes

Servings: 12

Ingredients

- 1 cup buckwheat flour
- 1¾ cups milk
- 1/8 teaspoon kosher salt
- 1 tablespoon extra-virgin olive oil
- ½ tablespoon ground flaxseed (optional)

Directions

1. Combine the buckwheat flour, milk, salt, extra-virgin olive oil, and flaxseed (if using), in a bowl and whisk thoroughly, or in a blender and pulse until well combined.

2. Heat a nonstick medium skillet over medium heat. Once it's hot, add a ¼ cup of batter to the skillet, spreading it out evenly. Cook until bubbles appear and the edges crisp like a pancake, 1 to 3 minutes, then flip and cook for another 2 minutes.

3. Repeat until all the batter is used up, and the crêpes are cooked. Layer parchment paper or tea towels between the crêpes to keep them from sticking to one another while also keeping them warm until you're ready to eat.

4. Serve with the desired fillings.

Nutrition Calories: 130 Fat: 5g Carbohydrates: 18g Fiber: 2g

Protein: 5g Calcium: 89mg

Shakshuka

Preparation Time: 5 minutes

Cooking Time: 25minutes

Servings: 4

Ingredients

- 2 tablespoons extra-virgin olive oil
- 1 onion, diced
- 2 tablespoons tomato paste
- 2 red bell peppers, diced
- 2 tablespoons Harissa (optional)
- 4 garlic cloves, minced
- 2 teaspoons ground cumin
- ½ teaspoon ground coriander (optional)
- 1 teaspoon smoked paprika
- 2 (14-ounce) cans diced tomatoes
- 4 large eggs
- ½ cup plain Greek yogurt
- Bread, for dipping (optional)

Directions

1. Heat the extra-virgin olive oil in a Dutch oven or large saucepan over medium heat. When it starts to shimmer, add the onion and cook until translucent, about 3 minutes.

2. Add the tomato paste, peppers, harissa (if using), garlic, cumin, coriander (if using), paprika, and tomatoes. Bring to a simmer and cook 10 to 15 minutes, until the

peppers are cooked and the sauce is thick. Adjust the seasoning as desired.

3.   Make four wells in the mixture with the back of a large spoon and gently break one egg into each well. Cover the saucepan and simmer gently until the egg whites are set but the yolks are still runny, 5 to 8 minutes.

4.   Remove the saucepan from the heat and spoon the tomato mixture and one cooked egg into each of four bowls. Top with the Greek yogurt and serve with bread (if using).

Nutrition Calories: 259 Fat: 14g Carbohydrates: 22g Fiber: 6g Protein: 12g Calcium: 88mg

Eggplant Breakfast Sandwich

Preparation Time: 5 minutes
Cooking Time: 20 minutes
Servings: 2-4

Ingredients

- 2 tablespoons extra-virgin olive oil, divided
- 1 eggplant, cut into 8 (½-inch-thick) rounds
- ¼ teaspoon kosher salt
- ¼ teaspoon freshly ground black pepper
- 4 large eggs
- 1 garlic clove, minced
- 4 cups fresh baby spinach
- Hot sauce or Harissa (optional)

Directions

1.   Heat 1 tablespoon of extra-virgin olive oil in a large skillet over medium heat. Add the eggplant in a single layer and cook until tender and browned on both sides, 4 to 5 minutes per side. Transfer the eggplant from the skillet to a plate and season it with salt and pepper. Wipe out the skillet and set aside.

2.   Meanwhile, place a large saucepan filled three-quarters full with water over medium-high heat and bring it to a simmer. Carefully break the eggs into small, individual bowls and pour slowly into a fine-mesh strainer over another bowl. Allow the excess white to drain, then lower the strainer into the water. Tilt the egg out into the water. Repeat with the remaining eggs. Swirl the water occasionally as the eggs cook and whites set, about 4 minutes. Remove the eggs with a slotted spoon, transfer them to a paper towel, and drain.

3.   Heat the remaining 1 tablespoon of extra-virgin olive oil over medium heat in the large skillet and add the garlic and spinach. Cook until the spinach is wilted, about 1 minute.

4.   Place one eggplant round on each of four plates and evenly divide the spinach among the rounds. Top the spinach with a poached egg on each sandwich and place the remaining eggplant round on the egg. Serve with hot sauce or harissa (if using).

Nutrition Calories: 362 Fat: 25g Carbohydrates: 21g Fiber: 10g Protein: 17g Calcium: 138mg

Perfect Egg Scramble with Simple Salad

Preparation Time: 17 minutes
Cooking Time: 5 minutes
Servings: 4

Ingredients

- 8 large eggs
- 3 tablespoons milk
- Kosher salt
- 6 cups arugula
- 1 tablespoon extra-virgin olive oil
- 2 tablespoons minced red onion
- 1 bunch radishes, thinly sliced
- 1 lemon, cut into wedges
- 2 tablespoons unsalted butter

Directions

1.   In a medium bowl, whisk the eggs, milk, and a pinch of salt until blended. Set aside for 15 minutes.

2.   Meanwhile, in a large bowl, toss the arugula with the extra-virgin olive oil, red onion, radishes, and a pinch of salt. Evenly divide the salad among four plates and garnish each with a lemon wedge.

3.   Melt the butter in a medium nonstick skillet over medium-high heat. Add the eggs to the skillet and cook by scraping the bottom very slowly, then folding. Repeat until the eggs have formed solid, moist curds. Portion the scrambled eggs evenly among the plates and serve immediately.

Nutrition Calories: 262 Fat: 20g Carbohydrates: 6g Fiber: 2g Protein: 14g Calcium: 128mg

Avocado-Tofu Scramble with Roasted Potatoes

Preparation Time: 5 minutes
Cooking Time: 25 minutes
Servings: 4

Ingredients

- 1½ pounds small potatoes, cut into bite-size pieces
- 4 tablespoons plant-based oil (safflower, olive, or grape seed), divided
- Kosher salt
- Freshly ground black pepper
- 1 ounce water
- 2 teaspoons ground cumin
- 2 teaspoons turmeric
- ¼ teaspoon paprika
- 1 yellow onion, finely chopped
- 1 bell pepper, finely chopped
- 3 cups kale, torn into bite-size pieces
- 3 ounces firm tofu, drained and crumbled
- 1 avocado, diced, for garnish

Directions

1. Preheat the oven to 425°F. Line a baking sheet with parchment paper.
2. Combine the potatoes with 2 tablespoons of oil and a pinch each of salt and pepper on the baking sheet, and then toss them to coat. Roast for 20 to 25 minutes or until tender and golden brown.
3. Meanwhile, stir together the water, cumin, turmeric, and paprika until well mixed to make the sauce. Set aside.
4. Heat the remaining 2 tablespoons of oil in a large skillet over medium heat. Add the onion and bell pepper and sauté for 3 to 5 minutes. Season with a pinch of salt and pepper.
5. Add the kale to the skillet, cover, and allow the steam to cook the kale for about 2 minutes.
6. Remove the lid and, using a spatula, push the vegetables to one side of the skillet and place the tofu and sauce on the empty side. Stir until the tofu is heated through, 3 to 5 minutes. Stir the tofu and vegetables.
7. Serve the tofu scramble with the roasted potatoes on the side and garnished with avocado.

Nutrition Calories: 256 Fat: 10g Carbohydrates: 36g Fiber: 7g Protein: 7g Calcium: 114mg

Blueberry-Chia Smoothie

Preparation Time: 5 minutes
Cooking Time: 0 minutes
Servings: 2

Ingredients

- 2 cups frozen blueberries
- ½ medium frozen banana
- 2 tablespoons peanut butter
- 2 tablespoons chia seeds
- 12 ounces unsweetened soy milk, plus extra if needed

Directions

1. Combine the blueberries, banana, peanut butter, chia seeds, and soy milk in a blender and blend on high speed until smooth. Use a spatula to scrape down the sides as needed.
2. Serve immediately. If it's too thick, add more soy milk or water by the tablespoonful until you've reached the desired consistency.

Nutrition Calories: 360 Fat: 16g Carbohydrates: 46g Fiber: 14g
Protein: 12g Calcium: 333mg

Cherry, Chocolate, and Almond Shake

Preparation Time: 5 minutes
Cooking Time: 0 minutes
Servings: 2

Ingredients

- 10 ounces frozen cherries
- 2 tablespoons cocoa powder
- 2 tablespoons almond butter
- 2 tablespoons hemp seeds
- 8 ounces unsweetened almond milk

Directions

1. Combine the cherries, cocoa, almond butter, hemp seeds, and almond milk in a blender and blend on high speed until smooth. Use a spatula to scrape down the sides as needed. Serve immediately.

Nutrition Calories: 28 Fat: 16g Carbohydrates: 32g Fiber: 7g Protein: 10g Calcium: 308mg

Stovetop Granola

Preparation Time: 10 minutes

Cooking Time: 10 minutes

Servings: 4

Ingredients

- 1½ cups grains (rolled oats, rye flakes, or any flaked grain)
- ¼ cup vegetable, grape seed, or extra-virgin olive oil
- ¼ cup honey or maple syrup
- 1 tablespoon spice (cinnamon, chai spices, turmeric, ginger, or cloves)
- 1 tablespoon citrus zest (orange, lemon, lime, or grapefruit) (optional)
- 1¼ cups roasted, chopped nuts (almonds, walnuts, or pistachios)
- ¾ cup seeds (sunflower, pumpkin, sesame, hemp, ground chia, or ground flaxseed)
- ½ cup dried fruit (golden raisins, apricots, raisins, dates, figs, or cranberries)
- Kosher salt

Directions

1. Heat a large dry skillet, preferably cast iron, over medium-high heat. Add the grains and cook, stirring frequently, until golden brown and toasty. Remove the grains from the skillet and transfer them to a small bowl.
2. Reduce the heat to medium, return the skillet to the heat, and add the vegetable oil, honey, and spice. Stir until thoroughly combined and bring to a simmer.
3. Once the mixture begins to bubble, reduce the heat to low and add the citrus zest (if using), toasted grains, nuts, seeds, and dried fruit. Stir and cook for another 2 minutes or until the granola is sticky and you can smell the spices. Adjust the seasonings as desired and add salt to taste.
4. Allow the granola to cool before storing it in an airtight container at room temperature for up to 6 months.

Nutrition Calories: 167 Fat: 11g Carbohydrates: 15g Fiber: 3g
Protein: 4g Calcium: 39mg

Seedy Muesli

Preparation Time: 5 minutes

Cooking Time: 0 minutes

Servings: 6

Ingredients

- 2 cups gluten-free rolled oats
- 1 cup roasted, slivered almonds
- ¾ cup raw sunflower seeds
- ½ cup raw pumpkin seeds
- ½ cup pistachios
- ½ cup apricots, sliced
- ¼ cup hemp seeds
- ¼ cup ground flaxseed
- ¼ cup toasted sesame seeds

Directions

1. In a medium bowl, combine the oats, almonds, sunflower seeds, pumpkin seeds, pistachios, apricots, hemp seeds, flaxseed, and sesame seeds.
2. Store the mixture in an airtight container at room temperature for up to 6 months.

Nutrition Calories: 430 Fat: 29g Carbohydrates: 30g Fiber: 8g Protein: 16g Calcium: 90mg

Apple Millet Porridge

Preparation Time: 3 minutes

Cooking Time: 12 minutes

Servings: 2

Ingredients

- 1 cup millet, rinsed and drained
- 2½ cups plant-based milk, divided
- 2 teaspoons ground cinnamon
- Pinch kosher salt
- 1 tablespoon honey
- 1 apple, cored and cut into bite-size pieces
- ¼ cup chopped walnuts, toasted

Directions

1. In a small saucepan, combine the millet, 2 cups of milk, the cinnamon, and salt and place over medium heat. Cook, stirring until the millet puffs up and is fully cooked, 10 to 12 minutes.

2. Remove the millet from the heat and slowly add the remaining ½ cup of milk along with the honey. Adjust the seasonings as desired.

3. Divide the millet between two bowls and top each with half of the apple and walnuts.

4. Store any leftovers in an airtight container in the refrigerator for up to 5 days.

Nutrition Calories: 605 Fat: 17g Carbohydrates: 102g Fiber: 14g Protein: 15g Calcium: 607mg

Breakfast Banana Barley

Preparation Time: 5 minutes
Cooking Time: 10 minutes
Servings: 2

Ingredients
- 3 cups water
- Pinch kosher salt
- 1½ cups quick barley, rinsed and drained
- 3 tablespoons natural peanut butter
- 1 banana, sliced

Directions

1. In a small saucepan, bring the water and salt to a boil over high heat.

2. Stir in the barley, cover, reduce the heat, and simmer for 10 minutes or until tender.

3. Remove the saucepan from the heat and add the peanut butter, stirring to blend. Adjust the salt as desired, and divide the mixture between two bowls.

4. Top with the sliced bananas and serve.

5. Store any leftovers in an airtight container in the refrigerator for up to 5 days.

Nutrition Calories: 725 Fat: 14g Carbohydrates: 136g Fiber: 26g Protein: 21g Calcium: 58mg

Harvest Blackberry Quinoa Bowl

Preparation Time: 5 minutes
Cooking Time: 20 minutes
Servings: 2

Ingredients
- 1½ cups water
- Pinch kosher salt
- ¾ cup quinoa, rinsed
- 1 cup halved blackberries

- Ground cinnamon, for garnish

Directions

1. In a medium saucepan, bring the water and salt to a boil over high heat, reduce the heat to low, and add the quinoa.

2. Cook until you see the grains are tender and the liquid is absorbed, about 15 minutes.

3. Remove the quinoa from the heat. If you prefer your quinoa to be fluffy, then cover with a lid for a few minutes and allow it to rest. Once the quinoa is rested, use a fork to fluff it up, top it with the blackberries and a sprinkle of cinnamon, and serve.

Nutrition Calories: 286 Fat: 3g Carbohydrates: 53g Fiber: 10g Protein: 10g Calcium: 51mg

High-Protein Oatmeal

Preparation Time: 2 minutes
Cooking Time: 8 minutes
Servings: 1

Ingredients
- 8 ounces vanilla soy milk
- ½ cup oats
- 1 tablespoon chia seeds
- ¼ cup blueberries
- 1 tablespoon sliced and toasted almonds

Directions

1. In a medium saucepan over medium-high heat, stir together the soy milk and oats.

2. Bring to a boil, reduce the heat to low, and simmer, stirring frequently, until cooked and tender, 5 to 8 minutes.

3. Remove the oatmeal from the heat and serve topped with chia seeds, blueberries, and almonds.

4. Store any leftovers in an airtight container in the refrigerator for up to 5 days.

Nutrition Calories: 373 Fat: 13g Carbohydrates: 49g Fiber: 12g Protein: 15g Calcium: 420mg

Carrot Cake Oatmeal

Preparation Time: 3 minutes
Cooking Time: 10 minutes
Servings: 1

Ingredients

- ½ cup unsweetened almond milk
- ½ cup water
- 1 carrot, grated
- 1/3 cup rolled oats
- 1 tablespoon golden raisins
- 1 teaspoon honey
- Pinch ground cinnamon
- 1½ tablespoons almond butter
- ½ cup cottage cheese

Directions

1. In a small saucepan, combine the almond milk, water, grated carrot, oats, golden raisins, honey, and cinnamon over medium heat. Bring the mixture to a boil, reduce the heat to low, and simmer, stirring occasionally, until the oats are cooked, about 7 minutes.

2. Mix in the almond butter, remove the saucepan from the heat, and transfer the oats to a bowl.

3. Serve immediately, topped with cottage cheese.

Nutrition Calories: 445 Fat: 21g Carbohydrates: 47g Fiber: 7g Protein: 21g Calcium: 431mg

Coconut-Berry Sunrise Smoothie

Preparation Time: 5 minutes
Cooking Time: minutes
Servings: 2

Ingredients:

- ½ cup mixed berries (blueberries, strawberries, blackberries)
- 1 tablespoon ground flaxseed
- 2 tablespoons unsweetened coconut flakes
- ½ cup unsweetened plain coconut milk
- ½ cup leafy greens (kale, spinach)
- ¼ cup unsweetened vanilla nonfat yogurt
- ½ cup ice

Directions:

1. In a blender jar, combine the berries, flaxseed, coconut flakes, coconut milk, greens, yogurt, and ice.

2. Process until smooth. Serve.

Ingredient tip: Flaxseed is a great source of anti-inflammatory omega-3 fatty acids as well as dietary fiber. Be sure to choose ground flaxseed (also known as flaxseed meal) instead of whole flaxseed, since it will be easier for your body to digest and absorb their nutritional benefits.

Nutrition Calories: 181 Fat: 15g Protein: 6g Carbohydrates: 8g Sugars: 3g Fiber: 4g

Greek Yogurt Sundae

Preparation Time: 5 minutes
Cooking Time: 0 minutes
Servings: 1

Ingredients:

- ¾ cup plain nonfat Greek yogurt
- ¼ cup mixed berries (blueberries, strawberries, blackberries)
- 2 tablespoons cashew, walnut, or almond pieces
- 1 tablespoon ground flaxseed
- 2 fresh mint leaves, shredded

Directions:

1. Spoon the yogurt into a small bowl. Top with the berries, nuts, and flaxseed.

2. Garnish with the mint and serve.

Substitution tip: Use fresh or frozen berries in this sundae, as available. If using frozen, take the berries out of the freezer about 10 or 15 minutes before you make the sundae, so they can thaw.

Nutrition: Calories: 237 Fat: 11g Protein: 21g Carbohydrates: 16g Sugars: 9g Fiber: 4g

Avocado and Goat Cheese Toast

Preparation Time: 5 minutes
Cooking Time: 0 minutes
Servings: 2

Ingredients:

- 2 slices whole-wheat thin-sliced bread (I love Ezekiel sprouted bread and Dave's Killer Bread)
- ½ avocado
- 2 tablespoons crumbled goat cheese
- Salt

Directions:

1.   In a toaster or broiler, toast the bread until browned.

2.   Remove the flesh from the avocado. In a medium bowl, use a fork to mash the avocado flesh. Spread it onto the toast.

3.   Sprinkle with the goat cheese and season lightly with salt.

4.   Add any toppings and serve.

Option tip: The options for topping avocado toast are endless. Some more ideas include adding a handful of microgreens, a tablespoon of crushed nuts, a tablespoon of Parmesan cheese, a couple of tomato slices, or a poached egg. Just remember that any add-ins will change the nutrient profile.

Nutrition: Calories: 137 Fat: 6g Protein: 5g Carbohydrates: 18g Sugars: 0g Fiber: 5g

Oat and Walnut Granola

Preparation Time: 10 minutes
Cooking Time: 30 minutes
Servings: 16

Ingredients:

- 4 cups rolled oats
- 1 cup walnut pieces
- ½ cup pepitas
- ¼ teaspoon salt
- 1 teaspoon ground cinnamon
- 1 teaspoon ground ginger
- ½ cup coconut oil, melted
- ½ cup unsweetened applesauce
- 1 teaspoon vanilla extract
- ½ cup dried cherries

Directions:

1.   Preheat the oven to 350°F. Line a baking sheet with parchment paper.

2.   In a large bowl, toss the oats, walnuts, pepitas, salt, cinnamon, and ginger.

3.   In a large measuring cup, combine the coconut oil, applesauce, and vanilla. Pour over the dry mixture and mix well.

4.   Transfer the mixture to the prepared baking sheet. Cook for 30 minutes, stirring about halfway through. Remove from the oven and let the granola sit undisturbed until completely cool. Break the granola into pieces, and stir in the dried cherries.

5.   Transfer to an airtight container, and store at room temperature for up to 2 weeks.

Option tip: For a higher-protein granola, mix in up to ½ cup hemp seeds or flaxseed after cooking, along with the cherries.

Nutrition: Calories: 224 Fat: 15g Protein: 5g Carbohydrates: 20g Sugars: 5g Fiber: 3g

Chocolate-Zucchini Muffins

Preparation Time: 15 minutes
Cooking Time: 20 minutes
Servings: 12

Ingredients:

- 1½ cups grated zucchini
- 1½ cups rolled oats
- 1 teaspoon ground cinnamon
- 2 teaspoons baking powder
- ¼ teaspoon salt
- 1 large egg
- 1 teaspoon vanilla extract
- ¼ cup coconut oil, melted
- ½ cup unsweetened applesauce
- ¼ cup honey
- ¼ cup dark chocolate chips

Directions:

1.   Preheat the oven to 350°F. Grease the cups of a 12-cup muffin tin or line with paper baking liners. Set aside.

2.   Place the zucchini in a colander over the sink to drain.

3.   In a blender jar, process the oats until they resemble flour. Transfer to a medium mixing bowl and add the cinnamon, baking powder, and salt. Mix well.

4.   In another large mixing bowl, combine the egg, vanilla, coconut oil, applesauce, and honey. Stir to combine.

5.   Press the zucchini into the colander, draining any liquids, and add to the wet mixture.

6.   Stir the dry mixture into the wet mixture, and mix until no dry spots remain. Fold in the chocolate chips.

7. Transfer the batter to the muffin tin, filling each cup a little over halfway. Cook for 16 to 18 minutes until the muffins are lightly browned and a toothpick inserted in the center comes out clean.

8. Store in an airtight container, refrigerated, for up to 5 days.

Option tip: Add more protein to the muffins by adding ½ cup walnut pieces along with the chocolate chips. If you make more muffins than you need, you can freeze them for up to 3 months to ensure you have a quick, healthy breakfast or snack for any day of the week.

Nutrition: Calories: 121 Fat: 7g Protein: 2g Carbohydrates: 16 Sugars: 7g Fiber: 2g Sodium: 106mg

Gluten-Free Carrot and Oat Pancakes

Preparation Time: 10 minutes
Cooking Time: 20 minutes
Servings: 4
Ingredients:
- 1 cup rolled oats
- 1 cup shredded carrots
- 1 cup low-fat cottage cheese
- 2 eggs
- ½ cup unsweetened plain almond milk
- 1 teaspoon baking powder
- ½ teaspoon ground cinnamon
- 2 tablespoons ground flaxseed
- ¼ cup plain nonfat Greek yogurt
- 1 tablespoon pure maple syrup
- 2 teaspoons canola oil, divided

Directions:
1. In a blender jar, process the oats until they resemble flour. Add the carrots, cottage cheese, eggs, almond milk, baking powder, cinnamon, and flaxseed to the jar. Process until smooth.

2. In a small bowl, combine the yogurt and maple syrup and stir well. Set aside.

3. In a large skillet, heat 1 teaspoon of oil over medium heat. Using a measuring cup, add ¼ cup of batter per pancake to the skillet. Cook for 1 to 2 minutes until bubbles form on the surface, and flip the pancakes. Cook for another minute until the pancakes are browned

and cooked through. Repeat with the remaining 1 teaspoon of oil and remaining batter.

4. Serve warm topped with the maple yogurt.

Ingredient tip: While oats are naturally gluten free, many brands are processed in facilities that also process grains with gluten, making cross-contamination risk high. If you are sensitive to gluten, be sure to select oats that are labeled as gluten free.

Nutrition: Calories: 226 Fat: 8g Protein: 15g Carbohydrates: 24g Sugars: 7g Fiber: 4g Sodium: 403mg

Breakfast Egg Bites

Preparation Time: 10 minutes
Cooking Time: 25 minutes
Servings: 8
Ingredients:
- Nonstick cooking spray
- 6 eggs, beaten
- ¼ cup unsweetened plain almond milk
- 1 red bell pepper, diced
- 1 cup chopped spinach
- ¼ cup crumbled goat cheese
- ½ cup sliced brown mushrooms
- ¼ cup sliced sun-dried tomatoes
- Salt
- Freshly ground black pepper

Directions:
1. Preheat the oven to 350°F. Spray 8 muffin cups of a 12-cup muffin tin with nonstick cooking spray. Set aside.

2. In a large mixing bowl, combine the eggs, almond milk, bell pepper, spinach, goat cheese, mushrooms, and tomatoes. Season with salt and pepper.

3. Fill the prepared muffin cups three-fourths full with the egg mixture. Bake for 20 to 25 minutes until the eggs are set. Let cool slightly and remove the egg bites from the muffin tin.

4. Serve warm, or store in an airtight container in the refrigerator for up to 5 days or in the freezer for up to 1 month.

Technique tip: For a busy morning, you can make these egg bites in single servings in the microwave. Spray a microwave-safe mug with nonstick cooking spray and add 1 beaten egg, along with 1 tablespoon unsweetened plain almond milk, 1 tablespoon minced bell pepper, a couple of tablespoons chopped spinach, and a few mushroom and sun-dried tomato slices. Season with a pinch salt and pepper. Microwave on high for 1½ to 2 minutes until the eggs begin to set.

Nutrition Calories: 67 Fat: 4g Protein: 6g Carbohydrates: 3g

Sugars: 2g Fiber: 1g Sodium: 127mg

Crispy Breakfast Pita with Egg and Canadian Bacon

Preparation Time: 5 minutes

Cooking Time: 15 minutes

Servings: 2

Ingredients:

- 1 (6-inch) whole-grain pita bread
- 3 teaspoons extra-virgin olive oil, divided
- 2 eggs
- 2 Canadian bacon slices
- Juice of ½ lemon
- 1 cup microgreens
- 2 tablespoons crumbled goat cheese
- Freshly ground black pepper

Directions:

1. Heat a large skillet over medium heat. Cut the pita bread in half and brush each side of both halves with ¼ teaspoon of olive oil (using a total of 1 teaspoon oil). Cook for 2 to 3 minutes on each side, and then remove from the skillet.

2. In the same skillet, heat 1 teaspoon of oil over medium heat. Crack the eggs into the skillet and cook until the eggs are set, 2 to 3 minutes. Remove from the skillet.

3. In the same skillet, cook the Canadian bacon for 3 to 5 minutes, flipping once.

4. In a large bowl, whisk together the remaining 1 teaspoon of oil and the lemon juice. Add the microgreens and toss to combine.

5. Top each pita half with half of the microgreens, 1 piece of bacon, 1 egg, and 1 tablespoon of goat cheese. Season with pepper and serve.

Ingredient tip: Microgreens are the immature edible greens of any number of vegetables. They are easy to grow yourself or can be found at farmers' markets and specialty and natural grocers year-round. There are many different varieties and you can play around and see which you prefer. If you can't find microgreens, feel free to substitute arugula, baby kale, spinach, or any other leafy green you like.

Nutrition: Calories: 250 Fat: 14g Protein: 13g Carbohydrates: 20g Sugars: 1g Fiber: 3g Sodium: 398mg

Brussels Sprout Hash and Eggs

Preparation Time: 15 minutes

Cooking Time: 15 minutes

Servings: 4

Ingredients:

- 3 teaspoons extra-virgin olive oil, divided
- 1 pound Brussels sprouts, sliced
- 2 garlic cloves, thinly sliced
- ¼ teaspoon salt
- Juice of 1 lemon
- 4 eggs

Directions:

1. In a large skillet, heat 1½ teaspoons of oil over medium heat. Add the Brussels sprouts and toss. Cook, stirring regularly, for 6 to 8 minutes until browned and softened. Add the garlic and continue to cook until fragrant, about 1 minute. Season with the salt and lemon juice. Transfer to a serving dish.

2. In the same pan, heat the remaining 1½ teaspoons of oil over medium-high heat. Crack the eggs into the pan. Fry for 2 to 4 minutes, flip, and continue cooking to desired doneness. Serve over the bed of hash.

Make-ahead tip: Brussels sprouts, like other brassica vegetables, are easy to prep in advance and hold up well both raw and cooked. Prep the Brussels sprouts up to 5 days in advance by slicing them when you have a free moment. Refrigerate in an airtight container until ready for use.

Nutrition: Calories: 158 Fat: 9g Protein: 10g Carbohydrates: 12g Sugars: 4g Fiber: 4g Sodium: 234mg

Spinach, Artichoke, and Goat Cheese Breakfast Bake

Preparation Time: 10 minutes
Cooking Time: 35 minutes
Servings: 8

Ingredients:
- Nonstick cooking spray
- 1 (10-ounce) package frozen spinach, thawed and drained
- 1 (14-ounce) can artichoke hearts, drained
- ¼ cup finely chopped red bell pepper
- 2 garlic cloves, minced
- 8 eggs, lightly beaten
- ¼ cup unsweetened plain almond milk
- ½ teaspoon salt
- ½ teaspoon freshly ground black pepper
- ½ cup crumbled goat cheese

Directions:
1. Preheat the oven to 375°F. Spray an 8-by-8-inch baking dish with nonstick cooking spray.
2. In a large mixing bowl, combine the spinach, artichoke hearts, bell pepper, garlic, eggs, almond milk, salt, and pepper. Stir well to combine.
3. Transfer the mixture to the baking dish. Sprinkle with the goat cheese.
4. Bake for 35 minutes until the eggs are set. Serve warm.

Option tip: Spice things up for breakfast by adding a scant teaspoon of red pepper flakes to this dish.

Nutrition: Calories: 104 Fat: 5g Protein: 9g Carbohydrates: 6g Sugars: 1g Fiber: 2g Sodium: 488mg

Homemade Turkey Breakfast Sausage

Preparation Time: 10 minutes
Cooking Time: 10 minutes
Servings: 8

Ingredients:
- 1 pound lean ground turkey
- ½ teaspoon salt
- ½ teaspoon dried sage
- ½ teaspoon dried thyme
- ½ teaspoon freshly ground black pepper
- ¼ teaspoon ground fennel seeds
- 1 teaspoon extra-virgin olive oil

Directions:
1. In a large mixing bowl, combine the ground turkey, salt, sage, thyme, pepper, and fennel. Mix well.
2. Shape the meat into 8 small, round patties.
3. Heat the olive oil in a skillet over medium-high heat. Cook the patties in the skillet for 3 to 4 minutes on each side until browned and cooked through.
4. Serve warm, or store in an airtight container in the refrigerator for up to 3 days or in the freezer for up to 1 month.

Technique tip: If you are using the turkey sausage for Sweet Potato, Onion, and Turkey Sausage Hash (here), skip steps 2 and 3, and add the bulk sausage to the pan as is when called for in the recipe.

Nutrition: Calories: 92 Fat: 5g Protein: 11g Carbohydrates: 0g Sugars: 0g Fiber: 0g Sodium: 156mg

Cottage Pancakes

Preparation Time: 10 minutes
Cooking Time: 20 minutes
Servings: 4

Ingredients:
- 2 cups low-fat cottage cheese
- 4 egg whites
- 2 eggs
- 1 tablespoon pure vanilla extract
- 1½ cups almond flour

From the Cupboard:
- Nonstick cooking spray

Directions:
1. Place the cottage cheese, egg whites, eggs, and vanilla in a blender and pulse to combine.
2. Add the almond flour to the blender and blend until smooth.
3. Place a large nonstick skillet over medium heat and lightly coat it with cooking spray.
4. Spoon ¼ cup of batter per pancake, 4 at a time, into the skillet. Cook the pancakes until the bottoms are firm and golden, about 4 minutes.
5. Flip the pancakes over and cook the other side until they are cooked through, about 3 minutes.

6. Remove the pancakes to a plate and repeat with the remaining batter.
7. Serve with fresh fruit.
Nutrition: Calories:345 Fat: 22.1gProtein: 29.1gCarbs: 11.1gFiber: 4.1gSugar: 5.1gSodium: 560mg

Tropical Yogurt Kiwi Bowl

Preparation Time: 5 minutes
Cooking Time: 0 minutes
Servings: 0
Ingredients:
- 1½ cups plain low-fat Greek yogurt
- 2 kiwis, peeled and sliced
- 2 tablespoons shredded unsweetened coconut flakes
- 2 tablespoons halved walnuts
- 1 tablespoon chia seeds

Directions:
1. Divide the yogurt between two small bowls.
2. Top each serving of yogurt with half of the kiwi slices, coconut flakes, walnuts, and chia seeds.
Nutrition: Calories: 261 Fat: 9.1gProtein: 21.1g Carbs: 23.1g Fiber: 6.1g Sugar: 14.1g Sodium: 84mg

Banana Crêpe Cakes

Preparation Time: 5 minutes
Cooking Time: 20 minutes
Servings: 4
Ingredients:
- 4 ounces (113 g) reduced-fat plain cream cheese, softened
- 2 medium bananas
- 4 large eggs
- ½ teaspoon vanilla extract
From the Cupboard:
- Avocado oil cooking spray
- 1/8 teaspoon salt

Directions:
1. Heat a large skillet over low heat. Coat the cooking surface with cooking spray, and allow the pan to heat for another 2 to 3 minutes.

2. Meanwhile, in a medium bowl, mash the cream cheese and bananas together with a fork until combined. The bananas can be a little chunky.
3. Add the eggs, vanilla, and salt, and mix well.
4. For each cake, drop 2 tablespoons of the batter onto the warmed skillet and use the bottom of a large spoon or ladle to spread it thin. Let it cook for 7 to 9 minutes.
5. Flip the cake over and cook briefly, about 1 minute.
Nutrition: Calories: 176 Fat: 9.1g Protein: 9.1g Carbs: 15.1g Fiber: 2.1g Sugar: 8.1g Sodium: 214mg

Cranberry Grits

Preparation Time: 10 minutes
Cooking Time: 15 minutes
Servings: 5
Ingredients:
- ¾ cup stone-ground grits or polenta (not instant)
- ½ cup unsweetened dried cranberries
- 1 tablespoon half-and-half
- ¼ cup sliced almonds, toasted
From the Cupboard:
- Pinch kosher salt
- 1 tablespoon unsalted butter or ghee (optional)

Directions:
1. In the electric pressure cooker, stir together the grits, cranberries, salt, and 3 cups of water.
2. Close and lock the lid. Set the valve to sealing.
3. Cook on high pressure for 10 minutes.
4. When the cooking is complete, hit Cancel and quick release the pressure.
5. Once the pin drops, unlock and remove the lid.
6. Add the butter (if using) and half-and-half. Stir until the mixture is creamy, adding more half-and-half if necessary.
7. Spoon into serving bowls and sprinkle with almonds.
Nutrition: Calories: 219 Fat: 10.2gProtein: 4.9g Carbs: 32.1g Fiber: 4.1g Sugar: 6.9g Sodium: 30mg

Goat Cheese and Avocado Toast

Preparation Time: 10 minutes

Cooking Time: 5 minutes

Servings: 2

Ingredients:

- 2 slices whole-wheat bread, thinly sliced
- ½ avocado
- 2 tablespoons goat cheese, crumbled
- 2 slices of crumbled bacon, for topping (optional)

From the Cupboard:

- Salt, to taste

Directions:

1. Toast the bread slices in a toaster for 2 to 3 minutes on each side until golden brown.
2. Using a large spoon, scoop the avocado flesh out of the skin and transfer to a medium bowl. Mash the flesh with a potato masher or the back of a fork until it has a spreadable consistency.
3. Spoon the mashed avocado onto the bread slices and evenly spread it all over.
4. Scatter with crumbled goat cheese and lightly season with salt.
5. Serve topped with crumbled bacon, if desired.

Nutrition: Calories: 140 Fat: 6.2gProtein: 5.2g Carbs: 18.2g Fiber: 5.1g Sugar: 0g Sodium: 197mg

Simple Cottage Cheese Pancakes

Preparation Time: 5 minutes

Cooking Time: 10 minutes

Servings: 2

Ingredients:

Batter:

- ½ cup low-fat cottage cheese
- ¼ cup oats
- 1/3 cup egg whites (about 2 egg whites)
- 1 tablespoon stevia
- 1 teaspoon vanilla extract

From the Cupboard:

- Olive oil cooking spray
- Directions:

Directions:

1. Add the cottage cheese, oats, egg whites, stevia and vanilla extract to a food processor. Pulse into a smooth and thick batter.
2. Coat a large skillet with cooking spray and place it over medium heat.
3. Slowly pour half of the batter into the pan, tilting the pan to spread it evenly. Cook for about 2 to 3 minutes until the pancake turns golden brown around the edges. Gently flip the pancake with a spatula and cook for 1 to 2 minutes more.
4. Transfer the pancake to a plate and repeat with the remaining batter.
5. Serve warm.

Nutrition: Calories: 188 Fat: 1.6g Protein: 24.6g Carbs: 18.9g Fiber: 1.9g Sugar: 2g Sodium: 258mg

Almond Berry Smoothie

Preparation Time: 5 minutes

Cooking Time: 0 minutes

Servings: 4

Ingredients:

- 2 cups frozen berries of choice
- 1 cup plain low-fat Greek yogurt
- 1 cup unsweetened vanilla almond milk
- ½ cup natural almond butter

Directions:

1. In a blender, add the berries, almond milk, yogurt, and almond butter. Process until fully mixed and creamy. Pour into four smoothie glasses.
2. Serve chilled or at room temperature.

Nutrition: Calories: 279 Fat: 18.2g Protein: 13.4g Carbs: 19.1g Fiber: 6.1g Sugar: 11.1g Sodium: 138mg

Feta Brussels sprouts and Scrambled Eggs

Preparation Time: 5 minutes

Cooking Time: 15 minutes

Servings: 4

Ingredients:

- 4 slices low-sodium turkey bacon
- 20 Brussels sprouts, halved lengthwise
- 8 large eggs, whisked
- ¼ cup crumbled feta cheese, for garnish

From the Cupboard:

- Avocado oil cooking spray

Directions:

1. Heat a large skillet over medium heat until hot. Coat the skillet with cooking spray.

2. Fry the bacon slices for about 8 minutes until evenly crisp, flipping occasionally.

3. With a slotted spoon, transfer the bacon to a paper towel-lined plate to drain and cool. Leave the bacon grease in the skillet.

4. Add the Brussels sprouts to the bacon grease in the skillet and cook as you stir for about 6 minutes until browned on both side.

5. Push the Brussels sprouts to one side of the skillet, add the whisked eggs and scramble for about 3 to 4 minutes until almost set.

6. Once the bacon is cooled, crumble into small pieces.

7. Divide the Brussels sprouts and scrambled eggs among four serving plates. Scatter the tops with crumbled bacon pieces and garnish with feta cheese before serving.

Nutrition: Calories: 255 Fat: 15.3g Protein: 21.3g Carbs: 10.2g Fiber: 4.2 Sugar: 4.2g Sodium: 340mg

Easy and Creamy Grits

Preparation Time: 5 minutes

Cooking Time: 10 minutes

Servings: 4

Ingredients:

- 1 cup fat-free milk
- 1 cup stone-ground corn grits
- From the Cupboard:
- 2 cups water

Directions:

1. Pour the milk and water into a saucepan over medium heat, and then bring to a simmer until warmed through.

2. Add the corn grits and stir well. Reduce the heat to low and cook covered for 5 to 7 minutes, whisking continuously, or until the grits become tender.

3. Remove from the heat and serve warm.

Nutrition: Calories: 168Fat: 1.1g Protein: 6.2g Carbs: 33.8gFiber: 1.1gSugar: 2.8g

Simple Grain-Free Biscuits

Preparation Time: 10 minutes

Cooking Time: 15 minutes

Servings: 4

Ingredients:

- ¼ cup plain low-fat Greek yogurt
- 1½ cups finely ground almond flour

From the Cupboard:

- 2 tablespoons unsalted butter
- Pinch salt

Directions:

1. Preheat the oven to 375°F (190°C). Line a baking sheet with parchment paper and set aside.

2. Place the butter in a microwave-safe bowl and microwave for 15 to 20 seconds, or until it is just enough to soften.

3. Add the yogurt and salt to the bowl of butter and blend well.

4. Slowly pour in the almond flour and keep stirring until the mixture just comes together into a slightly sticky, shaggy dough.

5. Use a ¼-cup measuring cup to mound balls of dough onto the parchment-lined baking sheet and flatten each into a rounded biscuit shape, about 1 inch thick.

6. Bake in the preheated oven for 13 to 15 minutes, or until the biscuits are lightly golden brown.

7. Let the biscuits cool for 5 minutes before serving.

Nutrition: Calories: 309 Fat: 28.1g Protein: 9.9g Carbs: 8.7g Fiber: 5.1g Sugar: 2.0g Sodium: 31mg

Brussels Sprout with Fried Eggs

Preparation Time: 10 minutes

Cooking Time: 15 minutes

Servings: 4

Ingredients:

- 1 pound (454 g) Brussels sprouts, sliced
- 2 garlic cloves, thinly sliced
- Juice of 1 lemon
- 4 eggs

From the Cupboard:

- 3 teaspoons extra-virgin olive oil, divided
- ¼ teaspoon salt

Directions:

1. Heat 1½ teaspoons of olive oil in a large skillet over medium heat.

2. Add the Brussels sprouts and sauté for 6 to 8 minutes until crispy and tender, stirring frequently.

3. Stir in the garlic and cook for about 1 minute until fragrant. Sprinkle with the salt and lemon juice.

4. Remove from the skillet to a plate and set aside.

5. Heat the remaining oil in the skillet over medium-high heat. Crack the eggs one at a time into the skillet and fry for about 3 minutes. Flip the eggs and continue cooking, or until the egg whites are set and the yolks are cooked to your liking.

6. Serve the fried eggs over the crispy Brussels sprouts.

Nutrition: Calories: 157 Fat: 8.9g Protein: 10.1g Carbs: 11.8g Fiber: 4.1g Sugar: 4.0g Sodium: 233mg

Easy Turkey Breakfast Patties

Preparation Time: 10 minutes
Cooking Time: 10 minutes
Servings: 8

Ingredients:

- 1 pound (454 g) lean ground turkey
- ½ teaspoon dried thyme
- ½ teaspoon dried sage
- ¼ teaspoon ground fennel seeds

From the Cupboard:

- ½ teaspoon salt
- ½ teaspoon freshly ground black pepper
- 1 teaspoon extra-virgin olive oil

Directions:

1. Mix the ground turkey, thyme, sage, salt, pepper, and fennel in a large bowl, and stir until well combined.

2. Form the turkey mixture into 8 equal-sized patties with your hands.

3. In a skillet, heat the olive oil over medium-high heat. Cook the patties for 3 to 4 minutes per side until cooked through.

4. Transfer the patties to a plate and serve hot.

Nutrition: Calories: 91 Fat: 4.8g Protein: 11.2g Carbs: 0.1g Fiber: 0.1g Sugar: 0g Sodium: 155mg

Quick Breakfast Yogurt Sundae

Preparation Time: 5 minutes
Cooking Time: 0 minutes
Servings: 1

Ingredients:

- ¾ cup plain Greek yogurt
- ¼ cup mixed berries (blueberries, strawberries, blackberries)
- 2 tablespoons cashew, walnut, or almond pieces
- 1 tablespoon ground flaxseed
- 2 fresh mint leaves, shredded

Directions:

1. Pour the yogurt into a tall parfait glass and scatter the top with the berries, cashew pieces, and flaxseed.

2. Sprinkle the mint leaves on top for garnish and serve chilled.

Nutrition: Calories: 238 Fat: 11.2g Protein: 20.9g Carbs: 15.8g Fiber: 4.1gSugar: 8.9gSodium: 63mg

Peanut Butter and Berry Oatmeal

Preparation Time: 5 minutes
Cooking Time: 5 minutes
Servings: 2

Ingredients:

- 1½ cups unsweetened vanilla almond milk
- ¾ cup rolled oats
- 1 tablespoon chia seeds
- 2 tablespoons natural peanut butter
- ¼ cup fresh berries, divided (optional)

Directions:

1. Add the almond milk, oats, and chia seeds to a small saucepan and bring to a boil.

2. Cover and continue cooking, stirring often, or until the oats have absorbed the milk.

3. Add the peanut butter and keep stirring until the oats are thick and creamy.

4. Divide the oatmeal into two serving bowls. Serve topped with the berries.

Nutrition: Calories: 260 Fat: 13.9g Protein: 10.1g Carbs: 26.9g Fiber: 7.1g Sugar: 1.0g Sodium: 130mg

Scrambled Egg Whites with Bell Pepper

Preparation Time: 5 minutes
Cooking Time: 10 minutes
Servings: 2

Ingredients:

- 1 green bell pepper, deseeded and finely chopped
- ½ red onion, finely chopped
- 4 eggs whites
- 2 ounces (57 g) pepper Jack cheese, grated

From the Cupboard:

- 2 tablespoons extra-virgin olive oil
- ½ teaspoon sea salt

Directions:

1. Heat the olive oil in a nonstick skillet over medium-high heat.
2. Add the bell pepper and onion to the skillet and sauté for 5 minutes or until tender.
3. Sprinkle the egg white with salt in a bowl, then pour the egg whites in the skillet. Cook for 3 minutes or until the egg whites are scrambled. Stir the egg whites halfway through.
4. Scatter with cheese and cook for an additional 1 minutes until the cheese melts.
5. Divide them onto two serving plates and serve warm.

Nutrition: Calories: 316 Fat: 23.3g Protein: 22.3g Carbs: 6.2g Fiber: 1.1g Sugar: 4.2g Sodium: 975mg

LUNCH

Quick Pork Diane

Preparation Time: 10 minutes
Cooking Time: 12 minutes
Servings: 4

Ingredients:

• Lemon juice [1 tsp.]
• Snipped fresh chives, parsley, or oregano [1 tbsp.]
• Water [1 tbsp.]
• Dijon-style mustard [1 tsp.]
• Butter [1 tbsp.]
• Worcestershire sauce [1 tbsp.]
• Lemon-pepper seasoning [1 tsp.]
• Four boneless pork top loin chops

Directions:

1. To make the sauce, add water, lemon juice, mustard, and Worcestershire sauce in a bowl and set aside. Remove the fat from the chops and sprinkle each side with lemon-pepper seasoning. Melt butter in a skillet and add the chops.
2. Cook for 12 minutes and turn to cook the other side. Remove from heat. Transfer to serving platter and cover with foil.
3. Pour the sauce into the skillet and then pour the sauce over the chops. Top the chops with chives. Serve.

Nutrition: Calories 178 Fat 11g Carbohydrates 1g Protein 18g
Sodium 302mg

Mediterranean Pork Chops: A - Ingredient Dish You Wouldn't Want To Miss

Preparation Time: 10 minutes
Cooking Time: 10 minutes
Servings: 1

Ingredients:

• Boneless or bone-in pork loin chops cut 1/2 inch thick (1 pc)
• Salt [1/4 tsp.]
• Freshly ground black pepper [1/4 tsp.]

• Finely snipped fresh rosemary or 1 tsp. dried rosemary, crushed [1 tbsp.]
• Garlic, minced [3 cloves]

Directions:

1. Prepare the oven by preheating to 425 deg. F. Line a roasting pan with foil and sprinkle the chops with salt and pepper. Set aside. A
2. Add rosemary and garlic, combine in a bowl. Sprinkle them evenly on the chops. Place the chops in the pan. Roast for 10 minutes. Reduce the oven temp to 350 deg. F and serve.

Nutrition: Calories 161 Fat 5g Carbohydrates 1g Protein 25 g Sodium 192mg

Spicy Grilled Portlets

Preparation Time: 20 minutes
Cooking Time: 15 minutes
Servings: 3-4

Ingredients:

• Sliced mango or chili peppers
• Lime juice [¼ cup]
• Olive oil [1 tbsp.]
• Salt [¼ tsp.]
• Garlic, minced [2 cloves]
• Ground cinnamon [1 tsp.]
• Chili powder [1 tbsp.]
• Ground cumin [2 tsp.]
• Hot pepper sauce [½ tsp.]
• Four pork rib chops, cut ¾ inch thick

Directions:

1. Place the chops in a plastic bag. To make the marinade, add chili powder, lime juice, cumin, oil, cinnamon, garlic, hot pepper, and salt.
2. Pour them over the chops and seal the bag. Turn the bag to coat chops well. Place the chops in the fridge for 24 hours.
3. Make sure to turn the bag to even out the marinade. Drain the chops and discard the marinade.
4. Grill the chops until pork juices run clear. Turn once. Garnish with mango or chili peppers. Serve.

Nutrition: Calories 196 Fat 9g Carbohydrates 3g Protein 25g Sodium 159mg

Tender Pork in Mushroom Sauce

Preparation Time: 10 minutes
Cooking Time: 8-9 hours
Servings: 4

Ingredients:
- Cooking oil [1 tbsp.]
- Worcestershire sauce [1½ tsp.]
- Dried thyme, crushed [¾ tsp.]
- 1 (10.75 ounces) can reduced-fat, reduced-sodium condensed cream of mushroom soup
- Pork loin chops, cut ¾ inch thick (4 pcs)
- Garlic powder [1 tsp.]
- Apple juice or apple cider [½ cup]
- One small onion, thinly sliced
- Sliced fresh mushrooms [1½ cups]
- Fresh thyme sprigs
- Quick-cooking tapioca [2 tbsp.]

Directions:
1. Remove the fat from the chops. Place a skillet over medium heat and add oil then warm. Add the chops and cook until brown.
2. Drain the fat. Add the onion in a slow cooker and add the chops. Crush the tapioca and add it to a bowl together with Worcestershire sauce, thyme, garlic powder, apple juice, mushrooms and mushroom soup. Pour the mixture over the chops.
3. Cover the slow cooker and cook on low heat for 8 to 9 hours. Garnished with thyme sprigs. Serve.

Nutrition: Calories 152 Fat 2g Carbohydrates 4g Protein26g
Sodium 286mg

Pork and Herb-Tomato Sauce

Preparation Time: 10 minutes
Cooking Time: 8 hours
Servings: 4

Ingredients:
- Quick-cooking tapioca crushed [2 tsp.]
- Salt [¼ tsp.]
- Worcestershire sauce [½ tsp.]
- Minced garlic (3 cloves)
- Four pork rib chops (with bone), cut ¾ inch thick
- Small onion, chopped [1 pc]
- Stewed tomatoes, undrained and unsalted [2 cans]
- Crushed red pepper [1/4 tsp.]
- Ground black pepper [½ tsp.]
- Dried Italian seasoning, crushed [1 tsp.]

Directions:
1. Remove the fat from the chops and lightly coat the skillet with cooking spray. Place skillet over medium-high heat.
2. Cook the chops until brown on both sides and set aside. In a slow cooker, add the garlic, onion, tapioca, black pepper, Italian seasoning, crushed red pepper, Worcestershire sauce, and salt. Add the chops and pour the tomatoes.
3. Cover the slow cooker and cook on low heat for 8 hours. Transfer the chops to a platter, add tomatoes on top and serve.

Nutrition: Calories 245 Fat 7g Carbohydrates 19g Protein 24 Sodium 568mg

Cranberry Pork Loin

Preparation Time: 10 minutes
Cooking Time: 15 minutes
Servings: 4

Ingredients:
- Cooking oil [1 tbsp.]
- Honey [1 tbsp.]
- Salt [1/8 tsp.]
- Ground nutmeg [1/8 tsp.]
- Ground black pepper [1/8 tsp.]
- Frozen orange juice concentrate, thawed [2 tbsp.]
- Ground ginger [¼ tsp.]
- Whole cranberry sauce [½ cup]
- 4 (5 ounces) boneless pork loin chops, cut ½-inch thick

Directions:
1. Coat a skillet with nonstick cooking spray and place over medium-high heat. Sprinkle salt and pepper on both sides of chops and put it on the skillet. Reduce the heat to medium and let the chops cook until done.

2. Make sure you turn the chops. Remove the chops from the skillet and cover with foil. Add orange juice concentrate, honey, nutmeg, ginger, and cranberry sauce in a bowl and mix. Add the mixture to the skillet and cook for 2 minutes until sauce thickens. Pour over the chops and serve.

Nutrition: Calories 277 Fat 9g Carbohydrates 22g Protein 26g Sodium 288mg

Sassy Pork Chops

Preparation Time: 15 minutes
Cooking Time: 7 hours
Servings: 2
Ingredients:
- Ground black pepper [1/4 tsp.]
- Reduced-sodium chicken broth [1/4 cup]
- Dried oregano, crushed [1/2 tsp.]
- Orange juice [1/4 cup]
- Cooking oil [2 tbsp.]
- Chopped onion [1/2 cup]
- Eight pork loin chops (with bone), cut 3/4 inch thick
- Medium red, green, and sweet yellow peppers cut into strips [2 pcs]
- Garlic salt [1/2 tsp.]
- Thinly sliced celery [1 cup]
- Chopped chipotle chili peppers in adobo sauce [1 tbsp.]

Directions:
1. In a slow cooker, add the celery, onion, and sweet peppers. Set aside. Season the chops with salt and pepper. Place in the skillet and cook over medium heat until brown on both sides.
2. Add the chops to the cooker. Add broth, chipotle peppers, orange juice, and oregano in a bowl. Mix and pour on the chops.
3. Cover the cooker and place the low heat. Cook for 7 hours. Place the chops and veggies on a platter and discard the liquid before serving.

Nutrition: Calories 215 Fat 7g Carbohydrates 4g Protein 33 Sodium 363mg

Louisiana Chicken

Preparation Time: 10 minutes
Cooking Time: 15 minutes
Servings: 2-3
Ingredients:
- Frozen cut okra [1 cup]
- Black pepper [1 tsp.]
- Stewed tomatoes, no salt [1 can]
- Skinned drumsticks [8 pcs]
- Louisiana hot sauce [1 ½ tbsp.]
- Whole grain noodles, cooked [2 cups]
- Dried thyme, ground [1 tsp.]
- Salt [1/4 tsp.]

Directions:
1. Coat a skillet lightly with cooking spray. Place it over medium-high heat and add chicken. Let it turn brown on all sides and don't forget to set them.
2. Add stewed tomatoes on top, thyme, hot sauce, okra, pepper, and salt. Let it boil and then reduce the heat. Cover and then simmer until the center is no longer pink. Add the chicken on a platter and then the sauce. Serve with the noodles and enjoy.

Nutrition: Calories 190 Fat 1g Carbohydrates 8g Protein 27g

Thai Chicken Wings

Preparation Time: 5 minutes
Cooking Time: 6 hours
Servings: 7-8
Ingredients:
- Lime juice [1 tbsp.]
- Ground ginger [1/4 tsp.]
- Peanut Sauce
- Chicken wing drummettes [24 pcs]
- Water [1/4 cup]
- Crushed red pepper [1/4 tsp.]
- Garlic, minced [2 cloves]
- Water [1/2 cup]
- Reduced-sodium soy sauce [2 tsp.]
- Almond butter [1/2 cup]
- Ground ginger [1/2 tsp.]

Directions:

1.   Put chicken in the slow cooker. Add the lime juice, water, and ginger. Cover and set to low heat. Let it cook for 5-6 hrs.

2.   Drain the chicken and discard the liquid. Add half of the peanut sauce to chicken and toss. Serve.

Nutrition: Calories 101 Fat 1g Carbohydrates 3g Protein 9g Sodium 159mg

Chicken Mac & Cheese

Preparation Time: 10 minutes

Cooking Time: 15 minutes

Servings: 2

Ingredients:

- Finely chopped onion [1/4 cup]
- Dried multigrain [1 ½ cups]
- Fresh baby spinach [2 cups]
- Skinless, boneless chicken breast halves, cut into 1-inch pieces [12 oz.]
- Fat-free milk [1 2/3 cups]
- Chopped, seeded tomatoes [1 cup]
- All-purpose flour [1 tbsp.]
- Shredded reduced-fat cheddar cheese [3/4 cup]
- Light semi soft cheese with garlic and herb [[1 6 1/2 oz.]

Directions:

1.   Cook the macaroni in a saucepan. Make sure to follow package directions. Don't add salt. Drain the macaroni. Coat a skillet with cooking spray. Heat the skillet over medium-high heat. Add the chicken and onions.

2.   Let it cook until onion is transparent and chicken is no longer pink. Stir frequently. Remove the skillet from heat. Add the cheese until it melts. Whisk flour and milk in another bowl. Add the chicken mixture.

3.   Cook over medium-high heat and stir. Wait until thick and bubbly then reduce the heat to low. Add the macaroni until heated. Add tomatoes and spinach. Serve.

Nutrition: Calories 169 Fat 3g Carbohydrates 24g Protein 11gSodium 210mg

Five Spice Chicken Wings

Preparation Time: 10 minutes

Cooking Time: 20 minutes

Servings: 4-5

Ingredients:

- Finely chopped onion [1/4 cup]
- Plum sauce [3/4 cup]
- Five-spice powder [1 tsp.]
- Butter melted [1 tbsp.]
- Slivered green onions
- Chicken wings [16 pcs]

Directions:

1.   Preheat your oven to 375 deg. F. Cut off the tips of the wings and discard the tips. Cut each wing into two pieces. Line a baking pan with foil and arrange the wings in it in a single layer. Bake the wings for 20 minutes. Drain. In a slow cooker, add the butter, five spice powder, plum sauce and chicken. Stir to coat the chicken with sauce. Cover and cook on low heat. Do this for 4 hours. Serve.

Nutrition: Calories 32 Fat 1g Carbohydrates 3g Protein 3g Sodium 45mg

Balsamic and Dijon Chicken

Preparation Time: 10 minutes

Cooking Time: 7 minutes

Servings: 2

Ingredients:

- Balsamic vinegar [3 tbsp.]
- Snipped fresh thyme [2 tsp.]
- Dijon-style mustard [1/3 cup]
- Garlic, minced [2 cloves]
- Skinless, boneless chicken breast halves [4 pcs]
- Fresh thyme sprigs

Directions:

1.   In a resealable plastic bag placed over a shallow dish, add the chicken and set aside. Prepare the marinade by stirring the balsamic vinegar, mustard, thyme, and garlic until smooth.

2.   Pour the marinade on the chicken inside the plastic and seal the bag. Turn bag to coat the chicken and leave in the fridge for 24 hours. Turn the bag if needed.

3.   Drain the chicken, don't discard the marinade. Place the chicken on the grill directly over coals. Grill,

the chicken for 7 minutes and brush with marinade. Turn the chicken and coat again with marinade. Garnish with thyme sprigs. Serve.

Nutrition: Calories 161Fat 1gCarbohydrates 3g Protein 26g Sodium 537mg

Buffalo-Style Chicken Salad

Preparation Time: 10 minutes
Cooking Time: 2 minutes
Servings: 2

Ingredients:
- Paprika [1 tsp.]
- Fat-free blue cheese salad dressing [1 tbsp.]
- Cracked black pepper [1/4 tsp.]
- Cooked chicken breast, chopped [3/4 cup]
- Fat-free milk [1 tsp.]
- Celery, cut into sticks [1 pc]
- Buffalo wing sauce [2 tbsp.]
- Light blue cheese, crumbled
- Heart of romaine sliced [Half]

Directions:
1. Place the romaine in a bowl. Place chopped chicken and sauce in a microwave-safe bowl. Microwave the diced chicken and sauce on high for a minute.
2. Add the microwaved mixture over the romaine. Add cheese and pepper for toppings. Combine milk and salad dressing and then drizzle over your salad. Add celery sticks and serve.

Nutrition: Calories 297 Fat 10g Carbohydrates 13g Protein 37g
Sodium 596mg

Red Clam Sauce & Pasta

Preparation Time: 10 minutes
Cooking Time: 3 Hours
Servings: 4
Cooking Time:

Ingredients:
- 1 onion, diced
- ¼ cup fresh parsley, diced
- What you'll need from store cupboard:
- 2 6 ½ oz. cans clams, chopped, undrained
- 14 ½ oz. tomatoes, diced, undrained

- 6 oz. tomato paste
- 2 cloves garlic, diced
- 1 bay leaf
- 1 tbsp. sunflower oil
- 1 tsp. Splenda
- 1 tsp. basil
- ½ tsp. thyme
- ½ Homemade Pasta, cook & drain

Directions:
1. Heat oil in a small skillet over med-high heat. Add onion and cook until tender, Add garlic and cook 1 minute more. Transfer to crock pot.
2. Add remaining Ingredients, except pasta, cover and cook on low 3-4 hours.
3. Discard bay leaf and serve over cooked pasta.

Nutrition: Calories 223 Carbs 32g Protein 12gFat 6gSugar 15g Fiber 5g

Grilled Herbed Salmon with Raspberry Sauce & Cucumber Dill Dip

Preparation Time: 10 minutes
Cooking Time: 30 minutes
Servings: 4

Ingredients:
- 3 salmon fillets
- 1 tablespoon olive oil
- Salt and pepper to taste
- 1 teaspoon fresh sage, chopped
- 1 tablespoon fresh parsley, chopped
- 2 tablespoons apple juice
- 1 cup raspberries
- 1 teaspoon Worcestershire sauce
- 1 cup cucumber, chopped
- 2 tablespoons light mayonnaise
- ½ teaspoon dried dill

Directions:
1. Coat the salmon fillets with oil.
2. Season with salt, pepper, sage and parsley.
3. Cover the salmon with foil.
4. Grill for 20 minutes or until fish is flaky.
5. While waiting, mix the apple juice, raspberries and Worcestershire sauce.

6. Pour the mixture into a saucepan over medium heat.

7. Bring to a boil and then simmer for 8 minutes.

8. In another bowl, mix the rest of the ingredients.

9. Serve salmon with raspberry sauce and cucumber dip.

Nutrition: Calories 256 Fat 15 g Cholesterol 68 mg Carbohydrate 6 g Fiber 1 g Protein 23 g Potassium 359 mg

Shrimp with Green Beans

Preparation Time: 10 minutes

Cooking Time: 2 minutes

Servings: 4

Ingredients:

- ¾ pound fresh green beans, trimmed
- 1 pound medium frozen shrimp, peeled and deveined
- 2 tablespoons fresh lemon juice
- 2 tablespoons olive oil
- Salt and ground black pepper, as required

Directions:

1. Arrange a steamer trivet in the Instant Pot and pour cup of water.

2. Arrange the green beans on top of trivet in a single layer and top with shrimp.

3. Drizzle with oil and lemon juice.

4. Sprinkle with salt and black pepper.

5. Close the lid and place the pressure valve to "Seal" position.

6. Press "Steam" and just use the default time of 2 minutes.

7. Press "Cancel" and allow a "Natural" release.

8. Open the lid and serve.

Nutrition: Calories: 223Fats: 1gCarbs: 7.9gSugar: 1.4gProteins: 27.4gSodium: 322mg

Crab Curry

Preparation Time: 10 minutes

Cooking Time: 20 minutes

Servings: 2

Ingredients:

- 0.5lb chopped crab

- 1 thinly sliced red onion
- 0.5 cup chopped tomato
- 3tbsp curry paste
- 1tbsp oil or ghee

Directions:

1. Set the Instant Pot to sauté and add the onion, oil, and curry paste.

2. When the onion is soft, add the remaining ingredients and seal.

3. Cook on Stew for 20 minutes.

4. Release the pressure naturally.

Nutrition: Calories 2Carbs 11Sugar 4Fat 10Protein 24; GL 9

Mussels in Tomato Sauce

Preparation Time: 10 minutes

Cooking Time: 3 minutes

Servings: 4

Ingredients:

- 2 tomatoes, seeded and chopped finely
- 2 pounds mussels, scrubbed and de-bearded
- 1 cup low-sodium chicken broth
- 1 tablespoon fresh lemon juice
- 2 garlic cloves, minced

Directions:

1. In the pot of Instant Pot, place tomatoes, garlic, wine and bay leaf and stir to combine.

2. Arrange the mussels on top.

3. Close the lid and place the pressure valve to "Seal" position.

4. Press "Manual" and cook under "High Pressure" for about 3 minutes.

5. Press "Cancel" and carefully allow a "Quick" release.

6. Open the lid and serve hot.

Nutrition: Calories 213 Fats 25.2g Carbs 11gSugar 1 Proteins 28.2g Sodium 670mg

Shrimp Salad

Preparation Time: 10 minutes

Cooking Time: 4 minutes

Servings: 6

Ingredients:

For Salad:

- 1 pound shrimp, peeled and deveined
- Salt and ground black pepper, as required
- 1 teaspoon olive oil
- 1½ cups carrots, peeled and julienned
- 1½ cups red cabbage, shredded
- 1½ cup cucumber, julienned
- 5 cups fresh baby arugula
- ¼ cup fresh basil, chopped
- ¼ cup fresh cilantro, chopped
- 4 cups lettuce, torn
- ¼ cup almonds, chopped

For Dressing:

- 2 tablespoons natural almond butter
- 1 garlic clove, crushed
- 1 tablespoon fresh cilantro, chopped
- 1 tablespoon fresh lime juice
- 1 tablespoon unsweetened applesauce
- 2 teaspoons balsamic vinegar
- ½ teaspoon cayenne pepper
- Salt, as required
- 1 tablespoon water
- 1/3 cup olive oil

Directions:

1. Slowly, add the oil, beating continuously until smooth.
2. For salad: in a bowl, add shrimp, salt, black pepper and oil and toss to coat well.
3. Heat a skillet over medium-high heat and cook the shrimp for about 2 minutes per side.
4. Remove from the heat and set aside to cool.
5. In a large bowl, add the shrimp, vegetables and mix well.
6. For dressing: in a bowl, add all ingredients except oil and beat until well combined.
7. Place the dressing over shrimp mixture and gently, toss to coat well.
8. Serve immediately.

Nutrition: Calories 274 Fat 17.7 g Cholesterol 159 mg Carbs 10 g Sugar 3.8 g Fiber 2.9 g Sodium 242 mg Potassium 481 mg

Parmesan Herb Fish

Preparation Time: 10 minutes

Cooking Time: 15 minutes

Servings: 4

Ingredients:

- 16 oz. tilapia fillets
- 1/3 cup almonds, sliced and chopped
- ½ teaspoon parsley, chopped
- ¼ cup dry bread crumbs
- What you will need from the store cupboard:
- ½ teaspoon garlic powder
- ¼ teaspoon black pepper, ground
- ½ teaspoon paprika
- 3 tablespoons Parmesan cheese, grated
- Olive oil

Directions:

1. Preheat your oven to 350 ᵒF.
2. Mix the bread crumbs, almonds, seasonings and Parmesan cheese in a dish.
3. Brush oil lightly on the fish.
4. Coat the almond mix evenly.
5. Now keep the fish on a greased foil-lined baking pan.
6. Bake for 10-12 minutes. The fish should flake easily with your fork.

Nutrition: Calories 225Carbohydrates 7gFiber 1gCholesterol 57mgFat 9g, Protein 29gSodium 202mg

Lemony Salmon

Preparation Time: 10 minutes

Cooking Time: 3 minutes

Servings: 3

Ingredients:

- 1 pound salmon fillet, cut into 3 pieces
- 3 teaspoons fresh dill, chopped
- 5 tablespoons fresh lemon juice, divided
- Salt and ground black pepper, as required

Directions:

1. Arrange a steamer trivet in Instant Pot and pour ¼ cup of lemon juice.

2. Season the salmon with salt and black pepper evenly.

3. Place the salmon pieces on top of trivet, skin side down and drizzle with remaining lemon juice.

4. Now, sprinkle the salmon pieces with dill evenly.

5. Close the lid and place the pressure valve to "Seal" position.

6. Press "Steam" and use the default time of 3 minutes.

7. Press "Cancel" and allow a "Natural" release.

8. Open the lid and serve hot.

Nutrition: Calories: 20 Fats: 9.6gCarbs: 1.1gSugar: 0.5g Proteins: 29.7gSodium: 74mg

Garlicky Clams

Preparation Time: 10 minutes
Cooking Time: 5 minutes
Servings: 4
Ingredients:

- 3 lbs. clams, clean
- 4 garlic cloves
- 1/4 cup olive oil
- 1/2 cup fresh lemon juice
- 1 cup white wine
- Pepper
- Salt

Directions:

1. Add oil into the inner pot of instant pot and set the pot on sauté mode.

2. Add garlic and sauté for 1 minute.

3. Add wine and cook for 2 minutes.

4. Add remaining ingredients and stir well.

5. Seal pot with lid and cook on high for 2 minutes.

6. Once done, allow to release pressure naturally. Remove lid.

7. Serve and enjoy.

Nutrition: Calories 332 Fat 13.5 g Carbohydrates 40.5 g Sugar 12.4 g Protein 2.5 g Cholesterol 0 mg

Cauliflower in Vegan Alfredo Sauce

Preparation Time: 10 minutes

Cooking Time: 35 minutes
Servings: 1
Ingredients:

- Olive oil: 1 tablespoon
- Garlic: 2 cloves
- Vegetable broth: 1 cup
- Sea salt: ½ teaspoon
- Pepper: as per taste
- Chili flakes: 1 teaspoon
- Onion (diced):·1 medium
- Cauliflower florets (chopped): 4 cups
- Lemon juice (freshly squeezed): 1 teaspoon
- nutritional yeast: 1 tablespoon
- Vegan butter: 2 tablespoons
- Zucchini noodles: for serving

Directions:

1. Begin by positioning a cooking pot on low heat. Stream in the oil and allow it to heat through.

2. Immediately you're done, toss in the chopped onion and set on fire for about 4 minutes. The onion should be translucent.

3. Put in the garlic and Prepare for about 30 seconds. Continuously stir to prevent them from sticking.

4. Put in the vegetable broth and shredded cauliflower florets. Ensure you mix well and cover the stockpot with a lid. Allow the cauliflower cook for 5 minutes and then extract it from the flame.

5. Get a blender and move the cooked cauliflower into it. Palpitate until the puree is smooth and creamy in texture. (Add 1 tablespoon of broth if required for.)

6. Put salt, lemon juice, nutritional yeast, butter, chili flakes, and pepper to the blender. Mix until all the ingredients fully combine to form a smooth puree.

7. Position the zucchini noodles over a dishing platter and stream the Prepare cauliflower Alfredo sauce over the noodles.

Nutrition: Fat: 9.1 g Protein: 3.9 g Carbohydrates: 10 g

Citrus Sautéed Spinach

Preparation Time: 10 minutes

Cooking Time: 5 minutes

Servings: 4

Ingredients:

- 2 tablespoons extra-virgin olive oil
- 4 cups fresh baby spinach
- 1 teaspoon orange zest
- ¼ cup freshly squeezed orange juice
- ½ teaspoon sea salt
- 1/8 teaspoon freshly ground black pepper

Directions:

1. In a large skillet over medium-high heat, heat the olive oil until it shimmers.

2. Add the spinach and orange zest. Cook for about 3 minutes, stirring occasionally, until the spinach wilts.

3. Stir in the orange juice, sea salt, and pepper. Cook for 2 minutes more, stirring occasionally. Serve hot.

Nutrition: Calories: 74 Protein: 7g Carbohydrates: 3g Sugars: 1gFiber: 1g Fat: 7g Cholesterol: 0mg Sodium: 258mg

Tempeh with Bell Peppers

Preparation Time: 10 minutes

Cooking Time: 15 minutes

Servings: 3

Ingredients:

- 2 tablespoons balsamic vinegar
- 2 tablespoons low-sodium soy sauce
- 2 tablespoons tomato sauce
- 1 teaspoon maple syrup
- ½ teaspoon garlic powder
- 1/8 teaspoon red pepper flakes, crushed
- 1 tablespoon vegetable oil
- 8 ounces' tempeh, cut into cubes
- 1 medium onion, chopped
- 2 large green bell peppers, seeded and chopped

Directions:

1. In a small bowl, add the vinegar, soy sauce, tomato sauce, maple syrup, garlic powder, and red pepper flakes and beat until well combined. Set aside.

2. Heat 1 tablespoon of oil in a large skillet over medium heat and cook the tempeh about 2–3 minutes per side.

3. Add the onion and bell peppers and heat for about 2–3 minutes.

4. Stir in the sauce mixture and cook for about 3–5 minutes, stirring frequently.

5. Serve hot.

Nutrition: Calories 241 Fat 13 g Cholesterol 0 mg Sodium 65 mg Carbs 19.7 g Fiber 2.1 g Sugar 8.1 g Protein 16.1 g

Mushroom Curry

Preparation Time: 10 minutes

Cooking Time: 20 minutes

Servings: 3

Ingredients:

- 2 cups tomatoes, chopped
- 1 green chili, chopped
- 1 teaspoon fresh ginger, chopped
- ¼ cup cashews
- 2 tablespoons canola oil
- ½ teaspoon cumin seeds
- ¼ teaspoon ground coriander
- ¼ teaspoon ground turmeric
- ¼ teaspoon red chili powder
- 1½ cups fresh shiitake mushrooms, sliced
- 1½ cups fresh button mushrooms, sliced
- 1 cup frozen corn kernels
- 1¼ cups water
- ¼ cup unsweetened coconut milk
- Salt and ground black pepper, to taste

Directions:

1. In a food processor, add the tomatoes, green chili, ginger, and cashews, and pulse until a smooth paste forms.

2. In a pan, heat the oil over medium heat and sauté the cumin seeds for about 1 minute.

3. Add the spices and sauté for about 1 minute.

4. Add the tomato paste and cook for about 5 minutes.

5. Stir in the mushrooms, corn, water, and coconut milk, and bring to a boil.

6. Cook for about 10–12 minutes, stirring occasionally.

7. Season with salt and black pepper and remove from the heat.

8. Serve hot.

Nutrition: Calories 311 Fat 20.4 g Cholesterol 0 mg Sodium 244 mg Carbs 32g Fiber 5.6 g Sugar 9 g Protein 8 g

Chicken Cacciatore

Preparation Time: 10 minutes

Cooking Time: 10 minutes

Servings: 4

Ingredients:

- 8 chicken drumsticks; bone-in
- 1/2 cup black olives; pitted and sliced
- 1 bay leaf
- 1 tsp. garlic powder
- 1 yellow onion; chopped
- 28 oz. canned tomatoes and juice; crushed
- 1 tsp. oregano; dried
- Salt and black pepper to the taste

Directions:

1. In a heat proof dish that fits your air fryer, mix chicken with salt, pepper, garlic powder, bay leaf, onion, tomatoes and juice, oregano and olives; toss, introduce in your preheated air fryer and cook at 365 °F, for 20 minutes. Divide among plates and serve.

Nutrition: Calories: 300Fat: 12Fiber: 8Carbs: 20Protein: 24

Crock-pot Buffalo Chicken Dip

Preparation Time: 10 minutes

Cooking Time: 3 Hours

Servings: 10

Ingredients:

- 2 cups cooked chicken, chopped into small pieces
- 1 cup ranch dressing
- 16 oz. cream cheese, cubed and softened
- 5 ounces' hot sauce

Directions:

1. Add 5 oz. hot sauce, 16 ounces cubed cream cheese, and 1 cup ranch dressing to a 3-quart Crock-Pot slow cooker. Cover it and cook for about 2 hours on Low, with occasional stirring.

2. Once cheese is melted, add 2 cups of cooked chicken. Cover the Crock-Pot slow cooker again and cook again for 1 hour on Low.

3. Serve buffalo chicken along with veggies or any of your favorite chips.

Nutrition: 344 calories29 g fat5 g total carbs15 g protein

Chicken & Tofu

Preparation Time: 10 minutes

Cooking Time: 25 minutes

Servings: 6

Ingredients:

- 2 tablespoons olive oil, divided
- 2 tablespoons orange juice
- 1 tablespoon Worcestershire sauce
- 1 tablespoon low-sodium soy sauce
- 1 teaspoon ground turmeric
- 1 teaspoon dry mustard
- 8 oz. chicken breast, cooked and sliced into cubes
- 8 oz. extra-firm tofu, drained and sliced into cubed
- 2 carrots, sliced into thin strips
- 1 cup mushroom, sliced
- 2 cups fresh bean sprouts
- 3 green onions, sliced
- 1 red sweet pepper, sliced into strips

Directions:

1. In a bowl, mix half of the oil with the orange juice, Worcestershire sauce, soy sauce, turmeric and mustard.

2. Coat all sides of chicken and tofu with the sauce.

3. Marinate for 1 hour.

4. In a pan over medium heat, add 1 tablespoon oil.

5. Add carrot and cook for 2 minutes.

6. Add mushroom and cook for another 2 minutes.

7. Add bean sprouts, green onion and sweet pepper.

8. Cook for two to three minutes.

9. Stir in the chicken and heat through.
Nutrition: Calories 285 Fat 9 g Cholesterol 32 mg Sodium 331 mg Carbohydrate 30 Fiber 4 g Sugars 4 g Protein 20 g Potassium 559 mg

Peppered Broccoli Chicken

Servings: 4
Cooking Time: 30 Minutes
Ingredients:
- 1 tbsp. Sage (sliced)
- 1 cup Broccoli florets
- 1 lb. (no bones and skin) Chicken breast
- 3 pieces Garlic cloves
- 1 cup Tomato pasta
- What you'll need from the store cupboard:
- Salt and Black pepper to taste
- 2 tbsp. Olive oil

Directions:
1. Put the instant pot on Sauté option, then put the oil and cook it. After that, put the chicken and garlic then heats it for 5 minutes.
2. Put the other ingredients, then cover it and heat it for 25 minutes on high temperature.
3. Release the pressure gradually for 10 minutes then split them among your plates before eating.
Nutrition: Calories: 217Fat: 10.1gFiber: 1.8gCarbs: 5.9gProtein: 25.4g

Beef with Mushrooms

Preparation Time: 10 minutes
Cooking Time: 40 minutes
Servings: 4
Ingredients:
- 300 g beef
- 150 g mushrooms
- 1 onion
- 1 teaspoon olive oil
- 100 g vegetable broth
- 1 teaspoon basil
- 1 teaspoon chili
- 30 g tomato juice

Directions:

1. For this recipe, you should take a solid piece of beef. Take the beef and pierce the meat with a knife.
2. Rub it with olive oil, basil, and chili and lemon juice.
3. Chop the onion and mushrooms and pour it with vegetable broth.
4. Cook the vegetables for 5 minutes.
5. Take a big tray and put the meat in it. Add vegetable broth to the tray too. It will make the meat juicy.
6. Preheat the air fryer oven to 180 C and cook it for 35 minutes.
Nutrition: Calories 175 kcal Proteins – 24.9 gramsFats – 6.2 gramsCarbohydrates – 4.4 grams

Russian Steaks with Nuts and Cheese

Preparation Time: 10 minutes
Cooking Time: 20 minutes
Servings: 4
Ingredients:
- 800g of minced pork
- 200g of cream cheese
- 50g peeled walnuts
- 1 onion
- Salt
- Ground pepper
- 1 egg
- Breadcrumbs
- Extra virgin olive oil

Directions:
1. Put the onion cut into quarters in the Thermo mix glass and select 5 seconds speed 5.
2. Add the minced meat, cheese, egg, salt, and pepper.
3. Select 10 seconds, speed 5, turn left.
4. Add the chopped and peeled walnuts and select 4 seconds, turn left, speed 5.
5. Pass the dough to a bowl.
6. Make Russian steaks and go through breadcrumbs.
7. Paint the Russian fillets with extra virgin olive oil on both sides with a brush.

8. Put in the basket of the air fryer, without stacking the Russian fillets.

9. Select 1800C, 15 minutes.

Nutrition: Calories: 1232 Fat: 3.41gCarbohydrates: 0g Protein: 20.99g Sugar: 0g Cholesterol: 63mg

Beef Patty

Preparation Time: 10 minutes
Cooking Time: 30 minutes
Servings: 4

Ingredients:

- Prepared dough
- 300g beef
- 1 large onion
- 1 red pepper
- 2 hard-boiled eggs
- Salt
- Pepper to taste.
- 1 tsp. oil

Directions:

1. Remove the dough from the refrigerator 10 minutes before.

2. In a pan, place oil, 1 onion, 1 pepper, garlic, seasoning. Add ground beef until cooked well. Season with salt and pepper to taste.

3. Let the filling cool

4. Place the filling in each circle of the dough and seal with egg white at the edges.

5. Butter a refractory mold and accommodate the patty.

6. Preheat the oven to 190°C for 10 minutes by pressing the Convection button

7. Place the refractory on the metal rack and bring to the preheated oven for 30 minutes at 190°C.

Nutrition: Calories: 269 Fat: 3.41g Carbohydrates: 0g Protein: 20.99g Sugar: 0g Cholesterol: 25mg

Light Cheese Cake with Strawberry Syrup

Preparation Time: 10 minutes
Cooking Time: 20 minutes
Servings: 4

Ingredients:

- 500g cottage cheese

- 3 whole eggs
- 2 tbsp. powdered sweetener
- 2 tbsp. oat bran
- ½ tbsp. baking yeast
- 2 tbsp. cinnamon
- 2 tbsp. vanilla aroma
- 1 lemon (the skin

Directions:

1. Mix in a bowl the cottage cheese, the sweetener, the cinnamon, the vanilla aroma, and the lemon zest. Mix very well until you get a homogeneous cream.

2. Incorporate the eggs one by one.

3. Finally, add oats and yeast mixing well.

4. Put the whole mixture in a container to fit in the air fryer.

5. Preheat the air fryer a few minutes at 1800C.

6. Insert the mold into the basket of the air fryer and set the timer for about 20 minutes at 180°C.

Nutrition: Calories: 191 Fat: 12g Carbohydrates: 29g Protein: 4g Sugar: 100g Cholesterol: 7g

Nutty Chicken Nuggets

Preparation Time: 10 minutes
Cooking Time: 10-13 minutes
Servings: 4

Ingredients:

- 1 egg white
- 1 tablespoon freshly squeezed lemon juice
- ½ teaspoon dried basil
- ½ teaspoon ground paprika
- 1 pound low-sodium boneless skinless chicken breasts, cut into 1½-inch cubes
- ½ cup ground almonds
- 2 slices low-sodium whole-wheat bread, crumbled

Directions:

1. In a shallow bowl, beat the egg white, lemon juice, basil, and paprika with a fork until foamy.

2. Add the chicken and stir to coat.

3. On a plate, mix the almonds and bread crumbs.

4. Toss the chicken cubes in the almond and bread crumb mixture until coated.

5. Bake the nuggets in the air fryer, in two batches, for 10 to 13 minutes, or until the chicken reaches an internal temperature of 165°F on a meat thermometer. Serve immediately.

Nutrition: Calories: 249 Fat: 8g Carbohydrates: 13g Sodium: 137mg Fiber: 3g Sugar: 3g

North Carolina Style Pork Chops

Preparation Time: 10 minutes
Cooking Time: 10 minutes
Servings: 2

Ingredients:
- 2 boneless pork chops
- 15 ml of vegetable oil
- 25g dark brown sugar, packaged
- 6g of Hungarian paprika
- 2g ground mustard
- 2g freshly ground black pepper
- 3g onion powder
- 3g garlic powder
- Salt and pepper to taste

Directions:
1. Preheat the air fryer a few minutes at 1800C.
2. Cover the pork chops with oil.
3. Put all the spices and season the pork chops abundantly, almost as if you were making them breaded.
4. Place the pork chops in the preheated air fryer.
5. Select Steak, set the time to 10 minutes.
6. Remove the pork chops when it has finished cooking. Let it stand for 5 minutes and serve.

Nutrition: Calories: 118 Fat: 6.85g Carbohydrates: 0 Protein:13.12g Sugar: 0g Cholesterol: 39mg

Air Fryer Bacon

Preparation Time: 10 minutes
Cooking Time: 10 minutes
Servings: 4

Ingredients:
- 11 slices bacon

Directions:
1. Divide the bacon in half, and place the first half in the air fryer.

2. Set the temperature at 401 degrees F, and set the timer to 11 mins.
3. Check it halfway through to see if anything needs to be rearranged.
4. Cook remainder of the time. Serve.

Nutrition: Calories: 91 kcal Carbs: 0g Protein: 2g Fat: 8g

Tuna and Fruit Kebabs

Preparation Time: 10 minutes
Cooking Time: 8 To 12 minutes
Servings: 4

Ingredients:
- 1 pound tuna steaks, cut into 1-inch cubes
- ½ cup canned pineapple chunks, drained, juice reserved
- ½ cup large red grapes
- 1 tablespoon honey
- 2 teaspoons grated fresh ginger
- 1 teaspoon olive oil
- Pinch cayenne pepper

Directions:
1. Thread the tuna, pineapple, and grapes on 8 bamboo (see Tip) or 4 metal skewers that fit in the air fryer.
2. In a small bowl, whisk the honey, 1 tablespoon of reserved pineapple juice, the ginger, olive oil, and cayenne. Brush this mixture over the kebabs. Let them stand for 10 minutes.
3. Grill the kebabs for 8 to 12 minutes, or until the tuna reaches an internal temperature of at least 145°F on a meat thermometer, and the fruit is tender and glazed, brushing once with the remaining sauce. Discard any remaining marinade. Serve immediately.

Nutrition: Calories: 181 Fat: 2g Protein: 18g Carbohydrates: 13g Sodium: 43mg Fiber: 1g Sugar: 12g

Meatloaf

Preparation Time: 10 minutes
Cooking Time: 20 minutes
Servings: 4

Ingredients:
- 1-pound ground beef, grass-fed

- 1 tablespoon minced garlic
- 1 cup white onion, peeled and diced
- 1 tablespoon minced ginger
- 1/4 cup chopped cilantro
- 2 teaspoons garam masala
- 1 teaspoon cayenne pepper
- 1 teaspoon salt
- 1/2 teaspoon ground cinnamon
- 1 teaspoon turmeric powder
- 1/8 teaspoon ground cardamom
- 2 eggs, pastured

Directions:

1. Switch on the air fryer, insert fryer basket, then shut with its lid, set the fryer at 360 degrees F and preheat for 5 minutes.

2. Meanwhile, place all the ingredients in a bowl, stir until well mixed, then take an 8-inches round pan, grease it with oil, add the beef mixture in it and spread it evenly.

3. Open the fryer, place the pan in it, close with its lid and cook for 15 minutes until the top is nicely golden and meatloaf is thoroughly cooked.

4. When air fryer beeps, open its lid, take out the pan, then drain the excess fat and take out the meatloaf.

5. Cut the meatloaf into four pieces and serve.

Nutrition: Calories: 260 Cal Carbs: 6 gFat: 13 g Protein: 26 g

Fiber: 1 g

Spicy Chicken Meatballs

Preparation Time: 10 minutes

Cooking Time: 12 minutes

Servings: 24

Ingredients:

- 1 medium red onion, minced
- 2 garlic cloves, minced
- 1 jalapeño pepper, minced
- 2 teaspoons olive oil
- 3 tablespoons ground almonds
- 1 egg
- 1 teaspoon dried thyme
- 1 pound ground chicken breast

Directions:

1. In a 6-by-2-inch pan, combine the red onion, garlic, -jalapeño, and olive oil. Bake for 3 to 4 minutes in the air fryer, or until the vegetables are crisp-tender. Transfer to a medium bowl.

2. Mix in the almonds, egg, and thyme to the vegetable -mixture. Add the chicken and mix until just combined.

3. Form the chicken mixture into about 24 (1-inch) balls. Bake the meatballs, in batches, for 8 to 10 minutes, until the chicken reaches an internal temperature of 165°F on a meat thermometer.

Nutrition: Calories: 185 Fat: 7g Protein: 29g Carbohydrates: 5g Sodium: 55mg Fiber: 1g Sugar: 3g

Tuna Wraps

Preparation Time: 10 minutes

Cooking Time: 4-7 minutes

Servings: 4

Ingredients:

- 1 pound fresh tuna steak, cut into 1-inch cubes
- 1 tablespoon grated fresh ginger
- 2 garlic cloves, minced
- ½ teaspoon toasted sesame oil
- 4 low-sodium whole-wheat tortillas
- ¼ cup low-fat mayonnaise
- 2 cups shredded romaine lettuce
- 1 red bell pepper, thinly sliced

Directions:

1. In a medium bowl, mix the tuna, ginger, garlic, and sesame oil. Let it stand for 10 minutes.

2. Grill the tuna in the air fryer for 4 to 7 minutes, or until done to your liking and lightly browned

3. Make wraps with the tuna, tortillas, mayonnaise, lettuce, and bell pepper. Serve immediately.

Nutrition: Calories: 288 Fat: 7g Protein: 31g Carbohydrates: 26g Sodium: 135mg Fiber: 1g Sugar: 1g

Cinnamon Toasted Almonds

Preparation Time: 10 minutes

Cooking Time: 25 Minutes

Servings: 8

Ingredients:

- 2 cups whole almonds

- 1-tablespoon olive oil
- 1-teaspoon ground cinnamon
- ½-teaspoon salt

Directions:

1. Preheat the oven to 325°F and line a baking sheet with parchment.

2. Toss together the almonds, olive oil, cinnamon, and salt.

3. Spread the almonds on the baking sheet in a single layer.

4. Bake for 25 minutes, stirring several times, until toasted.

Nutrition: Calories 150 Fat 13.6g Carbs 5.3g, Carbs 2.2g Protein 5g Sugar 1g Fiber 3.1g Sodium 148mg

Scallops with Green Vegetables

Preparation Time: 10 minutes

Cooking Time: 8-11 minutes

Servings: 4

Ingredients:

- 1 cup green beans
- 1 cup frozen peas
- 1 cup frozen chopped broccoli
- 2 teaspoons olive oil
- ½ teaspoon dried basil
- ½ teaspoon dried oregano
- 12 ounces sea scallops

Directions:

1. In a large bowl, toss the green beans, peas, and broccoli with the olive oil. Place in the air fryer basket. Air-fry for 4 to 6 minutes, or until the vegetables are crisp-tender.

2. Remove the vegetables from the air fryer basket and sprinkle with the herbs. Set aside.

3. In the air fryer basket, put the scallops and air-fry for 4 to 5 minutes, or until the scallops are firm and reach an internal temperature of just 145°F on a meat thermometer.

4. Toss scallops with the vegetables and serve immediately.

Nutrition: Calories: 124 Fat: 3gProtein: 14g Carbohydrates: 11g Sodium: 56mg Fiber: 3g Sugar: 3g

Low-fat Steak

Preparation Time: 10 minutes

Cooking Time: 10 minutes

Servings: 3

Ingredients:

- 400 g beef steak
- 1 teaspoon white pepper
- 1 teaspoon turmeric
- 1 teaspoon cilantro
- 1 teaspoon olive oil
- 3 teaspoon lemon juice
- 1 teaspoon oregano
- 1 teaspoon salt
- 100 g water

Directions:

1. Rub the steaks with white pepper and turmeric and put it in the big bowl.

2. Sprinkle the meat with salt, oregano, cilantro and lemon juice.

3. Leave the steaks for 20 minutes.

4. Combine olive oil and water together and pour it into the bowl with steaks.

5. Grill the steaks in the air fryer for 10 minutes from both sides.

6. Serve it immediately.

Nutrition: Calories– 268 kcal Proteins – 40.7 grams Fats – 10.1 grams Carbohydrates – 1.4 grams

Chicken in Tomato Juice

Preparation Time: 10 minutes

Cooking Time: 15 minutes

Servings: 3

Ingredients:

- 350 g chicken fillet
- 200 g tomato juice
- 100 g tomatoes
- 2 teaspoon basil
- 1 teaspoon chili
- 1 teaspoon oregano
- 1 teaspoon rosemary
- 1 teaspoon olive oil
- 1 teaspoon mint

- 1 teaspoon lemon juice

Directions:

1. Take a bowl and make the tomato sauce: combine basil, chili, oregano, rosemary, and olive oil, mint and lemon juice and stir the mixture very carefully.

2. You can use a hand mixer to mix the mass. It will make the mixture smooth.

3. Take a chicken fillet and separate it into 3 pieces.

4. Put the meat to the tomato mixture and leave for 15 minutes.

5. Meanwhile, preheat the air fryer oven to 230 C.

6. Put the meat mixture on the tray and put it in the oven for at least 15 minutes.

Nutrition: Calories– 258 kcal Proteins – 34.8 grams Fats – 10.5 grams Carbohydrates – 5.0 grams

Spicy Lamb Sirloin Steak

Preparation Time: 10 minutes

Cooking Time: 20 minutes

Servings: 4

Ingredients:

- 1-pound lamb sirloin steaks, pastured, boneless
- For the Marinade:
- ½ of white onion, peeled
- 1 teaspoon ground fennel
- 5 cloves of garlic, peeled
- 4 slices of ginger
- 1 teaspoon salt
- 1/2 teaspoon ground cardamom
- 1 teaspoon garam masala
- 1 teaspoon ground cinnamon
- 1 teaspoon cayenne pepper

Directions:

1. Place all the ingredients for the marinade in a food processor and then pulse until well blended.

2. Make cuts in the lamb chops by using a knife, then place them in a large bowl and add prepared marinade in it.

3. Mix well until lamb chops are coated with the marinade and let them marinate in the refrigerator for a minimum of 30 minutes.

4. Then switch on the air fryer, insert fryer basket, grease it with olive oil, then shut with its lid, set the fryer at 330 degrees F and preheat for 5 minutes.

5. Open the fryer, add lamb chops in it, close with its lid and cook for 15 minutes until nicely golden and cooked, flipping the steaks halfway through the frying.

6. When air fryer beeps, open its lid, transfer lamb steaks onto a serving plate and serve.

Nutrition: Calories: 182 Cal Carbs: 3 g Fat: 7 g Protein: 24 g Fiber: 1 g

Pork Head Chops With Vegetables

Preparation Time: 10 minutes

Cooking Time: 20 minutes

Servings: 2-4

Ingredients:

- 4 pork head chops
- 2 red tomatoes
- 1 large green pepper
- 4 mushrooms
- 1 onion
- 4 slices of cheese
- Salt
- Ground pepper
- Extra virgin olive oil

Directions:

1. Put the four chops on a plate and salt and pepper.

2. Put two of the chops in the air fryer basket.

3. Place tomato slices, cheese slices, pepper slices, onion slices and mushroom slices. Add some threads of oil.

4. Take the air fryer and select 1800C, 15 minutes.

5. Check that the meat is well made and take out.

6. Repeat the same operation with the other two pork chops.

Nutrition: Calories: 106 Fat: 3.41g Carbohydrates: 0g Protein: 20.99g Sugar: 0g Cholesterol: 0mg

Pork Fillets with Serrano Ham

Preparation Time: 10 minutes

Cooking Time: 20 minutes

Servings: 4

Ingredients:

- 400g of very thin sliced pork fillets
- 2 boiled and chopped eggs
- 100g chopped Serrano ham
- 1 beaten egg

- Breadcrumbs

Directions:

1. Make a roll with the pork fillets. Introduce half-cooked egg and Serrano ham. So that the roll does not lose its shape, fasten with a string or chopsticks.

2. Pass the rolls through the beaten egg and then through the breadcrumbs until it forms a good layer.

3. Adjust the temperature of the air fryer for a few minutes at 180° C.

4. Insert the rolls in the basket and set the timer for about 8 minutes at 180º C.

5. Serve.

Nutrition: Calories: 424 kcal Fat: 15.15gCarbs: 37.47g Protein: 31.84g

Beef with Sesame and Ginger

Preparation Time: 10 minutes
Cooking Time: 23 minutes
Servings: 4-6

Ingredients:

- ½ cup tamari or soy sauce
- 3 tbsp. olive oil
- 2 tbsp. toasted sesame oil
- 1 tbsp. brown sugar
- 1 tbsp. ground fresh ginger
- 3 cloves garlic, minced
- 1 to 1½ pounds skirt steak, boneless sirloin, or low loin

Directions:

1. Put together the tamari sauce, oils, brown sugar, ginger, and garlic in small bowl. Add beef to a quarter-size plastic bag and pour the marinade into the bag. Press on the bag as much air as possible and seal it.

2. Refrigerate for 1 to 1½ hours, turning half the time. Remove the meat from the marinade and discard the marinade. Dry the meat with paper towels. Cook at a temperature of 350°F for 20 to 23 minutes, turning halfway through cooking.

Nutrition: Calories: 381 Fat: 5g Carbohydrates: 9.6g Protein: 38g Sugar: 1.8g Cholesterol: 0mg

Sirloin Steak

Preparation time: 10 minutes

Cooking Time: 15 Minutes
Servings: 6

Ingredients:

- 2 sirloin steaks, grass-fed
- 1 tablespoon olive oil
- 2 tablespoons steak seasoning

Directions:

1. Switch on the air fryer, insert fryer basket, grease it with olive oil, then shut with its lid, set the fryer at 392 degrees F and preheat for 5 minutes.

2. Meanwhile, pat dries the steaks, then brush with oil and then season well with steak seasoning until coated on both sides.

3. Open the fryer, add steaks in it, close with its lid and cook for 10 minutes until nicely golden and crispy, flipping the steaks halfway through the frying.

4. When air fryer beeps, open its lid, transfer steaks onto a serving plate and serve.

Nutrition: Calories: 253.6 Cal Carbs: 0.2 g Fat: 18.1 g Protein: 21.1 g Fiber: 0.1 g

Cinnamon Spiced Popcorn

Preparation Time: 10 minutes
Cooking Time: 5 minutes
Servings: 4

Ingredients:

- 8 cups air-popped corn
- 2 teaspoons sugar
- ½ to 1 teaspoon ground cinnamon
- Butter-flavored cooking spray

Directions:

1. Preheat the oven to 350°F and line a shallow roasting pan with foil.

2. Pop the popcorn using your preferred Directions.

3. Spread the popcorn in the roasting pan and mix the sugar and cinnamon in a small bowl.

4. Lightly spray the popcorn with cooking spray and toss to coat evenly.

5. Sprinkle with cinnamon and toss again.

6. Bake for 5 minutes until just crisp then serve warm.

Nutrition: Calories 70 Fat 0.7g Carbs 14.7g Carbs 12.2g Protein 2.1g Sugar 2.2g Fiber 2.5g Sodium 1mg

Garlic Rosemary Lamb Chops

Preparation Time: 10 minutes

Cooking Time: 12 minutes

Servings: 4

Ingredients:

- 4 lamb chops, pastured
- 1 teaspoon ground black pepper
- 2 teaspoons minced garlic
- 1 ½ teaspoon salt
- 2 teaspoons olive oil
- 4 cloves of garlic, peeled
- 4 rosemary sprigs

Directions:

1. Take the fryer pan, place lamb chops in it, season the top with ½ teaspoon black pepper and ¾ teaspoon salt, then drizzle evenly with oil and spread with 1 teaspoon minced garlic.

2. Add garlic cloves and rosemary and then let the lamb chops marinate in the pan into the refrigerator for a minimum of 1 hour.

3. Then switch on the air fryer, insert fryer pan, then shut with its lid, set the fryer at 360 degrees F and cook for 6 minutes.

4. Flip the lamb chops, season them with remaining salt and black pepper, add remaining minced garlic and continue cooking for 6 minutes or until lamb chops are cooked.

5. When air fryer beeps, open its lid, transfer lamb chops onto a serving plate and serve.

Nutrition: Calories: 616 Cal Carbs: 1 g Fat: 28 g Protein: 83 g
Fiber: 0.3 g

Saucy Chicken with Zucchini and Mushrooms

Preparation Time: 10 minutes

Cooking Time: 5 hours

Servings: 6

Ingredients:

- 24 ounces Chicken Breast, sliced
- 8 ounces Button Mushrooms, sliced
- 3 cups chopped Zucchini

- 1 Onion, diced
- 3 Tomatoes, chopped
- 1 Bell Pepper, diced
- 2 Garlic Cloves, minced
- 1 tsp. dried Thyme
- ¼ cup Chicken Broth
- Salt and Pepper, to taste

Directions:

1. If you want to, you can cook the chicken slices in a pan until no longer pink first, although this is optional.

2. Place all of the ingredient in your Slow Cooker.

3. Give the mixture a gentle stir to combine.

4. Put the lid on and cook for at least 5 hours on LOW.

5. Serve and enjoy!

Nutrition Calories 240 Fats 8g Carbs 15g Protein 27g Fiber: 3g

Carribbean Chicken

Preparation Time: 10 minutes

Cooking Time: 6 hours

Servings: 6

Ingredients:

- 1 ½ cups Coya Mojo Criollo Marinade (or another sauce by choice)
- 1 tbsp. Curry Powder
- 1 tsp. Pepper
- 1 tsp. Garlic Powder
- 1 Onion, sliced
- 8 Chicken Thighs

Directions:

1. In a small bowl, combine the spices.

2. Brush the mixture over the chicken.

3. Place the chicken thighs in your Slow Cooker and arrange the onion slices over.

4. Pour the marinade over – do NOT stir at this point.

5. Close the lid and cook for 6 hours on LOW.

6. Serve over rice or your preferred side dish and enjoy!

Nutrition Calories 210 Fats 10g Carbs 7g Protein 22g Fiber: 1g

Turkey with Gravy

Preparation Time: 10 minutes
Cooking Time: 5 hours
Servings: 12
Ingredients:

- 6 pounds Turkey, bone-in
- 2 Onions, chopped
- 3 Carrots, sliced
- 3 Celery Ribs, chopped
- ¼ cup Whole-Wheat Flour
- ½ cup Water
- ½ tsp. Pepper
- ½ tsp. Paprika
- 1 tsp. Chicken Seasoning
- 1 tsp. Salt

Directions:

1. Combine the spices in a small bowl.
2. Massage the rub into the turkey meat.
3. Place the veggies at the bottom of your Slow Cooker.
4. Top with the turkey.
5. Put the lid on and cook for 6 hours on LOW.
6. Transfer the turkey to a cutting board.
7. Pour the cooking juices from the Slow Cooker into a saucepan.
8. Whisk the water and flour and add to the juices.
9. Cook over medium heat until thickened.
10. Slice the turkey and pour the gravy over.
11. Serve and enjoy!

Nutrition Calories 200 Total Fats 1g Carbs 2g Protein 43g Fiber: 0.5g

Lemon and Garlic Chicken

Preparation Time: 10 minutes
Cooking Time: 5 hours
Servings: 6
Ingredients:

- 2 pounds Chicken Breast, boneless and skinless
- 3 tbsp. Lemon Juice
- 2 tbsp. Butter
- 3 Garlic Cloves, minced
- 1 tbsp. Chicken Bouillon Granules
- ¼ cup Water
- Salt and Pepper, to taste

Directions:

1. Turn on your Slow Cooker and place the butter inside.
2. When melted, add the garlic and chicken, and gently cover the chicken with the buttery and garlicky mixture.
3. Place the chicken inside.
4. Combine the water, lemon, and bouillon granules, and pour over the chicken.
5. Season with salt and pepper.
6. Put the lid on and cook for 5 hours on LOW.
7. Serve and enjoy!

Nutrition Calories 190 Fats 4g Carbs 1g Protein 21g Fiber: 0g

Cheesy Tomato Chicken

Preparation Time: 10 minutes
Cooking Time: 8 hours and 15 minutes
Servings:
Ingredients:

- 1 ½ pounds Chicken Breast, boneless and skinless
- 28 ounces canned diced Tomatoes
- 3 cups shredded Mozzarella Cheese
- ½ cup chopped Kalamata Olives
- 1 tsp. Basil
- ¼ tsp. Oregano
- Salt and Pepper, to taste

Directions:

1. Place Combine the chicken and tomato sauce in your Slow Cooker.
2. Put the lid on and cook for 8 hours on LOW.
3. Open the chicken and shred the chicken within the pot.
4. Add the remaining ingredients.
5. Stir well to combine.
6. Cook on HIGH for 15 more minutes.
7. Serve as desired and enjoy!

Nutrition Calories 241 Fats 7g Carbs 4g Protein 25g Fiber: 1g

Turkey with Berries

Preparation Time: 10 minutes

Cooking Time: 5 hours

Servings: 12

Ingredients:

- 2 Turkey Breast Halves, boneless and skinless
- 2 cups Raspberries
- 1 cup White Grape Juice
- 2 cups Blueberries
- ½ cup Water
- 2 Apples, peeled and chopped
- ¼ tsp. ground Ginger
- ½ tsp. Rosemary
- ½ tsp. Garlic Powder
- Salt and Pepper, to taste

Directions:

1. Combine the garlic, rosemary, salt, and pepper, and rub the meat with the mixture.
2. Place inside the Slow Cooker.
3. Pour the water around (NOT OVER) the turkey.
4. Put the lid on and cook for 4 hours on LOW.
5. In a large bowl, combine the remaining ingredients.
6. Pour over the turkey and cook for another hour on LOW.
7. Serve and enjoy!

Nutrition Calories 215 Fats 1g Carbs 12g Protein 38g Fiber: 2g

Lemon and Dill Salmon

Preparation Time: 10 minutes

Cooking Time: 70 minutes

Servings: 4

Ingredients:

- 4 Salmon Fillets
- 1 Lemon, sliced
- Handful of Dill, chopped
- 1 Garlic Clove, minced
- Salt and Pepper, to taste
- 1 tsp. Olive Oil

Directions:

1. Brush the olive oil on the inside of your Slow Cooker.
2. Add the salmon and season with salt and pepper.
3. Sprinkle with garlic and dill.
4. Arrange the lemon slices on top.
5. Close the lid and cook for 70 minutes on HIGH.
6. Serve and enjoy!

Nutrition Calories 190 Fats 9g Carbs 1.8g Protein 24g Fiber: 0.4g

Saucy Fennel Shrimp

Preparation Time: 10 minutes

Cooking Time: 5 hours and 15 minutes

Servings: 6

Ingredients:

- 1 1 Large Potato, cut into cubes
- 1 ½ cups chopped Celery
- 1 ½ cups chopped Leek
- 1 pound Shrimp, peeled and deveined
- 28 ounces canned diced Tomatoes
- 2 cups sliced Fennel
- 2 tsp. minced Garlic
- ¼ cup dry White Wine
- ¼ cup Clam Juice
- Salt and Pepper, to taste

Directions:

1. Place all of the ingredients, except the shrimp, in your Slow Cooker.
2. Stir well to combine the mixture.
3. Close the lid and cook for 5 hours on LOW.
4. Open the lid, add the shrimp and increase to HIGH.
5. Stir the mixture well, close the lid, and cook for 15 minutes.
6. Serve over rice and enjoy!

Nutrition Calories 190 Fats 5g Carbs 20g Protein 13g Fiber: 3g

Tilapia Au Gratin

Preparation Time: 15 minutes

Cooking Time: 90 minutes

Servings: 6

Ingredients:

- 3 pounds Frozen Tilapia Fillets
- 1 cup grated Cheese
- 1 ¼ cup Milk
- ½ tbsp. Dry Mustard
- 1 ½ tsp. Lemon Juice
- 3 tbsp. Flour
- 6 tbsp. Butter
- ½ tsp. Nutmeg

Directions:

1. Grab a pan and add the butter to it.
2. Place over medium heat and melt it.
3. Stir in the flour, nutmeg, and dry mustard.
4. Slowly pour in the milk while constantly whisking, making sure that the mixture is lump-free and smooth.
5. Stir in the cheese and set aside.
6. Place the fish at the bottom of your Slow Cooker.
7. Pour the cheesy mixture over.
8. Place the lid and cook for 90 minutes on HIGH.
9. Serve and enjoy!

Nutrition Calories 410 Fats 21g Carbs 6g Protein 45g Fiber: 3g

Foil-Wrapped Haddock

Preparation Time: 10 minutes
Cooking Time: 5 hours
Servings: 6

Ingredients:

- 1 pound Haddock
- 1 tsp. Cajun seasoning
- ½ tsp. Garlic Powder
- Salt and Pepper, to taste

Directions:

1. Grab a larger piece of aluminum fillet and place the 1-pound Haddock onto it.
2. Combine the seasonings together and rub over the fish.
3. Bring the corners of the together, closing it off completely, making a packet.
4. Place the packet inside your Slow Cooker and close the lid.
5. Cook on LOW for 3 hours.

6. Serve and enjoy!

Nutrition Calories 160 Fats 9g Carbs 0g Protein 17g Fiber: 0g

Mustardy Parmesan Salmon

Preparation Time: 10 minutes
Cooking Time: 90 minutes
Servings: 4

Ingredients:

- 1 pound Salmon
- 1 tbsp. Mustard
- ¼ cup grated Parmesan Cheese
- 2 tsp. Basil
- Salt and Pepper, to taste

DIRECTIONS:

1. Place an aluminum foil inside the Slow Cooker, leaving enough on the sides so you can grab the foil and lift the fish when cooked.
2. Combine the mustard basil, salt, and pepper.
3. Brush over the salmon.
4. Coat the fillet with parmesan cheese.
5. Place it inside the cooker, on top of the foil, with the skin side down.
6. Put the lid on and cook for 90 minutes on LOW.
7. Serve and enjoy!

Nutrition Calories 194Fats 6.6gCarbs 0.5gProtein 31gFiber: 0.1g

Garlicky Creole Shrimp

Preparation Time: 10 minutes
Cooking Time: 55 minutes
Servings: 6

Ingredients:

- 1 ½ pounds Shrimp, peeled and deveined
- ¼ cup Olive Oil
- 2 tsp. minced Garlic
- 1 tsp. Creole Seasoning
- ¼ cup Butter
- Salt and Pepper, to taste

Directions:

1. Place the butter, garlic, oil, creole, and some salt and pepper, to your Slow Cooker.

2.	Put the lid on and cook for 15 minutes on HIGH.

3.	Add the shrimp and stir gently to coat them completely.

4.	Put the lid back on and cook for another 40 minutes.

5.	Serve and enjoy!

Nutrition Calories 260Fats 18gCarbs 0.3gProtein 24g Fiber: 0g

White Fish with Tomatoes

Preparation Time: 10 minutes

Cooking Time: 5 hours

Servings: 6

Ingredients:
- 1-pound Fish
- 1/3 cup Chicken Broth
- 1 Bell Pepper, diced
- 1 tsp. minced Garlic
- 1 can diced Tomatoes, undrained
- 1 tsp. Dill
- ½ Onion, chopped
- Salt and Pepper, to taste

Directions:

1.	Pour the tomatoes and broth into your Slow Cooker.

2.	Add the pepper, onion, dill, and garlic.

3.	Stir well to combine.

4.	Add the fish and season with salt and pepper.

5.	Close the lid and cook for 150 minutes on LOW.

6.	Serve and enjoy!

Nutrition Calories 150Fats 2.7gCarbs 8gProtein 25gFiber: 1.3g

Sweet & Sour Scallops

Preparation Time: 10 minutes

Cooking Time: 5 hours

Servings: 6

Ingredients:
- 1 pound Sea Scallops
- 1 small Onion, diced
- 1 small Red Bell Pepper, diced

- ¼ cup sugar-free Orange Juice
- 1/3 cup diced Tomatoes
- 2 tbsp. Cornstarch
- 1 tbsp. low-sodium Soy Sauce
- 1 Jalapeno, diced
- 3 tbsp. Rice Vinegar

Directions:

1.	Place all of the ingredients, except the scallops, in your Slow Cooker.

2.	Stir well to combine and place the lid on.

3.	Cook on LOW for 4 hours.

4.	Open the lid and add the scallops in.

5.	Put it back on and cook for 10 minutes on HIGH.

6.	Serve and enjoy!

Nutrition Calories 240Fats 2gCarbs 25gProtein 18gFiber: 1g

Creamy Trout & Asparagus

Preparation Time: 10 minutes

Cooking Time: 150 minutes

Servings: 4

Ingredients:
- 1 pound Trout, cut into pieces
- 8 Asparagus Spears, chopped
- ½ cup Milk
- ¼ cup Chicken Broth
- 2 tbsp. Butter, melted
- 4 tbsp. grated Parmesan Cheese
- Salt and Pepper, to taste

Directions:

1.	Set your Slow Cooker on HIGH and add the butter inside.

2.	When melted, turn it to LOW, and add the milk, broth, cheese, and some salt and pepper. Stir to combine.

3.	Place the asparagus and trout pieces inside and cover the lid.

4.	Cook on LOW for 150 minutes.

5.	Serve and enjoy!

Nutrition Calories 270Fats 15gCarbs 3.4gProtein 30gFiber: 0.7g

Tomato "Baked" Beans

Preparation Time: 10 minutes

Cooking Time: 5 hours

Servings: 12

Ingredients:

- 3 15-ounce cans Navy Beans, drained
- 1 Large Onion, chopped
- ½ cup chopped Celery
- ½ cup Tomato Juice
- 2 tbsp. Swerve
- ½ cup Tomato Sauce
- ½ cup Sugar-Free Ketchup
- 1 tsp. minced Garlic
- 1 tsp. Dry Mustard
- ½ tsp. Oregano
- Salt and Pepper, to taste

Directions:

1. Place all of the ingredients in the pot of your Slow Cooker.
2. Stir well to combine.
3. Put the lid on and set the cooker to LOW.
4. Cook for about 5 hours.
5. Serve as desired and enjoy!

Nutrition Calories 130Fats 2gCarbs 24gProtein 6.4gFiber: 5.9g

Quinoa & Black Bean Stuffed Peppers

Preparation Time: 15 minutes

Cooking Time: 6 hours

Servings: 6

Ingredients:

- 1 cup uncooked Quinoa, rinsed
- 1 ½ cup Enchilada Sauce
- 6 Bell Peppers
- 14 ounces canned Black Beans, drained
- 14 ounces canned Refried Beans
- 1 ½ cups shredded Cheese
- 1 tsp. Cumin
- 1 tsp. Onion Powder
- ½ tsp. Paprika
- Salt and Pepper, to taste
- ½ cup Water

Directions:

1. Cut the peppers' tops and remove the seeds.
2. In a bowl, place the quinoa, beans, 1 cup of the cheese, enchilada sauce, and spices.
3. Mix together well.
4. Fill the peppers with the quinoa/bean mixture.
5. Pour the water inside your Slow Cooker.
6. Arrange the peppers inside the Slow Cooker, so they are 'sitting' at the bottom.
7. Sprinkle with the remaining cheese.
8. Place the lid on and cook on LOW for 6 hours.
9. Serve and enjoy!

Nutrition Calories 393Fats 3.5gCarbs 50gProtein 21gFiber: 14.5g

Cheesy and Creamy Corn

Preparation Time: 10 minutes

Cooking Time: 4 hours and 10 minutes

Servings: 8

Ingredients:

- ½ cup Milk
- 24 ounces Frozen Corn
- 4 tbsp. Butter
- 8 ounces Cream Cheese
- 1 cup shredded Cheese
- Salt and Pepper, to taste

Directions:

1. Turn your Slow Cooker on and add the butter there.
2. When melted, add the milk, cream cheese, and corn.
3. Stir to combine and season with some salt and pepper.
4. Put the lid on and cook for 4 hours on LOW.
5. Open the lid and stir in the cheese.
6. Cook uncovered until the cheese is melted,
7. Serve and enjoy!

Nutrition Calories 300Fats 21gCarbs 23gProtein 9gFiber: 3g

Veggie Fajitas

Preparation Time: 10 minutes

Cooking Time: 3 hours and 30 minutes

Servings: 3

Ingredients:

- 1 Onion, chopped
- 8 ounces Cherry Tomatoes, halved
- 3 Peppers, cut into strips
- 1 tsp. Paprika
- 1 tsp. Chili Powder
- 1 tbsp. Olive Oil
- 6 Mini Tortillas

Directions:

1. Place the onion, peppers, olive oil, chili powder, and paprika, inside your Slow Cooker.

2. Put the lid on and cook for 90 minutes on HIGH.

3. Open the lid and stir in the tomatoes.

4. Put the lid back on and cook for 2 more hours.

5. Serve inside the flour tortillas.

6. Enjoy!

Nutrition Calories 250Fats 6gCarbs 16gProtein 5gFiber: 2.4g

Lemon Pepper Chicken Wings

Preparation Time: 10 minutes

Cooking Time: 40 minutes

Servings: 6

Ingredients:

- Chicken wings – 3 pounds
- Olive oil – 3 tablespoons
- Lemon pepper seasoning – ¼ cup
- Baking powder – 2 teaspoons

Directions:

1. Begin by preheating the oven by setting the temperature to 400 degrees Fahrenheit.

2. Take a large baking sheet pan and place an oven-safe rack onto the same. Set aside.

3. Take a large glass mixing bowl and add in the chicken wings. Pour the oil over the chicken wings and toss well. Make sure all the wings are evenly coated.

4. Sprinkle the lemon pepper seasoning over the chicken and use your hands to nicely rub it over the skin.

5. Also, sprinkle the baking powder over the chicken and give it a nice toss.

6. Place the seasoned wings over the rack and arrange them in a single layer. Make sure there is a slight gap between each of the chicken pieces.

7. Place the baking pans into the oven and bake for about 45 minutes. The skin should be slightly browned and crispy. Cook in batches if necessary.

8. Transfer onto a platter and serve with the dip of your choice.

Nutrition: Fat – 26.8 gProtein – 22.6 gCarbohydrates – 1 gSugar – 0.2 g

Balsamic and Garlic Chicken Thighs

Preparation Time: 10 minutes

Cooking Time: 25 minutes

Servings: 6

Ingredients:

- Chicken thighs (skinless and boneless) – 12 medium
- Olive oil – ¼ cup
- Balsamic vinegar – ¼ cup
- Garlic (minced) – 6 cloves
- Italian seasoning – 1 teaspoon
- Sea salt – 1 teaspoon
- Black pepper – ¼ teaspoon

Directions:

1. Take a large glass mixing bowl and add in the balsamic vinegar, olive oil, minced garlic, salt, pepper, and Italian seasoning. Whisk well to combine.

2. Add in the chicken and toss until the chicken thighs are well coated with the marinade.

3. Place the marinated chicken in the refrigerator and let it sit for around 2 hours. Flip halfway to ensure the chicken retains the flavor.

4. Once the chicken is almost done marinating, preheat the oven by bringing the temperature up to 425 degrees Fahrenheit.

5. Take a large baking sheet and line it with a parchment paper sheet.

6. Place the chicken on the lined baking sheet. Make sure you arrange the chicken pieces in a single layer and leave some space between the pieces.

7. Place the baking sheet into the preheated oven and bake for around 20 minutes. Cook in batches if necessary.

8. Take the chicken thighs out of the oven and transfer onto a serving platter.

9. Serve hot!

Nutrition: Fat – 18.3 gProtein – 43.8 gCarbohydrates – 3.1 gSugar – 1.6 g

Buffalo Chicken and Cheese Meatballs

Preparation Time: 10 minutes

Cooking Time: 15 minutes

Servings: 6

Ingredients:

- Chicken (ground) – 1 ½ pounds
- Egg whites – 2 medium
- Blue cheese – ½ cup
- Green onions (chopped) – ½ cup
- Buffalo sauce – ½ cup
- Olive oil – 1 tablespoon

Directions:

1. Start by preheating the oven by setting the temperature to 400 degrees Fahrenheit.

2. Take a baking sheet and line it with parchment paper.

3. In a large mixing bowl, add the ground chicken, egg whites, ¾ of buffalo sauce, and scallions. Mix well.

4. Take the blue cheese and crumble it well. Now add the crumbled cheese to the chicken mixture and fold it gently.

5. Use a large spoon or an ice cream scooper to scoop out the mixture. Roll it into balls measuring about an inch. Place the prepared meatballs onto the lined baking sheet. Repeat the process with the remaining meat and cheese mixture.

6. Place the baking sheet into the preheated oven and bake for around 15 minutes.

7. In the meantime, take a small bowl and add in the olive oil and buffalo sauce. Whisk well to combine.

8. Once the meatballs are done, transfer them onto a fresh sheet of parchment paper. Drizzle the meatballs with prepared buffalo sauce and olive oil mixture.

9. Return the meatballs to the oven and bake for another couple of minutes.

10. Serve hot!

Nutrition: Fat – 15 gProtein – 23 gCarbohydrates – 1 gSugar – 1 g

Creamy Garlic Chicken

Preparation Time: minutes

Cooking Time: minutes

Servings: 4

Ingredients:

Total Time: 3 hours 15 minutes

Ingredients:

- Olive oil – 1 tablespoon
- Garlic (minced) – 6 cloves
- Heavy cream – 1 cup
- Chicken broth – 1/3 cup
- Parmesan cheese (grated) – ¾ cup
- Chicken breast – 4 large
- Italian seasoning – 1 tablespoon
- Sea salt – as per taste
- Black pepper – as per taste
- Sun-dried tomatoes (chopped) – ½ cup
- Spinach (chopped) – 2 cups

Directions:

1. Take a medium-sized saucepan and place it on a medium flame. Pour in the oil and let it heat through.

2. Once the oil is hot enough, toss in the minced garlic and stir for about 1 minute.

3. Add the chicken broth and cream to the saucepan; stir well. Once the chicken broth mixture starts to gently simmer, reduce the heat to low and cook for around 10 minutes or until the sauce is thickened.

4. Stir in the parmesan cheese and whisk until the cheese is completely dissolved.

5. Turn on the slow cooker and place the chicken breasts at the bottom of the cooker. Generously season with sea salt, black pepper, and Italian seasoning. Also, add in the sun-dried tomatoes and give them a nice toss.

6. Pour the prepared cream and cheese sauce over the chicken and turn on the slow cooker. Cook on high heat for about 4 hours.

7. Once done, use tongs to remove the chicken breast pieces from the slow cooker and place them onto a plate. Set aside.

8. Now add in the chopped spinach and stir well. Switch the heat to high and cook for a couple of minutes.

9. Return the cooked chicken to the slow cooker and baste it with liquid. Cook for a minute and put off the flame.

10. Transfer onto a shallow serving platter and top with sun-dried tomatoes from the sauce.

11. Serve hot with rice or flatbread of your choice.

Nutrition: Fat – 35 gProtein – 45 gCarbohydrates – 9 g Sugar – 1 g

Low-Carb Turkey Meatloaf

Preparation Time: 10 minutes
Cooking Time: 50 minutes
Servings: 12

Ingredients:

For the meatloaf:

- Turkey (ground) – 2 pounds
- Onion (finely chopped) – ½ large
- Garlic (minced) – 6 cloves
- Tomato sauce – 1/3 cup
- Italian seasoning – 2 teaspoons
- Sea salt – 1 ½ teaspoons
- Black pepper – ¼ teaspoon
- Almond flour (blanched) – ½ cup
- Eggs – 2 large

For the toppings:

- Bacon – 10 slices
- Barbeque sauce (sugar-free) – ¼ cup

Directions:

1. Start by preheating the oven by setting the temperature to 350 degrees Fahrenheit.

2. Prepare a baking sheet by lining it with a sheet of parchment paper.

3. Take a large glass mixing bowl and add in the ground turkey, onion, garlic, tomato sauce, Italian seasoning, sea salt, pepper, blanched almond flour, and eggs. Mix until well combined.

4. Transfer the meatloaf mixture onto the prepared baking sheet and form a loaf shape measuring around 6x10 inches.

5. Place the bacon slices on top of the meatloaf log by arranging them side by side. Ensure that the ends of the bacon slices are tucked under the meatloaf on both sides.

6. Place the baking sheet into the oven and bake for around 30 minutes.

7. Once the meatloaf is done baking, take the baking sheet out of the oven and top it with the barbeque sauce.

8. Return the baking sheet to the oven and let it cook for another 30 minutes.

9. Take the meatloaf out of the oven and let it rest for at least 10 minutes.

10. Transfer onto a serving platter and slice it into 12 equal portions with a serrated knife.

11. Serve hot!

Nutrition: Fat – 17 gProtein – 19 gCarbohydrates – 4 gSugar – 1 g

Drop Egg Soup

Preparation Time: 10 minutes
Cooking Time: 7 minutes
Servings: 4

Ingredients:

- Chicken broth – 4 cups
- Coconut aminos – 4 teaspoons
- Mushrooms (thinly sliced) – 8 medium
- Green onions (thinly sliced) – 4 medium
- Fresh ginger (grated) – 1 teaspoon
- Black pepper – 1 teaspoon
- Eggs – 4 large
- Sea salt – as per taste

Directions:

1. Start by adding the chicken broth, mushrooms, coconut aminos, ginger, black pepper, and onions into a medium-sized saucepan. Place the pan on a high flame and let it come to a boil. Reduce the flame and cook for a couple of minutes more.

2. Crack the eggs in a cup and whisk them well.

3. Slowly pour the whisked eggs in a stream into the simmering soup. Keep stirring to get some smooth egg ribbons.

4. Stir in the salt as soon as you finish cooking the soup.

5. Serve hot!

Nutrition: Fat – 6 gProtein – 10 gCarbohydrates – 5 gSugar – 1 g

Tuna Shirataki Bowl

Preparation Time: 10 minutes

Cooking Time: 20 minutes

Servings: 4

Ingredients:

- Ahi tuna (fresh) – 1 pound
- Soy sauce – 2 tablespoons
- Sesame oil – 1 tablespoon
- Avocados – 2
- Edamame (shelled) – ½ cup
- Shirataki noodle rice – 1 bag
- Scallion – 1 bunch
- Jalapeno – 1
- Sriracha mayonnaise – ¼ cup
- Salt – as per taste
- Pepper – as per taste
- Black sesame seeds – for garnishing
- White sesame seeds – for garnishing

Directions:

1. Begin by cutting the tuna fish into bite-sized cubes and transferring them into a small mixing bowl.

2. Pour the sesame oil and soy sauce over the fish and mix well. Cover with a cling film and place the fish in the refrigerator to marinate for around an hour.

3. Take the noodles and place them in a fine-mesh metal strainer. Rinse the noodle rice under running water for around 15 seconds.

4. Place a saucepan filled more than halfway with water over a medium-high flame and let it come to a boil. Add in the rinsed noodle rice and cook for a couple of minutes.

5. Once done, transfer the boiled noodles rice into the strainer and set aside.

6. Place a nonstick saucepan on a medium flame and let it heat through. Add in the cooked noodle rice and cook for around 5 minutes or until it is slightly dry. Set aside.

7. Peel the avocado and remove the core. Cut it into bite-sized cubes. Make sure they are about the same size as the tuna. Transfer them into a large mixing bowl.

8. Also, add the shelled edamame, cooked noodle rice, finely chopped jalapeno, and scallion to the avocados. Mix gently.

9. Take the ahi tuna out of the refrigerator and add it to the avocados after squeezing out excess liquid.

10. Also, add in the sriracha mayonnaise and lime juice; finish with a seasoning of pepper and salt. Gently combine using a wooden spoon.

11. Garnish with white and black sesame seeds.

12. Serve!

Nutrition: Fat – 23 gProtein – 27 gCarbohydrates – 1 gSugar – 3.9 g

Chipotle Spicy Fish Tacos

Preparation Time: 10 minutes

Cooking Time: 20 minutes

Servings: 4

Ingredients:

- Olive oil – 2 tablespoons
- Yellow onion (diced) – ½ small
- Jalapeño (chopped) – 1
- Garlic (pressed) – 2 cloves
- Chipotle peppers soaked in adobo sauce – 4 ounces
- Butter – 2 tablespoons
- Mayonnaise – 2 tablespoons
- Haddock fillets – 1 pound
- Tortillas (low-carb) – 4

Directions:

1. Take a large nonstick pan and place it on a medium-high flame. Pour in the olive oil and let it simmer.

2. Toss in the diced onion and sauté it for around 5 minutes. Keep stirring to prevent the onions from browning.

3. Reduce the flame and add in the chopped garlic and jalapeno. Stir and cook for around 2 minutes.

4. Take the chipotle peppers out of the adobo sauce and chop them finely. Transfer the chopped chipotle and adobo sauce to the hot pan.

5. Add the mayonnaise, butter, and fish fillets to the pepper sauce and stir well.

6. Cook the fish for around 8 minutes or until it is completely cooked. Divide into 4 equal portions

7. To prepare the taco shells, take a tortilla and fry it for around 2 minutes on both sides on high flame.

8. Place the taco onto a plate and let each taco cool in the desired shape. Fill each taco shell with ¼ of the fish mixture.

9. Top with freshly chopped chives and serve hot!

Nutrition: Fat – 20 gProtein – 24 gCarbohydrates – 7 g Sugar – 2.3 g

Seared Sesame Tuna Steak

Preparation Time: 10 minutes
Cooking Time: 20 minutes
Servings: 2
Ingredients:

- Ahi tuna steaks – 2 (6-ounce)
- Soy sauce – 2 tablespoons
- Sesame oil – 1 tablespoon
- Sesame seeds – 1 teaspoon
- Salt – as per taste
- Pepper – as per taste

Directions:

1. Begin by placing the ahi tuna steak into a shallow dish and generously season with pepper and salt.

2. Take a small bowl and add in the sesame oil and soy sauce. Whisk well and pour over the ahi tuna steak.

3. Flip over and set the dish aside for around 15 minutes at room temperature.

4. Take a nonstick pan and place it over a medium flame. Once the pan is hot, place the marinated ahi tuna steaks in it and cook for about 3 minutes. Flip over and cook for another 3 minutes.

5. Once done, transfer onto a wooden block and slice into slices measuring about ½ inch in thickness.

6. Transfer onto a serving platter and garnish with a sprinkle of black and white sesame seeds.

7. Serve hot!

Nutrition: Fat – 9 gProtein – 40.5 gCarbohydrates – 1 g Sugar – 0.3 g

Baked Parmesan Cod Fillets

Preparation Time: 10 minutes
Cooking Time: 20 minutes
Servings: 4
Ingredients:

- Butter (melted) – ¼ cup
- Garlic (minced) – 2 cloves
- Parmesan cheese (grated) – ¾ cup
- Paprika – 1 teaspoon
- Cod fillets (boneless) – 1 ½ pounds
- Fresh parsley (chopped) – 1 tablespoon
- Lemon zest (freshly grated) – 1 tablespoon

Directions:

1. Start by preheating the oven by setting the temperature to 400 degrees Fahrenheit.

2. Take a baking sheet and line it with a parchment paper sheet.

3. Take a shallow glass dish and add in the garlic and melted butter; mix well and set aside.

4. In another shallow dish, add in the paprika and parmesan; mix well and set aside.

5. Take a cod fillet and dip it in the butter mixture. Flip and dip the other side. Then dredge the fillet with the parmesan mixture. Place the fillet on the baking sheet. Repeat the process with the remaining fillets.

6. Sprinkle the cod fillets with lemon zest and parsley and place the baking sheet into the oven. Bake for around 15 minutes or until the fish flakes easily.

7. Take it out of the oven and transfer it onto a serving platter.

8. Serve hot!

Nutrition: Calories: 320 Fat – 17.5 gProtein – 36.5 g Carbohydrates – 1 gSugar – 1.1 g

Grilled Lemon Butter Salmon Kebobs

Preparation Time: 10 minutes

Cooking Time: 15 minutes

Servings: 4

Ingredients:

- Salmon – 1 ½ pounds
- Zucchini (chopped) – 2 cups
- Butter (melted) – 2 tablespoons
- Lemon juice – 1 tablespoon
- Lemon zest – ½ teaspoon
- Salt – ½ teaspoon
- Black pepper (ground) – ¼ teaspoon
- Parsley (chopped) – 2 tablespoons
- Dill (chopped) – 2 teaspoons
- Skewers (soaked)

Directions:

1. Start by preheating the grill by bringing the heat to medium-high.

2. Take a large glass mixing bowl and add in the lemon juice, butter, lemon zest, pepper, salt, dill, and parsley. Mix until well combined. Your marinade is ready.

3. Cut the salmon into bite-sized cubes measuring about 1 inch each. Transfer into the marinade.

4. Also, add the zucchini to the marinade and toss well.

5. Skewer the zucchini and salmon cubes (alternating) and then place them on the preheated grill. Cook for around 4 minutes. Flip over and cook for another 4 minutes.

6. Transfer onto a serving platter and serve right away!

Nutrition: Calories: 418 Fat – 29 gProtein – 36 gCarbohydrates – 1.7 gSugar – 1.1 g

Alfredo Shrimp

Preparation Time: minutes

Cooking Time: minutes

Servings: 5

Ingredients:

- Zucchini (spiral) – 4
- Olive oil – 1 tablespoon
- Shrimp (cleaned and peeled) – 1 pound
- Garlic (minced) – 2 cloves
- Butter (unsalted) – 2 tablespoons
- Heavy cream – ¾ cup
- Cream cheese – 4 ounces
- Fresh parmesan (grated) – ½ cup
- Salt – ¼ teaspoon
- Black pepper (ground) – ¼ teaspoon
- Fresh parsley – 2 tablespoons

Directions:

1. Start by placing a large nonstick skillet over a medium-high flame. Pour in the olive oil and let it heat through.

2. Once the oil is hot, toss in the garlic and shrimp. Cook for a couple of minutes or until the shrimp is pink. Transfer onto a plate and set aside.

3. Return the pan to the heat and add in the butter and cream cheese. Whisk until both melt and are nicely combined. Add in the heavy cream, pepper, salt, and parmesan cheese; stir until well combined.

4. Now toss in the zucchini spiral noodles and cooked shrimp; cook with the cheese sauce for around 3 minutes.

5. Finish with a nice sprinkle of parmesan and serve hot!

Nutrition: Calories: 403 Fat – 33 gProtein – 21 gCarbohydrates – 7 gSugar – 3.25 g

Hummus and Salad Pita Flats

Preparation Time: 15 minutes

Cooking Time: 0 minutes

Servings:

Ingredients

- 1/4 cup sweet roasted red pepper hummus
- 2-oz whole wheat pitas
- 8 pitted olives.
- 2 large eggs.
- 2 cups spring mix
- 2 tsp. extra virgin olive oil
- 1 tsp. dried oregano

Directions

1. Heat pitas (you can find Directions: on the package).

2. Spread hummus exactly over pitas.

3. Top with chopped hard-cooked eggs, pitted olives and dried oregano.

4. Add spring mix with extra virgin olive oil, and arrange properly on each pita.

5. The right diet is excellent diabetes remedy.

Nutrition: Calories 250 Protein 8 gFat 2 gCarbs 50 g

Lettuce Salad with Lemon

Preparation Time: 5 minutes

Cooking Time: 5 minutes

Servings:

Ingredients:

- 1/2 head chopped lettuce
- 2 oz. arugula
- 1 avocado
- 1 tbsp. lemon juice
- 2 tsp. extra virgin olive oil
- 1/8 tsp. salt
- 1/4 tsp. mustard
- 1/8 tsp. pepper

Directions

1. Whisk together fresh lemon juice, torn arugula, chopped avocado, extra virgin olive oil, salt, mustard, and pepper.

2. Add chopped lettuce and toss to coat.

This recipe is perfect for both 1 and 2 type diabetics.

Nutrition: Calories 15Protein 2 g Fat 2 g Carbs 1 g

Ground Turkey, Asparagus and Basil

Preparation Time: 10 minutes

Cooking Time: 10 minutes

Servings:

Ingredients:

- 1/2 lb. ground turkey
- 1 (9-oz) pkg asparagus (chopped)
- 2 green onions
- 1/2 (10-oz) pkg carrots
- 1,5 clove garlic
- 1,5 tbsp soy sauce (low-sodium)
- 1,5 tbsp sweet chili sauce
- 3 tbsp fresh basil

Directions

1. Cook ground turkey over medium heat until turkey is browned and crumbly.

2. Add chopped asparagus, matchstick carrots, greens thinly sliced onions and minced garlic; cook for 2 minutes.

3. Stir in low-sodium soy sauce and chili sauce; cook 2 minutes. Add fresh basil.

4. Enjoy easy diabetic recipes!

Nutrition: Calories 161 Protein 20 g Fat 8 g Carbs 0 g

Smoky Carrot and Black Bean Stew

Preparation Time: 15 minutes

Cooking Time: 25 minutes

Servings:

Ingredients:

- 1 (15-oz) can salt-free black beans
- 1 (14.5-oz) can salt-free diced tomatoes
- 1 cup carrots (chopped)
- 1 (14.5-oz) can chicken broth (low-sodium)
- 1,5 tsp extra virgin olive oil
- 3/4 cup onion (chopped)
- 2 tsp smoked paprika
- 2 cloves garlic
- 1 avocado

Directions

1. Heat extra virgin olive oil in a large saucepan.

2. Add carrots and onion; fry 5 minutes.

3. Stir in paprika and minced garlic; cook 1 minute.

4. Add broth, beans, and diced tomatoes; bring to boil.

5. Reduce heat; simmer until carrots are very tender.

6. Top each serving with chopped avocado.

7. Tastes great!

Nutrition: Calories 100 Protein 15 g Fat 7 g Carbs 16 g

Oven-Baked Potatoes and Green Beans

Preparation Time: 10 minutes

Cooking Time: 30 minutes

Servings:

Ingredients:

- 1/2 lb. potatoes
- 1/2 lb. green beans

- 2 tsp extra virgin olive oil
- 2 tsp Dijon mustard
- 1/2 tsp garlic powder
- 1/4 tsp salt
- 1/7 tsp pepper

Directions

1.   Preheat oven to 375°F.

2.   Mix potatoes cut into chunks, oil, and mustard. Spread into a baking sheet. Bake 15 minutes. Make the first layer.

3.   Add green beans, garlic powder, salt, and pepper to potatoes, and toss. Make another layer.

4.   Bake 15 minutes more.

Nutrition: Calories 35 Protein 1.3 g Fat 0.3 g Carbs 5.5 g

Corn Tortillas and Spinach Salad

Preparation Time: 3 minutes
Cooking Time: 5 minutes
Servings:

Ingredients:

- 4 corn tortillas
- 2 cups baby spinach
- 2 tbsp. red onion (chopped)
- 1 pepper
- 4 mini tomatoes (whole)
- 8 pitted small ripe olives
- 2 tsp. balsamic vinegar
- 1/8 tsp. salt
- 1/8 tsp. pepper
- 1 tbsp. extra virgin olive oil

Directions

1.   Heat tortillas according to package instruction.

2.   Mix remaining ingredients in a salad bowl.

3.   Serve tortillas and salad.

4.   I often cook this dish for dinner, my children adore it

Nutrition: Calories 200 Protein 10 g Fat 3 g Carbs 35 g

Beans with Mustard Sauce and Spicy Cucumbers

Preparation Time: 5 minutes

Cooking Time: 7 minutes
Servings:

Ingredients:

- 1,3 cups beans
- 1 cucumber
- 2 tbsp. mayonnaise (reduced-fat)
- 1 tbsp. Greek yogurt (fat-free)
- 1/2 tsp. mustard
- 1/8 tsp. salt
- 1/8 tsp. pepper
- 1 tbsp. fresh lemon juice
- 1 tsp. hot sauce

Directions

1.   Cook beans.

2.   Mix reduced-fat mayonnaise, fat-free yogurt, mustard, pepper, and salt.

3.   Toss beans with mayonnaise mixture.

4.   Add lemon juice and hot sauce over peeled and sliced cucumbers.

You can serve beans and cucumbers alongside any fish dish.

Bon Appetit!

Nutrition: Calories 60 Protein 7 g Fat 1 g Carbs 8 g

Simple Lemon Farro and Steamed Broccoli

Preparation Time: 5 minutes
Cooking Time: 10 minutes
Servings:

Ingredients:

- 1/3 cup pearled farro (substitute brown rice or quinoa, if desired)
- 1 (12-oz) pkg broccoli
- 1/2 tsp. lemon rind
- 1,5 tsp. lemon juice
- 1 tbsp. extra virgin olive oil
- 1/4 tsp. salt

Directions

1.   Cook farro (you can find Directions: on the package).

2.   Mix farro, grated lemon rind, lemon juice, 1 tsp oil, and 1/8 tsp salt.

3. Put broccoli in a steamer basket over boiling water. Steam 4 minutes.

4. Add 2 tsp. oil and 1/8 tsp. salt.

Nutrition: Calories 35 Protein 2 g Fat 1 g Carbs 7 g

Creamy Bell Pepper-Corn Salad and Seared Zucchini

Preparation Time: 7 minutes

Cooking Time: 20 minutes

Servings:

Ingredients:

- 2 zucchini
- 2 cups corn kernels
- 3 cherry tomatoes (whole)
- 1/2 cup celery
- 1/3 cup green bell pepper
- 2 tbsps. sour cream (reduced-fat)
- 1/4 cup mayonnaise (reduced-fat)
- 1/8 tsp. pepper
- 1 tsp. sugar
- 1/4 tsp. salt

Directions

1. Cook corn (you can find Directions: on the package).

2. Mix corn, chopped celery, chopped green bell pepper, whole cherry tomatoes, sour cream, mayonnaise, sugar, 1/8 tsp salt and pepper in a bowl.

3. Heat a large skillet and cook cut in half lengthwise zucchini 8 minutes (turn occasionally).

4. Sprinkle zucchini with 1/8 tsp salt.

5. Add zucchini to the corn mixture.

Nutrition: Calories 100 Protein 6 g Fat 3 g Carbs 34 g

Broccoli with Hot Sauce

Preparation Time: 3 minutes

Cooking Time: 4 minutes

Servings:

Ingredients:

- 3 cups broccoli florets
- 1/2 tsp hot sauce
- 1 tbsp extra virgin olive oil
- 1/8 tsp salt

- 1/8 tsp pepper

Directions

1. Arrange broccoli in a steamer basket. Steam about 4 minutes or until tender.

2. Drizzle with the oil and sprinkle with hot sauce, pepper, and salt.

Nutrition: Calories 30 Protein 4 g Fat 0 g Carbs 5 g

Cauliflower and Spinach Salad

Preparation Time: 10 minutes

Cooking Time: 15 minutes

Servings:

Ingredients:

- 1/2 (12-oz) pkg cauliflower florets
- 1 (5-oz) pkg spinach
- 1 (8.25-oz) can mandarin oranges (drained)
- 1/4 cup almonds
- 1 tbsp extra virgin olive oil
- 1 tbsp apple vinegar
- 2 tsp honey
- 1/8 tsp salt

Directions

1. Cook cauliflower.

2. Mix vinegar, oil, honey, and salt; add spinach and toss to combine.

3. Top salad with oranges and almonds.

4. Serve alongside any meat dish.

Nutrition: Calories 27 Protein 3 g Fat 0 g Carbs 2 g

Easy Barbecue Brisket

Preparation Time: 15 minutes

Cooking Time: 5 hours

Servings:

Ingredients:

- 1,5 lb. beef brisket
- 1 sweet onion
- 1/2 tbsp steak seasoning
- 1/2 cup barbecue sauce
- 1 cup beef broth

Directions

1. Place sliced onion in a slow cooker. Rub seasoning on all sides of trimmed brisket.

2. Cut brisket in pieces, if necessary.

3.   Pour beef broth and barbecue sauce over brisket.

4.   Cook on low 3 to 5 hours — slice before serving.

Nutrition: Calories 188 Protein 13 g Fat 8 g
Carbs 15 g

Chicken Thighs

Preparation Time: 10 minutes

Cooking Time: 38 minutes

Servings:

Ingredients:

- 1,4 lb. bone-in, skinless chicken thighs
- 1 clove garlic
- 1/4 tsp dry mustard
- 1 tbsp olive oil
- 2 tbsp soy sauce
- 1/2 tsp ginger
- 1/4 tsp allspice
- 1/4 tsp red pepper

Directions

1.   Preheat oven to 400°F. Sauté minced garlic, ground ginger, ground allspice, mustard, and crushed red pepper in hot oil 3 minutes. Remove from heat.

2.   Whisk in soy sauce. Place chicken on a baking sheet. Pour garlic mixture over chicken, and toss.

3.   Bake 35 minutes.

4.   Surprise your guests with this wonderful dish.

Nutrition: Calories 120 Protein 8 g Fat 5 g Carbs 3 g

Orange-Avocado Salad

Preparation Time: 10 minutes

Cooking Time: 0 minutes

Servings:

Ingredients:

- 1 navel orange
- 1 avocado
- 1 tbsp fresh lime juice
- 1 tbsp extra virgin olive oil
- 1/2 tsp arugula

Directions

1.   Mix lime juice, oil, and arugula in a bowl.

2.   Add peeled and sectioned orange sections, tossing well.

3.   Add diced avocado just before serving.

Nutrition: Calories 30 Protein 2 g Fat 2 g Carbs 1 g

Avocados with Walnut-Herb

Preparation Time: 7 minutes

Cooking Time: 4 minutes

Servings:

Ingredients:

- 1/4 cup walnuts
- 1 avocado
- 1 tbsp fresh basil
- 1,5 tsp lemon juice (fresh)
- 1,2 tsp extra virgin olive oil
- 1,8 tsp salt
- 1,4 tsp pepper

Directions

1.   Fry chopped nuts 3 to 4 minutes.

2.   Mix nuts, chopped basil, oil, lemon juice, salt, and pepper.

3.   Cut avocado in half lengthwise.

4.   Top avocado halves with nut mixture.

Nutrition: Calories 200 Protein 2 g Fat 17 g Carbs 7 g

Baked Salmon with Garlic Parmesan Topping

Preparation Time: 5 minutes

Cooking Time: 20 minutes

Servings: 4

Ingredients:

- 1 lb. wild caught salmon filets
- 2 tbsp. margarine

What you'll need from store cupboard:

- ¼ cup reduced fat parmesan cheese, grated
- ¼ cup light mayonnaise
- 2-3 cloves garlic, diced
- 2 tbsp. parsley
- Salt and pepper

Directions:

1.   Heat oven to 350 and line a baking pan with parchment paper.

2.   Place salmon on pan and season with salt and pepper.

3.   In a medium skillet, over medium heat, melt butter. Add garlic and cook, stirring 1 minute.

4.   Reduce heat to low and add remaining Ingredients. Stir until everything is melted and combined.

5.   Spread evenly over salmon and bake 15 minutes for thawed fish or 20 for frozen. Salmon is done when it flakes easily with a fork. Serve.

Nutrition: Calories 408Total Carbs 4gProtein 41gFat 24gSugar 1gFiber 0g

Baked Seafood Casserole

Preparation Time: 20 minutes

Cooking Time: 30 minutes

Servings: 6

Ingredients:

- 12 oz. shrimp, peeled and deveined
- 12 oz. cod, cut into 1-inch squares
- 2 medium leeks, white part only, cut into matchstick pieces
- 2 stalks celery, diced
- 1 cup half-n-half
- 4 tbsp. margarine

What you'll need from store cupboard:

- 1 cup dry white wine
- 1 cup water
- ½ cup reduced fat parmesan cheese, grated
- ¼ cup super fine almond flour
- 2 small bay leaves whole
- 2 ½ tsp. Old Bay Seasoning
- ½ tsp. xanthan gum
- ¼ tsp. sea salt

Directions:

1.   Heat oven to 400 degrees.

2.   Poach the seafood: In a large, heavy pot, combine wine, water, bay leaves, and ½ teaspoon Old bay. Bring just to boiling over med-high heat. Reduce heat to low and simmer 3 minutes.

3.   Add shrimp and cook until they start to turn pink. Transfer to a bowl. Repeat for cod.

4.   Turn heat back to med-high heat and continue simmering poaching liquid until it is reduced to about 1 cup. Remove from heat, strain and save for later.

5.   In a separate large sauce pan melt 2 tablespoons margarine over med-high heat. Add leeks and celery and season with salt. Cook, stirring occasionally, until vegetables are soft.

6.   In an 8-inch square baking dish, layer vegetables and seafood.

7.   In the same saucepan you used for the vegetables, melt 1 tablespoon of margarine. Stir in xanthan gum and stir to coat. After xanthan is coated gradually stir in reserved poaching liquid. Bring to a simmer scraping up the browned bits on the bottom of the pan.

8.   When sauce starts to thicken, stir in half-n-half. Bring back to a simmer and cook, stirring frequently, until the sauce has the same texture as gravy. Taste and adjust seasoning as desired. Pour over seafood in the baking dish.

9.   In a food processor, or blender, combine the almond flour, parmesan, 2 teaspoons Old Bay, and 1 tablespoon margarine. Process until thoroughly combined. Sprinkle over casserole and bake 20 minutes or until topping is brown and crisp. Serve.

Nutrition: Calories 344Total Carbs 9g Protein 30gFat 17gSugar 2gFiber 1g

BBQ Oysters with Bacon

Preparation Time: 20 minutes

Cooking Time: 10 minutes

Servings: 2

Ingredients:

- 1 dozen fresh oysters, shucked and left on the half shell
- 3 slices thick cut bacon, cut into thin strips
- Juice of ½ lemon

What you'll need from the store cupboard

- 1/3 cup sugar-free ketchup (chapter 16)
- ¼ cup Worcestershire sauce
- 1 tsp. horseradish
- Dash of hot sauce
- Lime wedges for garnish
- Rock salt

Directions:

1. Heat oven to broil. Line a shallow baking dish with rock salt. Place the oysters snugly into the salt.
2. In a large bowl, combine remaining Ingredients and mix well.
3. Add a dash of Worcestershire to each oyster then top with bacon mixture. Cook 10 minutes, or until bacon is crisp. Serve with lime wedges.

Nutrition: Calories 234Total Carbs 10gProtein 13gFat 13gSugar 9gFiber 0g

Blackened Shrimp

Preparation Time: 5 minutes
Cooking Time: 5 minutes
Servings: 4

Ingredients:
- 1 ½ lbs. shrimp, peel & devein
- 4 lime wedges
- 4 tbsp. cilantro, chopped

What you'll need from store cupboard:
- 4 cloves garlic, diced
- 1 tbsp. chili powder
- 1 tbsp. paprika
- 1 tbsp. olive oil
- 2 tsp. Splenda brown sugar
- 1 tsp. cumin
- 1 tsp. oregano
- 1 tsp. garlic powder
- 1 tsp. salt
- ½ tsp. pepper

Directions:
1. In a small bowl combine seasonings and Splenda brown sugar.
2. Heat oil in a skillet over med-high heat. Add shrimp, in a single layer, and cook 1-2 minutes per side.
3. Add seasonings, and cook, stirring, 30 seconds. Serve garnished with cilantro and a lime wedge.

Nutrition: Calories 252Total Carbs 7gProtein 39gFat 7gSugar 2gFiber 1g

Cajun Catfish

Preparation Time: 5 minutes
Cooking Time: 15 minutes
Servings: 4

Ingredients:
- 4 (8 oz.) catfish fillets

What you'll need from store cupboard:
- 2 tbsp. olive oil
- 2 tsp. garlic salt
- 2 tsp. thyme
- 2 tsp. paprika
- ½ tsp. cayenne pepper
- ½ tsp. red hot sauce
- ¼ tsp. black pepper
- Nonstick cooking spray

Directions:
1. Heat oven to 450 degrees. Spray a 9x13-inch baking dish with cooking spray.
2. In a small bowl whisk together everything but catfish. Brush both sides of fillets, using all the spice mix.
3. Bake 10-13 minutes or until fish flakes easily with a fork. Serve.

Nutrition: Calories 366Total Carbs 0gProtein 35gFat 24gSugar 0gFiber 0g

Cajun Flounder & Tomatoes

Preparation Time: 10 minutes
Cooking Time: 15 minutes
Servings: 4

Ingredients:
- 4 flounder fillets
- 2 ½ cups tomatoes, diced
- ¾ cup onion, diced
- ¾ cup green bell pepper, diced

What you'll need from store cupboard:
- 2 cloves garlic, diced fine
- 1 tbsp. Cajun seasoning
- 1 tsp. olive oil

Directions:
1. Heat oil in a large skillet over med-high heat. Add onion and garlic and cook 2 minutes, or until soft. Add tomatoes, peppers and spices, and cook 2-3 minutes until tomatoes soften.
2. Lay fish over top. Cover, reduce heat to medium and cook, 5-8 minutes, or until fish flakes easily with a fork. Transfer fish to serving plates and top with sauce.

Nutrition: Calories 194Total Carbs 8gNet Carbs 6gProtein 32gFat 3gSugar 5gFiber 2g

Cajun Shrimp & Roasted Vegetables

Preparation Time: 5 minutes
Cooking Time: 15 minutes
Servings: 4
Ingredients:
- 1 lb. large shrimp, peeled and deveined
- 2 zucchinis, sliced
- 2 yellow squash, sliced
- ½ bunch asparagus, cut into thirds
- 2 red bell pepper, cut into chunks

What you'll need from store cupboard:
- 2 tbsp. olive oil
- 2 tbsp. Cajun Seasoning
- Salt & pepper, to taste

Directions:
1.   Heat oven to 400 degrees.
2.   Combine shrimp and vegetables in a large bowl. Add oil and seasoning and toss to coat.
3.   Spread evenly in a large baking sheet and bake 15-20 minutes, or until vegetables are tender. Serve.

Nutrition: Calories 251Total Carbs 13gNet Carbs 9gProtein 30gFat 9gSugar 6g Fiber 4g

Cilantro Lime Grilled Shrimp

Preparation Time: 5 minutes
Cooking Time: 5 minutes
Servings: 6
Ingredients:
- 1 ½ lbs. large shrimp raw, peeled, deveined with tails on
- Juice and zest of 1 lime
- 2 tbsp. fresh cilantro chopped

What you'll need from store cupboard:
- ¼ cup olive oil
- 2 cloves garlic, diced fine
- 1 tsp. smoked paprika
- ¼ tsp. cumin
- 1/2 teaspoon salt
- ¼ tsp. cayenne pepper

Directions:
1.   Place the shrimp in a large Ziploc bag.

2.   Mix remaining Ingredients in a small bowl and pour over shrimp. Let marinate 20-30 minutes.
3.   Heat up the grill. Skewer the shrimp and cook 2-3 minutes, per side, just until they turn pick. Be careful not to overcook them. Serve garnished with cilantro.

Nutrition: Calories 317Total Carbs 4gProtein 39gFat 15gSugar 0gFiber 0g

Coconut Shrimp

Preparation Time: 15 minutes
Cooking Time: 20 minutes
Servings: 6
Ingredients:
- 2 lbs. jumbo shrimp, peel & devein & pat dry
- 2 eggs

What you'll need from store cupboard:
- ¾ cup unsweetened coconut
- ¾ cup coconut flour
- ½ cup sunflower oil
- 1 tbsp. Creole seasoning
- 2 tsp. Splenda
- 1 tsp. salt
- ½ tsp. garlic powder
- Sriracha Dipping Sauce, (chapter 16)

Directions:
1.   Heat oil in a pot over med-high heat, you need about 3 inches of oil.
2.   In a medium bowl, combine coconut, flour, Creole seasoning, salt, garlic powder, and Splenda.
3.   In a small bowl beat the eggs.
4.   Dip shrimp in the eggs then the coconut mixture to coat. Cook, 1/3 of the shrimp at a time, 2-3 minutes, or until golden brown. Transfer to paper towel lined plate.
5.   Serve hot with Sriracha dipping sauce, or your favorite dipping sauce.

Nutrition: Calories 316Total Carbs 10gNet Carbs 7gProtein 29gFat 17gSugar 6gFiber 3g

Crab Cakes

Preparation Time: 10 minutes
Cooking Time: 10 minutes
Servings: 8
Ingredients:
- 1 lb. lump blue crabmeat

- 1 tbsp. red bell pepper, diced fine
- 1 tbsp. green bell pepper, diced fine
- 1 tbsp. fresh parsley, chopped fine
- 2 eggs
- ¼ tsp. fresh lemon juice

What you'll need from store cupboard:
- ¼ cup + 1 tbsp. lite mayonnaise
- ¼ cup Dijon mustard
- 2 tbsp. sunflower oil
- 1 tbsp. baking powder
- 1 tbsp. Worcestershire sauce
- 1 ½ tsp. Old Bay

Directions:

1. In a small bowl, whisk together ¼ cup mayonnaise, Dijon mustard, Worcestershire, and lemon juice until combined. Cover and chill until ready to serve.

2. In a large bowl, mix crab, bell peppers, parsley, eggs, 1 tablespoon mayonnaise, baking powder, and Old Bay seasoning until Ingredients are combined.

3. Heat oil in a large skillet over med-high heat. Once oil is hot, drop 2 tablespoons crab mixture into hot skillet. They will be loose but as the egg cooks they will hold together.

4. Cook 2 minutes or until firm, then flip and cook another minutes. Transfer to serving plate. Serve with mustard dipping sauce.

Nutrition: Calories 96Total Carbs 3gProtein 12gFat 4g Sugar 1gFiber 0g

Crab Frittata

Preparation Time: 10 minutes
Cooking Time: 50 minutes
Servings: 4

Ingredients:
- 4 eggs
- 2 cups lump crabmeat
- 1 cup half-n-half
- 1 cup green onions, diced

What you'll need from store cupboard:
- 1 cup reduced fat parmesan cheese, grated
- 1 tsp. salt
- 1 tsp. pepper
- 1 tsp. smoked paprika

- 1 tsp. Italian seasoning
- Nonstick cooking spray

Directions:

1. Heat oven to 350 degrees. Spray an 8-inch spring form pan, or pie plate with cooking spray.

2. In a large bowl, whisk together the eggs and half-n-half. Add seasonings and parmesan cheese, stir to mix.

3. Stir in the onions and crab meat. Pour into prepared pan and bake 35-40 minutes, or eggs are set and top is lightly browned.

4. Let cool 10 minutes, then slice and serve warm or at room temperature.

Nutrition: Calories 276Total Carbs 5gNet Carbs 4gProtein 25gFat 17gSugar 1gFiber 1g

Crispy Baked Flounder with Green Beans

Preparation Time: 10 minutes
Cooking Time: 20 minutes
Servings: 4

Ingredients:
- 1 lb. flounder
- 2 cups green beans
- 4 tbsp. margarine
- 8 basil leaves

What you'll need from store cupboard:
- 1 ¾ oz. pork rinds
- ½ cup reduced fat parmesan cheese
- 3 cloves garlic
- Salt and pepper to taste
- Nonstick cooking spray

Directions:

1. Heat oven to 350 degrees. Spray a baking dish with cooking spray.

2. Steam green beans until they are almost tender, about 15 minutes, less if you use frozen or canned beans. Lay green beans in the prepared dish.

3. Place the fish filets over the green beans and season with salt and pepper.

4. Place the garlic, basil, pork rinds, and parmesan in a food processor and pulse until mixture resembles crumbs. Sprinkle over fish. Cut margarine into small pieces and place on top.

5. Bake 15-20 minutes or until fish flakes easily with a fork. Serve.

Nutrition: Calories 358Total Carbs 5gProtein 39gFat 20g Sugar 1gFiber 2g

Crock Pot Fish & Tomatoes

Preparation Time: 10 minutes

Cooking Time: 2 hours 30 minutes

Servings: 4

Ingredients:
- 1 lb. cod
- 1 bell pepper, diced
- 1 small onion, diced

What you'll need from store cupboard:
- 15 oz. can tomatoes, diced
- 1/3 cup low-sodium vegetable broth
- 1 clove garlic, diced fine
- ½ tsp. basil
- ½ tsp. oregano
- ½ tsp. salt
- ¼ tsp. pepper

Directions:
1. Place the onion, bell pepper, tomatoes, and garlic in the crock pot. Stir to mix.
2. Place fish on top. Sprinkle with herbs and seasonings. Pour broth over top.
3. Cover and cook on high 1-2 hours, or low 2-4 hours.

Nutrition: Calories 165Total Carbs 11g Net Carbs 8g Protein 28gFat 1gSugar 6gFiber 3g

Crunchy Lemon Shrimp

Preparation Time: 5 minutes

Cooking Time: 10 minutes

Servings: 4

Ingredients:
- 1 lb. raw shrimp, peeled and deveined
- 2 tbsp. Italian parsley, roughly chopped
- 2 tbsp. lemon juice, divided

What you'll need from store cupboard:
- 2/3 cup panko bread crumbs
- 2½ tbsp. olive oil, divided
- Salt and pepper, to taste

Directions:
1. Heat oven to 400 degrees.
2. Place the shrimp evenly in a baking dish and sprinkle with salt and pepper. Drizzle on 1 tablespoon lemon juice and 1 tablespoon of olive oil. Set aside.
3. In a medium bowl, combine parsley, remaining lemon juice, bread crumbs, remaining olive oil, and ¼ tsp. each of salt and pepper. Layer the panko mixture evenly on top of the shrimp.
4. Bake 8-10 minutes or until shrimp are cooked through and the panko is golden brown.

Nutrition: Calories 283Total Carbs 15gNet Carbs 14g Protein 28gFat 12gSugar 1gFiber 1g

Dill Smoked Salmon over Noodles

Preparation Time: 10 minutes

Cooking Time: 10 minutes

Servings: 4

Ingredients:
- 6 oz. smoked salmon, chopped
- Juice from 1/2 a lemon
- ¼ cup half-n-half
- 3 tbsp. margarine
- 2 tbsp. fresh dill, diced

What you'll need from store cupboard:
- Homemade noodles, chapter 14
- ½ cup low sodium chicken broth
- ½ cup dry white wine
- 1 tbsp. olive oil
- 2 cloves garlic, diced fine
- Salt & pepper, to taste

Directions:
1. Heat oil and margarine in a large skillet over med-high heat. Add garlic and cook 30 seconds.
2. Add broth, wine, and lemon juice. Cook until sauce is reduced by half, about 4 minutes.
3. Stir in the half-n-half and noodles and cook 2 minutes, or until noodles are done.
4. Stir in the salmon and salt and pepper to taste. Serve garnished with the fresh dill.

Nutrition: Calories 273Total Carbs 4gProtein 14gFat 21g Sugar 0gFiber 0g

Fisherman's Pie

Preparation Time: 15 minutes
Cooking Time: 25 minutes
Servings: 4

Ingredients:

- 12 shrimp, peel & devein
- 8 oz. cod, cut in 1-inch pieces
- 4 oz. salmon, cut in 1-inch pieces
- 1 slice bacon
- 4 cup cheesy cauliflower puree, (chapter 14)
- ½ cup onion, diced
- ¼ cup heavy cream
- 2 tbsp. butter
- 1 tbsp. fresh parsley, diced

What you'll need from store cupboard:

- 1 cup low sodium vegetable broth
- ½ cup dry white wine
- 1 clove garlic, diced fine
- ¼ tsp. celery salt
- Salt & pepper, to taste
- Nonstick cooking spray

Directions:

1. Heat oven to 400 degrees. Spray a large casserole dish, or 4 small ones with cooking spray.
2. Melt butter in a medium saucepan over medium heat. Add onion and cook until soft. Add the garlic and cook 1 minute more.
3. Pour in the wine and broth and cook 5 minutes.
4. Stir in cream, bacon, and celery salt and simmer 5 minutes, until bacon is cooked through and most of the fat has rendered off. Remove the slice of bacon, chop it up and add it back to the pot.
5. Add the seafood, parsley, salt, and pepper to taste and simmer 2-3 minutes. Transfer mixture to prepared casserole dish.
6. Place the cauliflower in a large Ziploc bag, or pastry bag, and snip off one corner. Pipe the cauliflower in small rosettes to cover the top. Bake 8-10 minutes, or until heated through and top is lightly browned, you may need to broil it for 1-2 minutes to reach the browned color. Serve.

Nutrition: Calories 338Total Carbs 10gNet Carbs 7gProtein 38gFat 14gSugar 3gFiber 3g

Garlic Shrimp with Sun Dried Tomatoes

Preparation Time: 10 minutes
Cooking Time: 30 minutes
Servings: 4

Ingredients:

- ½ lb. shrimp, peeled and deveined
- 4 oz. sun-dried tomatoes
- 1 cup half-n-half

What you'll need from store cupboard:

- 1 cup reduced fat parmesan cheese
- 4 cloves garlic, diced fine
- 2 tbsp. olive oil
- 1 teaspoon dried basil
- ¼ tsp. salt
- ¼ tsp. paprika
- ¼ teaspoon crushed red pepper
- ½ recipe homemade pasta, cook and drain, (chapter 14)

Directions:

1. Heat oil in a large skillet over medium heat. Add garlic and tomatoes and cook 1 minute.
2. Add shrimp, sprinkle with salt and paprika, and cook about 2 minutes.
3. Add half-n-half, basil, and crushed red pepper and bring to boil. Reduce heat to simmer. Whisk the parmesan cheese into the hot cream and stir to melt cheese, on low heat.
4. Remove from heat. Add pasta and stir to coat. Serve.

Nutrition: Calories 353Total Carbs 23gNet Carbs 20gProtein 37gFat 22gSugar 3gFiber 3g

Grilled Tuna Steaks

Preparation Time: 5 minutes

Cooking Time: 10 minutes

Servings: 6

Ingredients:

- 6 6 oz. tuna steaks
- 3 tbsp. fresh basil, diced

What you'll need from store cupboard:

- 4 ½ tsp. olive oil
- ¾ tsp. salt
- ¼ tsp. pepper
- Nonstick cooking spray

Directions:

1. Heat grill to medium heat. Spray rack with cooking spray.
2. Drizzle both sides of the tuna with oil. Sprinkle with basil, salt and pepper.
3. Place on grill and cook 5 minutes per side, tuna should be slightly pink in the center. Serve.

Nutrition: Calories 343Total Carbs 0gProtein 51gFat 14g Sugar 0gFiber 0g

Italian Steamed Mussels

Preparation Time: 10 minutes

Cooking Time: 10 minutes

Servings: 4

Ingredients:

- 2 lbs. mussels, cleaned
- 2 plum tomatoes, peeled, seeded and diced
- 1 cup onion, diced
- 2 tbsp. fresh parsley, diced

What you'll need from store cupboard:

- ¼ cup dry white wine
- 3 cloves garlic, diced fine
- 3 tbsp. olive oil
- 2 tbsp. fresh breadcrumbs
- ¼ teaspoon crushed red pepper flakes

Directions:

1. Heat oil in a large sauce pot over medium heat. Add the onions and cook until soft, about 2-3 minutes. Add garlic and cook 1 minute more.

2. Stir in wine, tomatoes, and pepper flakes. Bring to a boil, stirring occasionally. Add the mussels and cook 3-4 minutes, or until all the mussels have opened. Discard any mussels that do not open.

3. Once mussels open, transfer them to a serving bowl. Add bread crumbs to the sauce and continue to cook, stirring frequently, until mixture thickens. Stir in parsley and pour evenly over mussels. Serve.

Nutrition: Calories 340Total Carbs 18gNet Carbs 16g Protein 29gFat 16gSugar 4g Fiber 2g

Jambalaya

Preparation Time: 10 minutes

Cooking Time: 40 minutes

Servings: 6

Ingredients:

- 1 lb. raw shrimp, peel & devein
- 14 oz. Andouille sausage, cut into 1-inch pieces
- 1 medium cauliflower, riced
- 4 stalks celery, diced
- ½ white onion, diced
- ½ red bell pepper, diced
- 4 tbsp. margarine

What you'll need from store cupboard:

- 2 cups low sodium chicken broth
- ½ can tomatoes & green chilies
- 3 cloves garlic, diced fine
- 2 tsp. garlic powder
- 2 tsp. Old Bay
- 1 ½ tsp. onion powder
- 1 tsp. thyme
- 1 tsp. oregano
- 1 tsp. basil
- 1/2 tsp. cayenne pepper

Directions:

1. Place large stock pot over med-high heat.
2. In a small bowl, stir together garlic powder, onion powder, thyme, oregano, basil, Old Bay, and cayenne until combined.
3. Add 2 tablespoons margarine to the stock pot and let melt.

4.	Add the rice cauliflower with 2 teaspoons of the spice mixture. Cook, stirring frequently, about 5 minutes. Transfer to a bowl.

5.	Add the remaining margarine to the stock pot and melt. Then add the sausage and cook 5 minutes, stirring to brown all sides.

6.	Add onion, celery, and pepper and stir to combine. Cook about 3 minutes until vegetables start to get soft.

7.	Add the garlic and cook, stirring, 1 minute. Add the cauliflower and combine then add half the spice mixture and tomatoes, simmer 2-3 minutes.

8.	Pour in the broth and bring to a boil, cook 8-10 minutes.

9.	Season shrimp with remaining spice mixture and add to the pot, cook 3-4 minutes just until shrimp turn pink. Serve.

Nutrition: Calories 428Total Carbs 13gNet Carbs 10gProtein 33gFat 27gSugar 4gFiber 3g

DINNER

Snapper with Tahini Salad

Preparation Time: 5–10 minutes
Cooking Time: 20 minutes
Servings: 4

Ingredients

- ½ bunch flat parsley, trimmed and finely chopped
- 3 tablespoons olive oil
- 1 tablespoon tahini
- 4 wild-caught snapper fillets
- 8 celery sticks, white parts trimmed and sliced into 1/8-inch sticks
- Juice of 1 lemon
- ½ tablespoon honey
- Salt and pepper to taste

Directions

1. Preheat the oven to 350°F (175°C). Grease a baking sheet with some cooking spray or olive oil.
2. Season the fish fillets with salt and pepper; place them over the baking sheet.
3. Bake for around 15 minutes, or until the fish is easy to flake. Bake for 2–3 minutes more if needed.
4. Add the parsley and celery sticks to a mixing bowl. Mix well.
5. To another mixing bowl, add the tahini, olive oil, lemon juice, and honey. Combine well.
6. Place the fillets on a serving platter; top with the celery salad and dressing.
7. Serve fresh with some lemon wedges (optional).

Nutrition: Calories 313, Fat 15.5 g, Total carbs 6.5 g, Sugar 3.5 g, Protein 35 g, Sodium 292 mg

Baked Garlic Lemon Salmon

Preparation Time: 5 minutes
Cooking time 15 minutes
Servings: 4

Ingredients

- 3 tablespoons lemon juice
- 4 medium-sized salmon fillets
- ¼ cup unsalted butter, melted

- 2 cloves garlic, minced
- A handful of parsley, finely chopped
- Salt and pepper to taste

Directions

1. Preheat the oven to 400°F (200°C). Line a baking dish or tray with tin foil; grease with some cooking spray.
2. Place the salmon fillets over the baking dish.
3. Add the butter, garlic, lemon juice, salt and pepper to a mixing bowl. Mix well.
4. Brush the salmon fillets with the butter sauce, reserving some sauce.
5. Bake for around 15 minutes, or until the salmon is easy to flake. Bake for 2–3 minutes more if needed.
6. Brush with the reserved sauce and sprinkle some lemon juice on top.
7. Serve with chopped parsley on top.

Nutrition: Calories 350 Fat 25 g Total carbs 2 g Sugar 0.5 g,
Protein 28.5 g Sodium 68 mg

Wholesome Broccoli Pork Chops

Cooking time 10 minutes
Preparation Time: 10–15 minutes
Servings: 4

Ingredients

- 1½ tablespoons canola oil (divided)
- ¼ teaspoon red pepper flakes, crushed
- 1 clove garlic, minced
- 1 pound pork loin chops, boneless and divided into 4 equal parts
- 2 cups broccoli florets
- 2 tablespoons + 1 teaspoon reduced-sodium soy sauce
- 2 tablespoons water
- 3 tablespoons rice wine vinegar
- 2 tablespoons cilantro, chopped

Directions

1. Add the water, soy sauce, vinegar, red pepper, garlic, and 1 tablespoon of the canola oil to a mixing bowl. Mix well.

2.   Add the pork chops and combine well.

3.   Refrigerate for 20–30 minutes to marinate.

4.   Steam the broccoli florets over boiling water for 5 minutes; drain and set aside.

5.   Heat the remaining ½ tablespoon of canola oil over medium heat in a medium saucepan or skillet.

6.   Add the pork chops (reserve the marinade) and stir-cook for 4–5 minutes until evenly brown. Transfer the chops to a serving platter.

7.   In another saucepan, boil the reserved marinade.

8.   Cover and simmer the mixture over low heat for about 2–3 minutes until it thickens.

9.   Pour it over the pork chops; top with chopped cilantro and serve with cooked broccoli on the side.

Nutrition: Calories 235, Fat 13 g, Total carbs 5 g, Sugar 1 g,

Protein 23 gSodium 480 mg

Herbed Chicken Meal

Preparation Time: 5 minutes

Cooking time 25 minutes

Servings: 6

Ingredients:

- 3 cloves garlic
- 3 large boneless, skinless chicken breasts
- 3 tablespoons rosemary
- 3 tablespoons butter, melted
- 1½ tablespoons olive oil
- 1 teaspoon salt
- 1 cup dry vermouth
- ½ cup red wine vinegar
- ¾ teaspoon pink peppercorns

Directions

1.   Divide the chicken breasts into halves and pat dry with paper towels.

2.   Heat the butter and olive oil over medium heat in a medium saucepan or skillet.

3.   Add the garlic and stir cook for 30 seconds until softened.

4.   Add the chicken breasts and stir-cook for 1–2 minutes until evenly brown.

5.   Add the salt and vinegar; stir the mixture.

6.   Cover and simmer over low heat for about 5 minutes.

7.   Add the rosemary and vermouth; stir and simmer the mixture uncovered for about 10 minutes until the chicken is tender and well cooked. Transfer the chicken to serving plates.

8.   Add the peppercorns and simmer the mixture for 4–5 minutes.

9.   Pour the mixture over the chicken and serve warm.

Nutrition: Calories 187Fat 11.5 gTotal carbs 1 gSugar 0 g,

Protein 16.5 gSodium 183 mg

Avocado Orange Salmon

Preparation Time: 10 minutes

Cooking time 15 minutes

Servings: 8

Ingredients

- About 3 cups watercress, roughly chopped
- 3 tablespoons cucumbers, finely chopped
- 4 (4–6 ounces each) Alaska salmon fillets, rinsed and dried
- ¼ cup avocado oil (divided)
- 2 oranges, peeled and segmented, discard membranes
- 1 teaspoon white wine vinegar
- Salt and pepper to taste
- ½ avocado, pitted, peeled and sliced
- 2 cups mixed greens
- ¼ cup walnuts
- 2 tablespoons apple cider vinegar
- 1 pinch smoked paprika

Directions

1.   Heat 3 tablespoons of avocado oil over medium heat in a medium saucepan or skillet.

2.   Add the salmon and brown evenly for 3–4 minutes.

3.   Flip the salmon and season with salt and pepper; cook for 3–4 more minutes until opaque. Divide onto serving plates.

4.   Add the watercress, cucumber and orange segments to a mixing bowl; mix well.

5. Add the remaining oil, white wine vinegar, salt, and pepper.

6. Add the mixture to the serving plates beside the salmon; top with apple cider vinegar, avocado, and walnuts.

Nutrition: Calories 382 Fat 38 g Total carbs 7 g Sugar 0 g,Protein 46 g Sodium 160 mg

Mediterranean Chicken Breasts

Preparation Time: 5 minutes

Cooking time 35 minutes

Servings: 4

Ingredients

- 4 (4-ounce) boneless, skinless chicken breasts
- 2 tablespoons lemon juice
- 1 tablespoon olive oil
- 1 clove garlic, minced
- ½ teaspoon garlic powder
- ¼ teaspoon pepper
- 1 (15-ounce) can artichoke hearts, drained and chopped
- 1/3 cup low-sodium, fat-free chicken broth
- 3 tablespoons parmesan cheese, grated

Directions

1. Preheat the oven to 350°F (175°C). Grease a baking pan or dish with some cooking spray.

2. Place the chicken breasts in a plastic bag and pound them to ½ inch thick.

3. Pour the lemon juice over the chicken breasts and season with garlic powder and pepper.

4. Place the chicken breasts in the baking pan and bake for about 25 minutes.

5. Heat the olive oil over medium heat in a medium saucepan or skillet.

6. Add the garlic and stir cook for 1 minute until softened.

7. Add the artichoke hearts; stir-cook for about 3 minutes.

8. Add the chicken broth and simmer for 5 minutes. Mix in the cheese until it melts.

9. Pour the artichoke mixture over chicken breasts and bake for 10 more minutes until the chicken is cooked to perfection. Serve warm.

Nutrition: Calories 215 Fat 7 g Total carbs 9 g Sugar 1 g, Protein 28 g Sodium 340 mg

Hearty Pumpkin Chicken Soup

Preparation Time: 15–20 minutes

Cooking time 30 minutes

Servings: 6

Ingredients

- 1 small onion, thinly sliced
- 2 cloves garlic, minced
- 1 pound chicken breast, thinly sliced
- 1 tablespoon vegetable oil or coconut oil
- 1 medium zucchini, diced
- 1-inch piece ginger, peeled and minced
- ¾ pound pumpkin, cubed into ½-inch pieces
- 1 small chili or jalapeno pepper, seeded and thinly sliced
- 1 red bell pepper, seeded and thinly sliced
- 2 cups chicken broth
- 1 (14-ounce) can light coconut milk
- A handful of cilantro leaves
- Juice of 1 lime
- Salt and pepper to taste

Directions

1. Season the chicken slices with salt and pepper.

2. Heat the oil over medium-high heat in a large cooking pot.

3. Add the chicken and stir cook for 4–5 minutes to evenly brown.

4. Add the onion, ginger, and garlic and stir cook for 2–3 minutes until softened and translucent.

5. Add the zucchini and cubed pumpkin; stir well.

6. Add the chicken broth, coconut milk, bell pepper, chili or jalapeno pepper, and lime juice; stir again.

7. Bring to a boil, cover, and simmer over low heat for about 20 minutes, until the pumpkin is cooked well and softened.

8. Season with additional salt and pepper, if required.

9. Serve warm with cilantro leaves on top.

Note: You can store leftovers in an airtight container in the refrigerator for up to 3–4 days. Simply re-heat in a cooking pot and serve.

Nutrition: Calories 231 Fat 13 g Total carbs 11.5 g Sugar 5 g,
Protein 17 g Sodium 1207 mg

Crunchy Crusted Salmon

Preparation Time: 5–10 minutes
Cooking time 12–15 minutes
Servings: 4

Ingredients

- 2 slices whole-wheat bread, torn into pieces
- 4 teaspoons honey
- 2 teaspoons canola oil
- 3 tablespoons finely chopped walnuts
- 4 (4-ounce) salmon fillets
- 4 teaspoons Dijon mustard
- ½ teaspoon dried thyme

Directions

1. Preheat the oven to 400°F (200°C). Grease a baking sheet with some cooking spray.
2. Place the salmon over the baking sheet.
3. Combine the mustard and honey in a bowl. Brush the salmon with the honey mixture.
4. Add the bread pieces to a blender or food processor and blend to make fine crumbs.
5. Add the crumbs and walnuts to a mixing bowl. Mix well.
6. Add the thyme and canola oil; combine again.
7. Press the mixture over the salmon and bake for 12–15 minutes until the topping is evenly brown and the salmon is easy to flake.
8. Serve warm.

Nutrition: Calories 295 Fat 17 g Total carbs 13 g Sugar 7 g,
Protein 22 g Sodium 243 mg

Italian Pork Chops

Preparation Time: 5 minutes
Cooking time 25 minutes
Servings: 4

Ingredients

- 4 cloves garlic, sliced
- 4 thick pork chops, fat trimmed
- 1 small yellow onion, cut into rings

- ½ cup low-fat mozzarella cheese
- 1 (28-ounce) can diced tomatoes
- 1 teaspoon paprika
- 1 teaspoon dried oregano
- 1 chicken bouillon cube
- Salt and pepper to taste

Directions

1. Preheat the oven to 400°F (200°C). Grease a baking pan with some cooking spray.
2. Season the pork chops with pepper.
3. Grease a medium saucepan or skillet with cooking spray and heat it over medium heat.
4. Add the pork chops and stir-cook for 2 minutes per side until evenly brown.
5. Add the garlic and onion rings and stir-cook for 1–2 minutes until softened.
6. Add the spices, tomato and bouillon cube; simmer for 2–3 minutes.
7. Pour in the tomato sauce.
8. Add the mixture to the baking pan, top with the cheese, and bake for about 20 minutes until the top is golden brown.
9. Let cool slightly and serve warm.

Note: You can store leftovers in an airtight container in the refrigerator for up to 3–4 days. Simply reheat in a saucepan and serve.

Nutrition: Calories 405 Fat 17 g, Total carbs 16 g, Sugar 7.5 g,
Protein 43.5 gsodium 1275 mg

Mushroom Chicken Mania

Preparation Time: 10 minutes
Cooking time 20 minutes
Servings: 4

Ingredients

- 10 ounces white button mushrooms, sliced
- ¼ teaspoon pepper
- 1/3 cup balsamic vinegar
- ½ cup low sodium, fat-free chicken broth
- 1 pound boneless, skinless chicken breasts
- 1 tablespoon olive oil
- ¼ cup all-purpose flour
- 1 tablespoon low-fat margarine

Directions

1.   Add the chicken breasts to a plastic bag and pound to flatten with your palm.
2.   Coat them evenly with flour.
3.   Grease a medium saucepan or skillet with some cooking spray and heat it over medium heat.
4.   Add the chicken breasts and brown evenly for 4–5 minutes each side. Set aside.
5.   Melt the margarine in the pan, add mushrooms and pepper, and stir-cook for 4–5 minutes until softened.
6.   Add the balsamic vinegar and boil the mixture until the sauce thickens.
7.   Cover and simmer over low heat for about 2 minutes.
8.   Add the chicken and simmer for 5 more minutes.
9.   Serve warm.

Nutrition: Calories 240, Fat 9 g, Total carbs 12 g, Sugar 4 g,
Protein 27 g, Sodium 150 mg

Tomato Steak Kebabs

Preparation Time: 10–15 minutes
Cooking time 10 minutes
Servings: 4

Ingredients

- 1 teaspoon Dijon mustard
- 1 pound top sirloin steak, cut into 1-inch cubes
- ¼ cup balsamic vinaigrette
- 2 cups cherry tomatoes
- ¼ cup barbecue sauce

Directions

1.   Add the barbecue sauce, vinaigrette and mustard to a mixing bowl; mix well. Set aside ¼ of the mixture.
2.   Add the beef and coat well.
3.   Take four metal or soaked wooden skewers and thread them alternately with tomatoes and beef pieces.
4.   Preheat the grill to medium-high heat. Grease the grill rack with cooking spray.
5.   Grill the skewers for 6–8 minutes until the beef is tender. When 3–4 minutes remain, begin basting frequently with the reserved mixture.

Nutrition: Calories 194, Fat 7 g, Total carbs 7 gSugar 5 g, Protein 25 g, Sodium 288 mg

Baked Broccoli Chicken

Preparation Time: 10 minutes
Cooking time 45 minutes
Servings: 4

Ingredients

- 1 teaspoon vegetable oil
- 4 medium chicken fillets, chopped
- 1 medium onion, finely chopped
- 1 (10.5-ounce) can chicken or mushroom soup
- 1 pound broccoli florets, boiled and drained
- 1 teaspoon curry powder
- 2 ounces brown breadcrumbs
- 2 ounces low-fat cheddar cheese, grated
- ½ cup skimmed milk
- Salt and pepper to taste

Directions

1.   Preheat the oven to 425°F (220°C). Grease a baking dish or casserole dish with some cooking spray.
2.   Heat the oil over medium heat in a medium saucepan or skillet.
3.   Add the onion and stir-cook until softened and translucent.
4.   Add the chicken pieces; stir-cook for 10 minutes until evenly brown. Set aside.
5.   Add the chicken or mushroom soup, milk and curry powder to a mixing bowl. Mix well.
6.   Arrange the chicken mixture and broccoli in the baking dish; pour the soup mixture on top.
7.   Top with the crumbs and cheddar cheese.
8.   Bake for about 30 minutes until the top is evenly brown.
9.   Slice and serve warm.

Nutrition: Calories 332 Fat 9 g Total carbs 15 g Sugar 6 g, Protein 44.5 g Sodium 700 mg

Baked Creamed Chicken

Preparation Time: 5 minutes

Cooking time 25 minutes

Servings: 4

Ingredients

- 5 ounces low-fat cream cheese
- 20–40 basil leaves (more or less to taste)
- 4 boneless, skinless chicken breasts
- 5½ ounces prosciutto, finely sliced
- Pepper to taste

Directions

1. Preheat the oven to 375°F (190°C).
2. Arrange the prosciutto slices on a piece of aluminum foil so they overlap slightly. Spread the cream cheese over them and set aside for 15 minutes.
3. Place the basil leaves on top.
4. Wrap the prosciutto slices around the chicken breasts. Season with pepper.
5. Place them over a baking sheet.
6. Bake for 25–30 minutes until the chicken is tender.
7. Let cool slightly, slice and serve warm.

Note: You can store leftovers in an airtight container in the refrigerator for up to 3–4 days. Simply reheat in the oven and serve.

Nutrition: Calories 294,Fat 11.5 gTotal carbs 3 gSugar 2.5 g, Protein 38.5 g Sodium 934 mg

Pork Mushroom Stew

Preparation Time: 10 minutes

Cooking time 90 minutes

Servings: 5

Ingredients

- 1 (16-ounce) can unsalted tomato sauce
- 2 cups carrots, sliced
- 1 medium green pepper, chopped
- ½ pound mushrooms, sliced
- 1 teaspoon dried basil
- ½ teaspoon dried rosemary, crushed
- 1 pound lean boneless pork, cut into 1-inch cubes
- 1 cup onion, chopped
- ½ cup water
- ¼ teaspoon pepper

Directions

1. Grease a large cooking pot or Dutch oven with some cooking oil and heat it over medium heat.
2. Add the pork and stir-cook to brown evenly.
3. Add the onion, seasonings, water and tomato sauce; stir.
4. Bring to a boil, cover, and simmer over low heat for about 60 minutes until the pork is tender.
5. Add the other ingredients; combine and cook for 30 more minutes until the veggies are tender.
6. Serve warm.

Nutrition: Calories 201Fat 7 gTotal carbs 15 gSugar 0 g, Protein 18 gSodium 644 mg

Baked feta with delicious vegetables

Preparation Time: 60 minutes

Cooking Time: 20 minutes

Servings: 2

Ingredients:

- 200 g of feta; Max. 45% fat
- 4 organic cocktail tomatoes
- 1 tbsp. olive oil
- 1 tbsp. fresh herbs (e.g. marjoram, thyme, rosemary, basil)
- Sea salt and black pepper
- 4 onions, red
- 2 peppers, yellow
- 1 red pepper
- 1 tbsp. rapeseed oil
- 1-2 tbsp. balsamic vinegar, light
- 1 teaspoon paprika powder, noble sweet
- 1 teaspoon linden blossom honey
- ½ organic lemon
- Basil for garnish

Direction:

1. Preheat oven to 200 degrees. Quarter the feta cheese. Place a piece of baking paper approx. 30 × 50 cm on a baking sheet, place the feta cheese on top.
2. Wash, dry and slice cocktail tomatoes, wash, dry and chop herbs. Mix the olive oil with the herbs, season

with sea salt and pepper and distribute evenly over the cheese.

3. Gather the baking paper with the cheese at the ends like a piece of candy and seal (not completely). Then bake the parcels in the oven (middle rack) for about 15 minutes.

4. In the meantime, peel and halve the onions and cut into thin slices. Quarter the peppers, remove the stones and stem, wash and cut into fine strips. Squeeze the lemon.

5. Heat oil in a pan and sauté the onions for about 5 minutes. Add the peppers and fry for another 5 minutes. Season the finished vegetables with balsamic vinegar, the spices, herbs, and honey and lemon juice.

6. Remove the feta from the baking paper and arrange on two plates with the vegetables and garnish with basil.

Nutrition: Calories: 407 kcal Protein: 2.9 g Fat: 38.43 g Carbohydrates: 16.09 g

Mushroom salmon tarteflambée

Preparation Time: 10 minutes
Cooking Time: 30 minutes
Servings: 4

Ingredients:
- 2 organic eggs
- 100 g quark, lean level
- 20 g flax flour
- 1 pinch of sea salt
- Black pepper, freshly ground
- 100 g Gouda cheese, grated (30% fat)
- For covering:
- 60 g crème fraîche
- 1 teaspoon horseradish from the jar, sugar-free
- 30 g of organic rocket
- 4 mushrooms, brown
- 3 tbsp. olive oil
- Lemon pepper
- 50 g of salmon, smoked
- Dill, at will
- 30 g Gouda cheese, grated (30% fat)

Directions:

1. Preheat the oven to 180 degrees (top and bottom heat). Place parchment paper on a baking sheet.

2. Separate eggs. Put the egg yolks in a bowl together with the quark, flax flour, sea salt, black pepper and cheese and mix thoroughly.

3. Beat egg whites with a mixer until stiff and fold carefully into the quark mixture. Put the mixture on the baking sheet and smooth it out thinly. Then bake in the preheated oven for about 10-15 minutes.

4. Mix the crème fraîche and horseradish together. Wash and dry arugula. Clean the mushrooms and cut them in slices. Heat the oil in a pan, fry the mushrooms and season with lemon pepper.

5. Take the quark base out of the oven, spread the horseradish cream evenly over it, then spread the fried mushrooms and the salmon, rocket and cheese cut into pieces on top and then sprinkle with the dill.

6. Bake for another 5–8 minutes. The tarteflambée is ready when the cheese has melted.

Note: Linseed flour is ground and de-oiled linseed. Since it is de-oiled, it has a longer shelf life than simply ground flaxseed. The fibers in flax flour contain a lot of fiber and are therefore good for digestion.

Nutrition: Calories: 425 kcal Protein: 19.51 g Fat: 29.03 g Carbohydrates: 22.35 g

Meat skewers with polenta

Preparation Time: 10 minutes
Cooking Time: 15 minutes
Servings: 4

Ingredients:
- 130 g polenta, instant
- Vegetable broth
- 1 organic lemon
- 2 tbsp. parmesan, grated
- Chili flakes, to taste
- 250 g of green asparagus
- 2 carrots, large
- 1 ½ tbsp. oil for frying
- Sea salt and black pepper, fresh
- 4 tbsp. sour cream
- 250 g pork schnitzel
- Paprika powder, noble sweet & parsley, fresh

- Metal skewers

Directions:

1. Prepare the polenta with stock according to the instructions on the packet. Wash the lemon, make zest and squeeze. Season the polenta with 2 teaspoons of lemon juice, a little zest, cheese and chili to taste.

2. Wash and clean the asparagus and carrots, cut lengthways into thin strips with a peeler.

3. Dab the schnitzel with kitchen paper and pound, cut into strips, then slide on skewers in waves, season with sea salt and pepper. Wash, dry and chop parsley.

4. Heat a pan with oil and fry the skewers for about 5 minutes (the meat should be done).

5. Keep the skewers warm in the oven. Fry the vegetables in oil until al dente, then season with salt and pepper. Pour in a little broth, bring to the boil. And finally stir in the sour cream.

6. Arrange the skewers and vegetables on two plates and sprinkle with the parsley.

Note: Polenta is available in every supermarket.

Nutrition: Calories: 272 kcal Protein: 19.09 g Fat: 17.77 g Carbohydrates: 9.67 g

Cauliflower avocado mash with chicken breast

Preparation Time: 25 minutes

Cooking Time: 3 minutes

Servings: 4

Ingredients:

- 600 g of cauliflower
- Rock salt
- 1 small onion, light
- 25 g dried tomatoes
- 1 tbsp. rapeseed oil
- Black pepper
- 2 chicken breast fillets (125 g each)
- 1 organic lemon
- Milk (3.5% fat), to taste
- Vegetable broth, as needed
- ¼ avocado, ripe
- 40 g feta (9% fat)
- Chives for garnish

Directions:

1. Clean the cauliflower, cut into florets, wash thoroughly and cook in salted water for approx. 8–10 minutes until soft (over medium heat), drain.

2. In the meantime, peel and chop the onion. Chop the tomatoes.

3. Heat the oil in a pan, sauté the onion and tomatoes briefly, season with rock salt and pepper, remove from the pan. Wash, dry and chop the chives.

4. Season the chicken breast with salt and pepper. Heat the oil. Fry the meat for about 5–8 minutes on both sides. Squeeze the lemon and drizzle with lemon juice, put the pan aside and simmer the meat (covered).

5. Warm the milk together with the vegetable stock. Remove the stone and peel from the avocado, put the cauliflower and avocado in a container and mash them with a potato masher, gradually stirring in the milk, season with salt and freshly ground pepper.

6. Serve the mash with the chicken breast. Crumble the feta.

7. Finally, spread the onion and tomato mixture and the feta over the top and garnish with chives.

Note: The avocado is one of the superfoods, it can lower blood sugar and insulin levels at the same time. It tastes excellent and is very versatile.

Nutrition: Calories: 126 kcal Protein: 4.86 g Fat: 7.95 g Carbohydrates: 11.6 g

Colorful sweet potato salad

Preparation Time: 5 minutes

Cooking Time: 30 minutes

Servings: 4

Ingredients:

- 450 g sweet potato
- Sea salt and black pepper, curry powder, to taste
- 1 ½ tbsp. olive oil
- 100 g baby spinach
- ½ organic lemon
- 30 g of walnuts
- ½ organic apple, green
- ½ teaspoon maple syrup
- 1 tbsp. vegetable stock
- 2 tbsp. quinoa, puffed, approx. 15 g

- ½ handful of chive flowers

Directions:

1.   Preheat the oven to 200 degrees (convection). Line a baking sheet with parchment paper. Peel the sweet potato and cut into bite-sized pieces. Mix with sea salt, black pepper, curry and 1 tbsp. oil and place on the baking tray, cook for about 20 minutes, turning occasionally, then leave to cool.

2.   In the meantime, clean, wash and spin-dry the spinach. Halve the lemon, squeeze out the juice. Chop walnuts. Wash the apple, cut into quarters and remove the core, cut into bite-sized pieces and drizzle with a little lemon juice.

3.   For the dressing, stir together lemon juice, maple syrup, sea salt, pepper and oil vigorously.

4.   Finally, put all the ingredients in a bowl and mix with the dressing. Then divide the salad on two plates, sprinkle the quinoa on top and garnish with the chives flowers.

Note: Quinoa (puffed) is already available in many supermarkets, but also in health food stores and health food stores.

Nutrition: Calories: 211 kcal Protein: 5.49 g Fat: 14.41 g Carbohydrates: 19.38 g

Lentil salad with nuts and feta

Preparation Time: 20 minutes
Cooking Time: 10 minutes
Servings: 2

Ingredients:

- 200 ml orange juice, freshly squeezed
- 60 g lentils, red
- Lemon thyme, to taste
- 150 g small organic tomatoes
- 60 g feta (50% fat)
- 50 g of organic rocket
- 25 g walnut kernels
- 2 tbsp. organic apple cider vinegar
- ½ teaspoon mustard, sugar-free
- ½ teaspoon linden blossom honey
- 2 ½ tbsp. olive oil
- 1 organic apple, small approx. 300 g
- Sea salt and black pepper

Directions:

1.   Halve the oranges and squeeze them, put them in a saucepan and bring to the boil. Cook the lentils in the boiling orange juice according to the package instructions then cool for about 10 minutes.

2.   In the meantime, wash and dry the thyme and pluck the leaves off. Wash and clean tomatoes (remove green), halve or quarter larger. Crumble the feta. Sort, wash and dry the rocket. Roughly chop the walnuts and toast them in a pan without oil.

3.   Mix the vinegar, mustard, honey and oil well into a dressing. Wash and quarter the apple and core, cut into cubes and place in a bowl. Add lentils and dressing and mix well, season with sea salt and pepper. Add walnuts and the other ingredients and stir gently.

Note: Lenses are good for diabetics. They contain a lot of fiber, are high in iron, potassium, B1 and many vegetable proteins. These lower the glycemic index.

Nutrition: Calories: 279 kcal Protein: 6.82 g Fat: 21.32 g Carbohydrates: 19 g

Aromatic multicolor tomato salad

Preparation Time: 10 minutes
Cooking Time: 0 minutes
Servings: 2

Ingredients:

- 125 g small organic tomatoes
- 125 g small organic tomatoes, yellow
- ½ small onion, red
- ½ clove of garlic
- Basil, if you like
- 1 ½ tbsp. olive oil
- Sea salt and black pepper
- 1 handful of organic rocket
- 100 g of grainy cream cheese

Directions:

1.   Wash all tomatoes, remove greens and cut in half. Peel the onion and garlic. Cut the onion into rings. Chop the garlic very finely.

2.   Wash, dry and finely chop the basil.

3.   Put the tomatoes, onions, basil, garlic and olive oil in a bowl and mix.

4.   Season with sea salt and black pepper.

5. Wash the rocket, pat dry with a little paper towel. Arrange tomato salad with rocket and cream cheese in bowls or on plates.

Note: Tomatoes are excellent as a diabetic diet. Not only do they taste good, they are also very healthy, they provide us with minerals (e.g. potassium), numerous vitamins (vitamin C, provitamin A, E and folic acid) and not to forget with secondary plant substances (lycopene). Of course, tomatoes taste best in summer, as they unfold their full aroma when they are in the sun.

Nutrition: Calories: 275 kcal Protein: 5.4 g Fat: 24.8 g Carbohydrates: 10.05 g

Green omelette with smoked salmon

Preparation Time: 10 minutes
Cooking Time: 5 minutes
Servings: 2
Ingredients:
* ½ organic cucumber
* Sea salt
* 50 g of salmon, smoked
* 1 box of garden cress
* 20 g of dill
* 3 organic eggs
* pepper, freshly ground
* 2 tbsp. mineral water
* 80 grams of kefir
* 2 tbsp. olive oil for frying

Preparation:
1. Wash the cucumber thoroughly and cut into thin slices. Set aside a few slices. Spread the rest on two plates and sprinkle with sea salt and pepper.
2. Cut the smoked salmon into bite-sized pieces. Cut off the cress, wash, dry and finely chop the dill.
3. Put the eggs together with the sea salt, pepper, mineral water and kefir in a tall container and stir well with a whisk. Then mix in the dill. Heat two small pans with oil.
4. Put half of the egg mixture into each pan and let it set over a low heat for about 3–4 minutes.
5. Top the finished omelets with the salmon, cucumber slices (the ones that were set aside) and cress.

Finally, fold up the omelettes, cut in half and arrange on the plates with the cucumber slices.

Note: Cucumbers have hardly any calories, are rich in important nutrients and are 96 % water. This means that they can also be eaten in large quantities.

Nutrition: Calories: 382 kcal Protein: 20.57 g Fat: 30.4 g Carbohydrates: 6.04 g

Chicken breast on vegetable noodles

Preparation Time: 10 minutes
Cooking Time: 40 minutes
Servings: 4
Ingredients:
* 300 g of chicken breast fillet
* Sea salt
* 1 organic zucchini, yellow (300 g)
* 1 organic zucchini, green (300 g)
* 200 g organic carrots
* 125 g chicory
* 1 tbsp. sesame oil 3 tbsp.& soy sauce, light, sugar-free
* SambalOelek, at will
* 1 lime
* Black pepper
* Coconut oil for frying

Directions:
1. Dab the chicken breast with paper towels. Bring the pot with plenty of water and a little sea salt to the boil and cook the meat in it for about 20 minutes.
2. In the meantime, wash the zucchini, cut the ends, wash the carrots and peel thinly. Use a vegetable peeler or a spiral cutter to cut long strips from the courgette and carrots. Wash the chicory, remove the stalk and peel off the leaves.
3. Heat sesame oil in a pan, add the vegetable noodles and simmer over medium heat for about 5 minutes. Add the chicory and cook for another 2-3 minutes. Halve and squeeze the lime. Then season the vegetables with soy sauce, sambaloelek, approx. 1 tablespoon of lime juice, sea salt and black pepper.
4. Remove the cooked chicken breast fillets from the water, drain in a colander and pat dry a little. Then cut into slices. Heat a pan with coconut oil. Put the meat

in the pan and toss over a medium heat for about 4-5 minutes, deglaze with soy sauce.

5.   Finally season with pepper and sea salt. Divide the vegetable noodles on two plates and serve with the meat.

Nutrition: Calories: 163 kcal Protein: 15.26 gFat: 3.84 g Carbohydrates: 18.87 g

Glass chicken salad with fruits

Preparation Time: 20 minutes
Cooking Time: 5 minutes
Servings: 2
Ingredients:
- ½ Chinese cabbage, small
- ½ organic orange
- ½ small can of pineapple (2 slices, 236 ml), unsweetened
- 125 g yogurt, low in fat
- 1 tbsp. sour cream
- 1 organic lemon
- Parsley, to taste
- Sea salt and black pepper from the mill
- 1 chicken breast fillets, approx. 150 g
- Paprika, hot
- 1 tbsp. olive oil

Directions:
1.   Clean the Chinese cabbage, cut in half, cut out the stalk then wash and cut into strips. Cut off the peel of the orange all around with a knife, then cut out the fillets.
2.   Drain the pineapple in a colander and collect the juice. Cut the pineapple into small pieces, fill 25 ml of pineapple juice.
3.   Wash, dry and chop parsley. Put the yoghurt, sour cream, pineapple and lemon juice and parsley (set aside a bit) in a bowl, stir and season with sea salt and freshly ground salt and pepper.
4.   Dab the chicken breast fillet with kitchen paper, cut into strips and season with sea salt, pepper and paprika. Heat oil in a pan and fry the meat in it (approx. 3 minutes). Mix the ingredients for the salad with the dressing.
5.   Finally, fill into glasses, serve the chicken breast on top and garnish with the rest of the parsley.

Nutrition: Calories: 119 kcal Protein: 7.11 g Fat: 7.73 g Carbohydrates: 6.46 g

Stuffed eggplant

Preparation Time: 30 minutes
Cooking Time: 3 minutes
Servings: 4
Ingredients:
- 2 small organic eggplants
- sea salt
- olive oil, as needed
- ½ small cauliflower
- 1 small onion, red
- 1 clove of garlic
- 100 g cream cheese, natural
- Sea salt and black pepper from the mill
- Rosemary and thyme, fresh
- 50 g cheese, grated e.g. Gouda

Directions:
1.   Wash the eggplant, cut off the ends and cut in half lengthways. Cut out the pulp (except for a 1 cm wide edge) and cut into cubes.
2.   Heat the oil in a pan, salt the aubergines and fry them for approx. 5–8 minutes (with the cut surface facing down), remove and dab off the excess oil with kitchen paper. Preheat the oven to 200 degrees.
3.   Clean the cauliflower, cut into florets and wash thoroughly. Peel the onion and garlic, cut the onion into cubes and chop the garlic very finely.
4.   Heat a pan with a little oil, add the diced aubergine, cauliflower, onion and garlic and fry. Deglaze with a little water (approx. 50 ml), bring to the boil, cover with a lid and simmer for approx. 5 minutes.
5.   Wash and dry the rosemary and thyme, pluck off the leaves and place in a bowl with the cream cheese, stir, season with sea salt and pepper. Mix this mixture with the vegetables and fill the eggplant halves with it, sprinkle cheese on top and bake for about 20 minutes.

Note: Eggplants are healthy and versatile. They are high in fiber, which is important for health. They also promote our feeling of satiety.

Nutrition: Calories: 199 kcal Protein: 7.61 g Fat: 10.43 g Carbohydrates: 22.67 g

Stuffed tomatoes with quinoa

Preparation Time: 10 minutes

Cooking Time: 20 minutes

Servings: 2

Ingredients:

- 50 g of colorful quinoa
- 2 organic beefsteak tomatoes, large
- 50 g spinach, fresh or frozen
- 1 spring onion
- 50 g paprika, grilled out of the glass
- Walnut oil, as needed
- 1 tsp. white wine vinegar
- Sea salt and black pepper from the mill
- 1 whole grain baguette
- 2 cloves of garlic

Directions:

1. Cook the quinoa according to the instructions on the packet, place in a colander and drain. Wash tomatoes, cut off a lid, remove the pulp with a spoon and chop.

2. Sort the spinach and wash it thoroughly. Clean, wash and cut the spring onions into rings. Drain the peppers and cut into small pieces. Heat the oil in a pan, sauté the onions, add the spinach and let it collapse over a low heat.

3. Add paprika and quinoa and cook for another 3 minutes. Season to taste with vinegar, sea salt and pepper.

4. Season the tomatoes from the inside with salt and pepper, add the filling, and put the lid on the tomato.

5. Grease a baking dish a little and put the tomatoes in it, put the oven on the grill and cook for about 15–20 minutes.

6. In the meantime, peel off the garlic, cut the whole wheat baguette into slices, rub with garlic and either roast in a pan with a little oil, toast or also roast in the grill. Serve the filled tomatoes with the wholemeal baguette and enjoy.

Note: Quinoa is available in many supermarkets or in health food stores.

TIP: If you don't have colorful quinoa, use white.

Nutrition: Calories: 202 kcal Protein: 9.85 g Fat: 5.12 g Carbohydrates: 37.67 g

Colorful vegetable casserole

Preparation Time: 20 minutes

Cooking Time: 1 hour 20 minutes

Servings: 2

Ingredients:

- 1 organic zucchini
- 300 g of potatoes
- 1 onion, red
- 2 organic beefsteak tomatoes
- olive oil, as needed
- Sea salt and black pepper & thyme, fresh
- 100 g of feta
- 30 g of pitted olives
- Herbs for garnish, e.g. B. parsley, chives

Directions:

1. Wash zucchini and remove the ends, cut into cubes. Peel and wash the potatoes and cut into bite-sized pieces. Peel the onions and cut into slices. Wash tomatoes, remove greens and cut into large cubes.

2. Heat a pan with oil and fry the potatoes with the zucchini and onion. Pre heat the oven to 180 degrees.

3. Wash and dry the thyme, pick off the leaves. Mix the tomatoes and 1 tbsp. thyme, season well with sea salt and pepper. Put everything in a lightly greased casserole dish, cover with baking paper or aluminum foil and cook for about 50–60 minutes.

4. In the meantime, crumble the feta, cut the olives into rings and distribute them evenly on the casserole. Then cook for another 20 minutes.

5. Wash, dry and chop the herbs and finally garnish the casserole with the herbs.

Note: It is better to buy small zucchini, they have a much more intense taste.

Nutrition: Calories: 167 kcal Protein: 6.92 g Fat: 6.85 g Carbohydrates: 21.35 g

Lentil snack with tomato salsa

Preparation Time: 10 minutes
Cooking Time: 45 minutes
Servings: 2

Ingredients:

- 100 g of red lentils
- 1 small onion, red
- 80 g of wheat semolina
- 3 tbsp. paprika tomato paste
- 2 tbsp. mixed, chopped herbs (e.g. parsley, chervil, chives)
- ½ organic lemon
- Sea salt and black pepper
- 1 organic tomato
- ½ red chili pepper, small
- 1 spring onion
- Olive oil, as needed
- 1 teaspoon rice syrup or maple syrup

Directions:

1. Cook the lentils according to the package instructions. Peel the onion and cut into small cubes. Mix the semolina with the finished lentils and leave to swell (about 3 minutes).

2. In the meantime, wash, dry and chop herbs. Add onion, paprika tomato paste (if you like) and herbs, stir and season with lemon juice, sea salt and pepper, then let cool.

3. For the tomato salsa, wash the tomatoes, remove the greens and cut into small cubes. Wash the chili peppers, cut lengthways, remove the seeds and partitions, wash again and cut into very small pieces.

4. Clean, wash and cut the spring onions into rings. Mix tomatoes, spring onions, chili peppers and a little paprika tomato paste as well as olive oil and rice syrup and season with sea salt and pepper.

5. Shape the lentil mixture into small rolls or balls. Heat the oil in a pan and fry it brown all over or prepare it on the grill.

6. Arrange on plates and serve with the tomato salsa.

Nutrition: Calories: 394 kcal Protein: 20.1 gFat: 2.13 g Carbohydrates: 76.77 g

Clear soup with liver dumplings

Preparation Time: 10 minutes
Cooking Time: 40 minutes
Servings: 2

Ingredients:

For the dumplings:

- 75 g veal liver
- 1 red onion, small
- Parsley, to taste
- ½ tbsp. olive oil
- 35 g breadcrumbs
- 1 organic egg size M
- Sea salt and black pepper
- Nutmeg, grated, optional

For the soup:

- 1 organic carrot
- 50 g of celery
- 2 spring onions
- ½ tbsp. oil
- Bay leaf, optional
- 500 ml of vegetable stock

Directions:

1. Turn the liver through a meat grinder (or have it made by the butcher).

2. Peel and cut the onion. Wash, dry and chop parsley.

3. Heat oil in a saucepan, sauté the onion briefly, add the parsley and sauté briefly. Then let it cool down.

4. Place the liver with the breadcrumbs in a bowl, add the onion-parsley mixture and egg and knead, salt and pepper. If you like, add some nutmeg and knead. Shape the mixture into about 6 dumplings and place in the refrigerator.

5. Now wash and dry the vegetables for the soup thoroughly. Cut the carrot into slices, cut the celery into bite-sized pieces and finally cut the spring onion into rolls. Heat a little oil in a saucepan, cook the carrot, celery and spring onion together with the bay leaf for about 5 minutes. Then season with sea salt and pepper. Add the vegetable stock and simmer the soup over medium heat (about 10 minutes).

6. Finally add the dumplings and simmer for another 10 minutes.

7. When the dumplings float to the surface, they are done.

8. Serve the soup with the liver dumplings.

Note: Garnish the soup with fresh herbs as required.

Nutrition: Calories: 217 kcal Protein: 13.41 g Fat: 13.63 g Carbohydrates: 10.73 g

Beef steaks with green asparagus

Preparation Time: 15 minutes
Cooking Time: 20 minutes
Servings: 4
Ingredients:
- 500 g asparagus, green
- 40 g herb butter
- 2 beef fillet steaks (approx. 150 g each)
- 1 dried tomato pickled in oil
- 50 g ricotta
- Sea salt and black pepper
- Herbs, fresh e.g. B. oregano, basil
- 1 tbsp. oil for frying & capers, as desired (optional)

Also: aluminum foil and toothpicks or small wooden skewers

Directions:
1. Wash the asparagus and peel the lower ends. Prepare two pieces of baking paper or aluminum foil and spread the asparagus on top. Put the herb butter on the asparagus, close the foil tightly, put on the grill for about 10 - 15 minutes.

2. Dab steaks with a little paper towel, cut a pocket. Drain the tomatoes and cut into small pieces. Put the ricotta and capers in a bowl, wash, dry and chop the herbs and add them as well.

3. Mix everything well and season with sea salt and pepper. Pour the finished cream into the steaks and seal the openings with a toothpick.

4. Finally, season the steaks with sea salt and pepper, brush with the oil and grill depending on the degree of cooking required (approx. 5–8 minutes on each side).

5. Arrange the steaks with the asparagus, add the rest of the cream and serve hot.

Note: If you don't have a grill, you can prepare both the asparagus and the steaks in the oven. First fry the steaks briefly in the pan and then finish cooking in the oven.

Nutrition: Calories: 339 kcal Protein: 18.91 g Fat: 27.06 g Carbohydrates: 6.31 g

Broccoli Omelet

Preparation Time: 5 minutes
Cooking Time: 1.5-2 hours
Servings: 2
Ingredients:
- 2 garlic cloves, minced
- 3 eggs
- ½ yellow onion, chopped
- ¼ cup milk
- ½ cup broccoli florets, fresh or frozen
- ¼ teaspoon black pepper
- ½ tomato, chopped
- 1/8 teaspoon chili powder
- ½ tablespoon Parmesan cheese, shredded
- ¾ cups Cheddar cheese, shredded
- 1/8 teaspoon salt
- 1/8 cup green onions, chopped
- 1/8 teaspoon garlic powder

Directions:
1. Whisk the eggs, milk, and spices in a bowl.

2. To the egg mixture, add onions along with the garlic, parmesan cheese, and broccoli. Stir well until combined, and then pour the egg mixture into a slow cooker.

3. Close the lid and cook for about 1 ½ hour to 2 hours on high.

4. Remove the cover when the cooking time is over and then sprinkle the shredded cheddar cheese on top. Close the lid again and then turn off the slow cooker.

5. Let rest for about 10 minutes, until the cheddar cheese has melted.

6. When done, cut the omelet into quarters and then serve.

7. Garnish the servings with chopped green onion and fresh tomato. Enjoy!

Nutrition: Calories: 423 kcal Fat: 28g Carbohydrates: 13g
Protein: 29g

Apple Cinnamon Oatmeal

Preparation Time: 10 minutes

Cooking Time: 8 hours

Servings: 4

Ingredients

- 2 peeled and sliced apples
- 1 tbsp. cinnamon
- 1/3 Cup brown sugar
- 2 cups rolled oats, old-fashioned

What you'll need from store cupboard

- Pinch of salt
- 4 cups water

Directions:

1. Place the apples in the crockpot bottom then add cinnamon and sugar over the apples. Stir to mix.
2. Add the oats over apples evenly then add salt and water. Do not stir.
3. Cover and cook for about 8-9 hours on low or cook overnight.
4. Stir well, making sure oats are not at the bottom.
5. Serve.

Nutrition: Calories: 232.4, Fat: 3.1g, Carbs: 53g, Protein: 5.2g,

Sugars: 20.9g, Fiber: 6g, Sodium: 4.9mg,

Nutty Steel-cut Oatmeal with Blueberries

Preparation Time: 5 minutes

Cooking Time: 30 minutes

Servings: 2

Ingredients:

- 1 ½ cups water
- ½ cup steel-cut oats
- 1 ½ tablespoons almond butter
- ½ teaspoon ground cinnamon
- ¼ teaspoon ground nutmeg
- Pinch ground ginger
- ½ cup blueberries
- ¼ cup whole almonds

Directions:

1. Over high-heat, put the water in a medium saucepan, and bring the liquid to a boil.
2. Stir in the oats, and reduce the heat to low so they simmer gently.
3. Simmer the oats uncovered for about 20 minutes, until they are tender.
4. Stir in the almond butter, cinnamon, nutmeg, and ginger, and simmer for an additional 10 minutes.
5. Serve topped with blueberries and whole almonds.

Nutrition: Calories: 246 kcal Carbohydrates: 24g Glycemic Load: 17 Fiber: 5g Protein: 8g Sodium: 2mg Fat: 14g

Slow "Roasted" Tomatoes

Preparation Time: 5 minutes

Cooking Time: 1 hour 15 minutes

Servings: 2

Ingredients:

- ½ tablespoon balsamic vinegar
- 1 large firm under-ripe tomato, halved crosswise
- 1 garlic clove, minced
- 1 teaspoon olive oil
- ½ teaspoon dried basil, crushed
- ½ cup breadcrumbs, coarse, soft whole-wheat
- Dried rosemary, crushed
- 1 tablespoon Parmesan cheese, grated
- Salt
- ¼ teaspoon dried oregano, crushed
- Chopped fresh basil, optional

Directions:

1. Using cooking spray, coat the unheated slow cooker lightly. Then add tomatoes to the bottom of the slow cooker, cut side up.
2. In a bowl, combine vinegar together with garlic, oil, rosemary, dried basil, and salt, and then spoon the mixture over the tomatoes in the slow cooker evenly.
3. Close the lid and cook for either 2 hours on low, or 1 hour on high.
4. Over medium heat, preheat a skillet, and then add the breadcrumbs. Cook as you stir constantly until lightly browned, for about 2-3 minutes. Remove from heat when done and then stir in the parmesan.
5. When through, remove tomatoes from the slow cooker and put them on the serving plates, and then

drizzle over tomatoes with the cooking liquid. Then sprinkle with the breadcrumb mixture and let rest for 10 minutes in order to absorb the flavors.

6. Garnish with basil if need be and then serve. Enjoy!

Nutrition: Calories: 96 kcal Fat: 4g Carbohydrates: 13g Protein: 3g

Tomato-Herb Omelet

Preparation Time: 10 minutes

Cooking Time: 10 minutes

Servings: 2

Ingredients:

- 1 tablespoon coconut oil, divided
- 2 scallions, green and white parts, chopped
- 1 teaspoon minced garlic
- 2 tomatoes, chopped, liquid squeezed out
- 6 eggs, beaten
- ½ teaspoon chopped fresh thyme
- ½ teaspoon chopped fresh basil
- ½ teaspoon chopped fresh chives
- ½ teaspoon chopped fresh oregano
- 1/8 teaspoon sea salt
- Pinch ground nutmeg
- Pinch freshly ground black pepper
- Chopped fresh parsley, for garnish

Directions:

1. Put a small saucepan over medium heat before adding 1 teaspoon of coconut oil.

2. Sauté the scallions and garlic for about 3 minutes, until the vegetables are softened.

3. Add the tomatoes and sauté for 3 minutes. Remove the saucepan from the heat and set aside.

4. Whisk together the eggs, thyme, basil, chives, oregano, salt, nutmeg, and pepper in a medium bowl.

5. Put a large skillet over medium-high heat before adding the remaining 2 teaspoons of oil. Swirl the oil until it coats the skillet.

6. Pour in the egg mixture, and swirl until the eggs start to firm up—do not stir the eggs. Lift the edges of the firmed eggs to let the uncooked egg flow at the bottom.

7. When the eggs are almost done, spoon the tomato mixture onto one-half of the eggs.

8. Fold the uncovered side over the tomato mixture and cook for a minute longer.

9. Cut the omelet in half, sprinkle with parsley, and serve.

Nutrition: Calories: 306 kcal Carbohydrates: 13g Fiber: 6g

Protein: 19g Sodium: 312mg Fat: 21g

Mouth-Watering Egg Casserole

Preparation Time: 15 minutes

Cooking Time: 10 hours

Servings: 2

Ingredients

- 10oz ham, ½ -inch slices
- ½ cup thinly sliced button mushrooms
- 1 tbsp. seeded red capsicum, thinly sliced
- ¼ cup thawed artichoke hearts, frozen and quartered
- Whole basil leaves, fresh

What you'll need from store cupboard

- ¼ cup diced potatoes, cooked
- 1 tbsp. drained tomatoes, sun-dried and chopped up
- ¼ cup thawed and drained spinach, chopped and frozen
- 10oz diced Swiss cheese
- 10oz goat feta cheese
- 2 eggs
- 1 cup whole milk
- 1 tbsp. Dijon mustard
- Sea salt to taste
- Black pepper freshly cracked to taste

Directions:

1. Place a coated crockpot liner with cooking oil inside a crockpot, 2-qt

2. Grill the ham pieces for about 4 minutes until crisp. Retain the fat.

3. Sauté mushrooms and capsicum in the fat and butter for about 4 minutes until soft.

4. Place potatoes in the crockpot base and on top, then place an even layer of mushroom-capsicum mixture.

5. Add half of artichokes, tomatoes, and spinach in layers then sprinkle with half Swiss cheese, followed by remaining vegetables, then remaining cheese and feta cheese.

6. Meanwhile, combine eggs, milk, and mustard in a bowl then pour over to settle through on the dish.

7. Place ham on top.

8. Cover and cook for about 8 hours on low then use the liner to remove the casserole.

9. Rest for about 10 minutes, then remove the liner.

10. Slice the casserole and garnish with basil leaves.

11. Serve alongside with green salad, leafy.

Nutrition: Calories: 297, Fat: 17g, Carbs: 20.8g, Protein: 15.8g,

Sugars: 10.2g, Fiber: 2.4g, Sodium: 416mg, Potassium: 617mg

Amazing Overnight Apple and Cinnamon Oatmeal

Preparation Time: 10 minutes

Cooking Time: 7 hours

Servings: 2

Ingredients

- ¾ cup coconut milk
- 1 diced whole apple
- ½ cup steel cut oats
- ½ tbsp. raw honey

What you'll need from store cupboard

- 1 tbsp. coconut oil
- ¾ cup water, fresh
- ¼ tbsp. salt to taste, sea
- 1 tbsp. cinnamon

Directions:

1. Spray your crockpot with cooking oil. This is to prevent food from sticking.

2. Add water, coconut milk, apples, oats, coconut oil, raw honey, salt, and cinnamon. Stir to combine.

3. Cover and cook for about 6-7 hours on low.

4. Serve hot with favorite toppings.

Nutrition: Calories: 284, Fat: 17.9g, Carbs: 30.3g, Protein: 4.2g, Sugars: 1.3g, Fiber: 4.7g, Sodium: 30mg, Potassium: 90mg

Zoodles with Pea Pesto

Preparation Time: 10 minutes

Cooking Time: 10 minutes

Servings: 2

Ingredients:

- 1 ½ zucchini
- 1 tablespoon extra-virgin olive oil
- Pinch sea salt
- Pea Pesto

Directions:

1. Cut the zucchini lengthwise into long strips using a vegetable peeler. Use a knife to cut the strips into the desired width. Alternatively, use a spiralizer to cut the zucchini into noodles.

2. In a large skillet, the olive oil is heated until it shimmers over medium-high heat. Add the zucchini and cook until softened for about 3 minutes. Add the sea salt.

3. Toss the zucchini noodles with the pesto.

Nutrition: Calories: 348 kcal Fat: 30g Sodium: 343mg Carbohydrates: 13g Fiber: 1g Protein: 10g

Shrimp Peri-Peri

Preparation Time: 10 minutes

Cooking Time: 15 minutes

Servings: 2

Ingredients:

- Peri-Peri Sauce
- ½ lb. large shrimp, shelled and deveined
- 1 tablespoon extra-virgin olive oil
- Sea salt

Directions:

1. Preheat the oven broiler on high.

2. In a small pot, bring the Peri-Peri Sauce to a simmer.

3. Meanwhile, place the cleaned shrimp on a rimmed baking sheet, deveined-side down. Brush with olive oil and sprinkle with salt.

4. Broil until opaque, about 5 minutes. Serve with the sauce on the side for dipping or spooned over the top of the shrimp.

Nutrition: Calories: 279 kcal Fat: 16g Sodium: 464mg Carbohydrates: 10g Fiber: 3g Protein: 24g

Halibut with Lime and Cilantro

Preparation Time: 30 minutes

Cooking Time: 45 minutes

Servings: 2

Ingredients:

- 2 tablespoons lime juice
- 1 tablespoon chopped fresh cilantro
- 1 teaspoon olive or canola oil
- 1 clove garlic, finely chopped
- 2 halibut or salmon steaks (about ¾ lb.)
- Freshly ground pepper to taste
- ½ cup chunky-style salsa

Directions:

1. In a shallow glass or plastic dish or in a resealable food-storage plastic bag, mix lime juice, cilantro, oil, and garlic. Add halibut, turning several times to coat with marinade. Cover; refrigerate 15 minutes, turning once.
2. Heat gas or charcoal grill. Remove halibut from marinade; discard marinade.
3. Place halibut on the grill over medium heat. Cover grill; cook 10 to 20 minutes, turning once, until halibut flakes easily with a fork. Sprinkle it with pepper. Serve with salsa.

Nutrition: Calories: 190 kcal Fat: 4.5g Cholesterol: 90mg Sodium: 600mg Carbohydrates: 6g Fiber: 0g Sugars: 2g Protein: 32g

Autumn Pork Chops with Red Cabbage and Apples

Preparation Time: 15 minutes

Cooking Time: 30 minutes

Servings: 2

Ingredients:

- 1/8 Cup apple cider vinegar
- 1 tablespoon granulated sweetener
- 2 (4 oz.) pork chops, about 1 inch thick
- ½ tablespoon extra-virgin olive oil
- ¼ red cabbage, finely shredded
- ½ sweet onion, thinly sliced
- ½ apple, peeled, cored, and sliced
- ½ teaspoon chopped fresh thyme

Directions:

1. Scourge together the vinegar and sweetener. Set it aside.
2. Season the pork with salt and pepper.
3. Position a big skillet over medium-high heat and add the olive oil.
4. Cook the pork chops until no longer pink, turning once, about 8 minutes per side.
5. Put chops aside.
6. Add the cabbage and onion to the skillet and sauté until the vegetables have softened about 5 minutes.
7. Add the vinegar mixture and the apple slices to the skillet and bring the mixture to boiling point.
8. Adjust low-heat and simmer for 5 additional minutes.
9. Return the pork chops to the skillet, along with any accumulated juices and thyme, cover, and cook for 5 more minutes.

Nutrition: Calories: 223 kcal Fat: 12g Carbohydrates: 3g

Orange-Marinated Pork Tenderloin

Preparation Time: 2 hours

Cooking Time: 30 minutes

Servings: 2

Ingredients:

- 1/8 Cup freshly squeezed orange juice
- 1 teaspoon orange zest
- 1 teaspoon minced garlic
- ½ teaspoon low-sodium soy sauce
- ½ teaspoon grated fresh ginger
- ½ teaspoon honey
- ¾ pounds pork tenderloin roast
- ½ tablespoon extra-virgin olive oil

Directions:

1. Blend together the orange juice, zest, garlic, soy sauce, ginger, and honey.
2. Pour the marinade into a resealable plastic bag and add the pork tenderloin.
3. Remove as much air as possible and seal the bag. Marinate the pork in the refrigerator, turning the bag a few times, for 2 hours.
4. Preheat the oven to 400°F.

5. Pull out tenderloin from the marinade and discard the marinade.

6. Position a big ovenproof skillet over medium-high heat and add the oil.

7. Sear the pork tenderloin on all sides, about 5 minutes in total.

8. Position skillet to the oven and roast for 25 minutes.

9. Put aside for 10 minutes before serving.

Nutrition: Calories: 228 kcal Carbohydrates: 4g Sugar: 3g

Vegetarian Chipotle Chili

Preparation Time: 5 minutes
Cooking Time: 6 hours
Servings: 2
Ingredients:
- ¼ onion, diced
- 2 ¼ oz. corn, frozen
- ¾ carrots, diced
- Ground cumin
- 1 garlic clove, minced
- ½ medium sweet potatoes, diced
- ¼ teaspoon chipotle chili powder
- Ground black pepper
- 1 cup kidney beans, cooked from dried beans, or use rinsed canned beans
- ¼ tablespoon salt
- 7 oz. tomatoes, diced, undrained
- ½ avocados, diced

Directions:
- In a slow cooker, combine all the ingredients except the diced avocados.
- Cook for 3 hours on high, and then cook for 3 hours on low until done. If desired, you can also cook for 4-5 hours on high or 7-8 hours on low until cooked through.
- When done, serve with the diced avocado and enjoy!

Nutrition: Calories: 283 kcal Fat: 8g Carbohydrates: 45g Protein: 11g

Wild Rice

Preparation Time: 5 minutes
Cooking Time: 2-3 hours
Servings: 2
Ingredients:
- ¼ cup onions, diced
- ½ cup wild rice, or wild rice mixture, uncooked
- ¾ cups chicken broth, low sodium
- ¼ cup diced green or red peppers
- 1/8 teaspoon pepper
- ½ tablespoon oil
- 1/8 teaspoon salt
- ¼ cup mushrooms, sliced

Directions:
1. In a slow cooker, layer the rice and the vegetables, and then pour oil, pepper, and salt over the vegetables. Stir well.

2. Heat the chicken broth in a pot, and then pour over the ingredients in the slow cooker.

3. Close the lid and cook for 2 ½-3 hours on high, until the rice has softened and the liquid is absorbed.

4. Serve and enjoy!

Nutrition: Calories: 157 kcal Fat: 3g Carbohydrates: 27g Protein: 6g

Stuffed Bell Peppers with Quinoa

Preparation Time: 10 minutes
Cooking Time: 35 minutes
Servings: 2
Ingredients:
- 2 bell peppers
- 1/3 cup quinoa
- 3 oz. chicken stock ¼ cup onion, diced
- ½ teaspoon salt
- ¼ teaspoon tomato paste
- ½ teaspoon dried oregano
- 1/3 cup sour cream
- 1 teaspoon paprika

Directions:
1. Trim the bell peppers and take away the seeds.

2. Then combine chicken broth and quinoa in the pan.

3. Add salt and boil the ingredients for 10 minutes or until quinoa will soak all liquid.

4. Then combine cooked quinoa with dried oregano, ingredient, and onion.

5. Fill the bell peppers with the quinoa mixture and arrange them in the casserole mold.

6. Add soured cream and bake the peppers for 25 minutes at 365 F.

7. Serve the cooked peppers with soured cream sauce from the casserole mold.

Nutrition: Calories 237Fat 10.3Fiber 4.5Carbs 31.3Protein 6.9

Mediterranean Burrito

Preparation Time: 10 minutes
Cooking Time: 0minutes
Servings: 2
Ingredients:
- 2 wheat tortillas
- 2 oz. red kidney beans, canned, drained
- 2 tablespoons hummus
- 2 teaspoons tahini sauce
- 1 cucumber
- 2 lettuce leaves
- 1 tablespoon lime juice
- 1 teaspoon olive oil
- ½ teaspoon dried oregano

Directions:
1. Mash the red kidney beans until you get a puree.
2. Then spread the wheat tortillas with beans mash from one side.
3. Add hummus and tahini sauce.
4. Cut the cucumber into the wedges and place them over tahini sauce.
5. Then add lettuce leaves.
6. Make the dressing: misunderstanding together vegetable oil, dried oregano, and juice.
7. Drizzle the lettuce leaves with the dressing and wrap the wheat tortillas in burritos' shape.

Nutrition: Calories 288Fat 10.2Fiber 14.6Carbs 38.2Protein 12.5

Prosciutto Wrapped Mozzarella Balls

Preparation Time: 10 minutes
Cooking Time: 10 minutes
Servings: 4
Ingredients:
- 8 mozzarella balls, cherry size
- 4 oz. bacon, sliced
- ¼ teaspoon ground black pepper
- ¾ teaspoon dried rosemary
- 1 teaspoon butter

Directions:
1. Sprinkle the sliced bacon with ground black pepper and dried rosemary.
2. Wrap every mozzarella ball in the sliced bacon and secure them with toothpicks.
3. Melt butter.
4. Brush wrapped mozzarella balls with butter.
5. Line the tray with the baking paper and arrange mozzarella balls in it.
6. Bake the meal for 10 minutes at 365F.

Nutrition: Calories 323Fat 26.8Fiber 0.1Carbs 0.6Protein 20.6

Garlic Chicken Balls

Preparation Time: 15 minutes
Cooking Time: 10 minutes
Servings: 4
Ingredients:
- 2 cups ground chicken
- 1 teaspoon minced garlic
- 1 teaspoon dried dill
- 1/3 carrot, grated
- 1 egg, beaten
- 1 tablespoon olive oil
- ¼ cup coconut flakes
- ½ teaspoon salt

Directions:
1. In the mixing bowl, mix up together ground chicken, minced garlic, dried dill, carrot, egg, and salt.
2. Stir the chicken mixture with the assistance of the fingertips until homogeneous.
3. Then, make medium balls from the mixture.
4. Coat every chicken ball in coconut flakes.
5. Heat vegetable oil in the skillet.

6. Add chicken balls and cook them for 3 minutes from all sides. The cooked chicken balls will have a golden-brown color.

Nutrition: Calories 200Fat 11.5Fiber 0.6Carbs 1.7Protein 21.9

Monkey Salad

Preparation Time: 4 minutes

Cooking Time: 7 minutes

Servings: 1

Ingredients:

- 2 tablespoon butter
- 1 cup unsweetened coconut flakes
- 1 cup raw, unsalted cashews
- 1 cup raw, unsalted s
- 1 cup 90% dark chocolate shavings

Directions:

1. In a skillet, melt the butter on medium heat.
2. Add the cashews and s and sauté for 3 minutes. Remove from the warmth and sprinkle with bittersweet chocolate shavings.
3. Serve!

Nutrition: Calories: 321Carbs: 5 gFat: 12 gProtein: 6 gFiber: 5 g

Jarlsberg Lunch Omelet

Preparation Time: 5 minutes

Cooking Time: 10 minutes

Servings: 2

Ingredients:

- 4 medium mushrooms, sliced, 2 oz.
- 1 green onion, sliced
- 2 eggs, beaten
- 1 oz. Jarlsberg or Swiss cheese, shredded
- 1 oz. ham, diced

Directions:

1. In a skillet, cook the mushrooms and scallion until tender.
2. Add the eggs and blend well.
3. Sprinkle with salt and top with the mushroom mixture, cheese, and therefore the ham.
4. When the egg is set, fold the plain side of the omelet on the filled side.

5. Close up the heat and let it stand until the cheese has melted.
6. Serve!

Nutrition: Calories: 288Carbs: 22 gFat: 12 gProtein: 27 g

Fiber: 6 g

Mu Shu Lunch Pork

Preparation Time: 5 minutes

Cooking Time: 10 minutes

Servings: 2

Ingredients:

- 4 cups coleslaw mix, with carrots
- 1 small onion, sliced thin
- 1 lb. cooked roast pork, cut into ½ cubes
- 2 tablespoon hoisin sauce
- 2 tablespoon soy sauce

Directions:

1. In a large skillet, heat the oil on high heat.
2. Stir-fry the cabbage and onion for 4 minutes until tender.
3. Add the pork, hoisin, and soy.
4. Cook until browned. Enjoy!

Nutrition: Calories: 388Carbs: 16 g Fat: 21 gProtein: 25 g

Fiber: 16 g

Fiery Jalapeno Poppers

Preparation Time: 10 minutes

Cooking Time: 40 minutes

Servings: 4

Ingredients:

- 5 oz. cream cheese
- ¼ cup mozzarella cheese
- 8 medium jalapeno peppers
- ½ teaspoon Mrs. Dash Table Blend
- 8 slices bacon

Directions:

1. Preheat your fryer to 400°F/200°C.
2. Cut the jalapenos in half.
3. Use a spoon to scrape out the insides of the peppers.

4. In a bowl, add together the cheese, mozzarella cheese, and spices of your choice.

5. Pack the cheese mixture into the jalapenos and place the peppers on top.

6. Wrap each pepper in 1 slice of bacon, ranging from rock bottom and dealing up.

7. Bake for half-hour. Broil for a further 3 minutes. Serve!

Nutrition: Calories: 238 Carbs: 4 g Fat: 10 g Protein: 24 g Fiber: 14 g

Bacon & Chicken Patties

Preparation Time: 5 minutes

Cooking Time: 15 minutes

Servings: 2

Ingredients:

- 1 ½ oz. can chicken breast
- 4 slices bacon
- ¼ cup parmesan cheese
- 1 large egg
- 3 tablespoon flour

Directions:

1. Cook the bacon until crispy.

2. Chop the chicken and bacon together in a food processor until fine.

3. Add in the parmesan, egg, flour, and blend.

4. Make the patties by hand and fry on medium heat in a pan with some oil.

5. Once browned, flip over, continue cooking, and lay them to empty. Serve!

Nutrition: Calories: 387 Carbs: 13 g Fat: 16 g Protein: 34 g Fiber: 28 g

Cheddar Bacon Burst

Preparation Time: 25 minutes

Cooking Time: 90 minutes

Servings: 8

Ingredients:

- 30 slices bacon
- 2 ½ cups cheddar cheese
- 4-5 cups raw spinach
- 1-2 tablespoon Tones Southwest Chipotle Seasoning

- 2 teaspoon Mrs. Dash Table Seasoning

Directions:

1. Preheat your fryer to 375°F/190°C.

2. Weave the bacon into 15 vertical pieces & 12 horizontal pieces. Cut the additional 3 in half to fill in the rest horizontally.

3. Season the bacon.

4. Add the cheese to the bacon.

5. Add the spinach and depress to compress.

6. Tightly roll up the woven bacon.

7. Line a baking sheet with kitchen foil and add salt to it.

8. Put the bacon on top of a cooling rack and put that on top of your baking sheet.

9. Bake for 60-70 minutes.

10. Let cool for 10-15 minutes before 11. Slice and enjoy!

Nutrition: Calories: 218 Carbs: 20 g Fat: 9 g Protein: 21 g Fiber: 5 g

Prosciutto Spinach Salad

Preparation Time: 5 minutes

Cooking Time: 5 minutes

Servings: 2

Ingredients:

- 2 cups baby spinach
- 1/3 lb. prosciutto
- 1 cantaloupe
- 1 avocado
- ¼ cup diced red onion handful of raw, unsalted walnuts

Directions:

1. Put a cup of spinach on each plate.

2. Top with the diced prosciutto, cubes of melon balls, slices of avocado, a couple of purple onions, and a couple of walnuts.

3. Add some freshly ground pepper, if you wish. Serve!

Nutrition: Calories: 348 Carbs: 11 g Fat: 9 g Protein: 26 g Fiber: 22 g

Riced Cauliflower & Curry Chicken

Preparation Time: 15 minutes

Cooking Time: 30 minutes

Servings: 6

Ingredients:

- 2 lbs. chicken (4 breasts)
- 1 packet curry paste
- 3 tablespoon ghee (can substitute with butter)
- ½ cup heavy cream
- 1 head cauliflower (around 1 kg)

Directions:

1. In a large skillet, melt the ghee.
2. Add the curry paste and blend.
3. Once combined, add a cup of water and simmer for five minutes.
4. Add the chicken, cover the skillet, and simmer for 18 minutes.
5. Cut a cauliflower head into florets and blend in a food processor to make the riced cauliflower.
6. When the chicken is cooked, uncover, add the cream and cook for a further 7 minutes. Serve!

Nutrition: Calories: 267 Carbs: 42 g Fat: 31 g Protein: 34 g Fiber: 32 g

Lasagna Spaghetti Squash

Preparation Time: 30 minutes

Cooking Time: 90 minutes

Servings: 6

Ingredients:

- 25 slices mozzarella cheese
- 1 large jar (40 oz.) Rao's Marinara sauce
- 30 oz. whole-milk ricotta cheese
- 2 large spaghetti squash, cooked (44 oz.)
- 4 lbs. ground beef

Directions:

1. Preheat your fryer to 375°F/190°C.
2. Slice the spaghetti squash and place it face down inside a fryer proof dish. Fill with water until covered.
3. Bake for 45 minutes until the skin is soft.
4. Sear the meat until browned.
5. In a large skillet, heat the browned meat and marinara sauce. Put aside when warm.
6. Scrape the flesh off the cooked squash to resemble strands of spaghetti.
7. Layer the lasagna in a large greased pan in alternating layers of spaghetti squash, meat sauce, mozzarella, and ricotta. Repeat until all increases are used.
8. Bake for half-hour and serve!

Nutrition: Calories: 508 Carbs: 32 g Fat: 8 g Protein: 22 g Fiber: 21 g

Blue Cheese Chicken Wedges

Preparation Time: 20 minutes

Cooking Time: 45 minutes

Servings: 4

Ingredients:

- Blue cheese dressing
- 2 tablespoon. crumbled blue cheese
- 4 strips of bacon
- 2 chicken breasts (boneless)
- 3/4 cup of your favorite buffalo sauce

Directions:

1. Boil in a large pot of salted water.
2. Add two chicken breasts to the pot and cook for 28 minutes.
3. Close up the heat and let the chicken rest for 10 minutes. Using a fork, pull the chicken apart into strips.
4. Cook and funky the bacon strips and put them to the side.
5. On medium heat, combine the chicken and buffalo sauce. Stir until hot.
6. Add the bleu and buffalo pulled chicken. Top with the cooked bacon crumbles.
7. Serve and enjoy.

Nutrition: Calories: 309 Carbs: 27 g Fat: 18 g Protein: 34 g Fiber: 29 g

'Oh so Good' Salad

Preparation Time: 5 minutes
Cooking Time: 10 minutes
Servings: 2

Ingredients:

- 6 Brussels sprouts
- ½ teaspoon apple cider vinegar
- 1 teaspoon olive/grape seed oil
- 1 grind of salt
- 1 tablespoon freshly grated parmesan

Directions:

1. Slice the clean Brussels sprouts in half.
2. Oppositely cut thin slices.
3. Once sliced, cut the roots off and discard.
4. Toss alongside the apple cider, oil, and salt.
5. Sprinkle with the parmesan cheese, combine and enjoy!

Nutrition: Calories: 438 Carbs: 31 g Fat: 23 g Protein: 24 g Fiber: 16 g

Low Carb Pumpkin Pie Pudding

Preparation Time: 10 minutes
Cooking Time: 20 minutes
Servings: 2

Ingredients

- 3 eggs, whisked
- 1/3 cup of almond milk, whipping
- ¼ cup of stevia sweetener
- 16 ounces of pumpkin puree
- 2 teaspoons pumpkin pie spice

Directions

1. In a bowl, whisk eggs and add almond milk, stevia, pumpkin puree, and pumpkin pie spice.
2. Grease the oil in a steel pan and then pour egg mixture in it.
3. Pour 2 cups of water inside the instant pot and set trivet in the pot.
4. Place steel pan on top of the trivet. Cover the pan with the aluminum foil.
5. Close the pot and set the timer to 20 minutes at high pressure.
6. Once timer beeps, quick release the steam. Remove the lid of the instant pot.
7. Chill for 2 hours and then serve with whipping cream.

Nutrition: Calories: 220 kcal Protein: 13.8 g Fat: 15.17 g Carbohydrates: 6.41 g

Red Cabbage Mix

Preparation Time: 10 minutes
Cooking Time: 5 minutes
Servings: 6

Ingredients

- 4 tablespoons of coconut oil
- 1 teaspoon of butter
- 2 garlic cloves
- 6 cups of red cabbage, shredded
- Salt and black pepper to taste
- 1/3 cup of water

Directions

1. Turn on the sauté mode of the instant pot. Add coconut oil and butter to the instant pot.
2. Heat the butter to let it melt. Add salt, pepper, and garlic cloves.
3. Cook until aroma comes. Add cabbage and pour water.
4. Lock the lid and set the timer to 5 minutes.
5. Once timer beeps, release the steam naturally. Serve and enjoy.

Nutrition: Calories: 609 kcal Protein: 81.01 g Fat: 29.66 g Carbohydrates: 4.39 g

Irish Lamb Stew

Preparation Time: 10 minutes
Cooking Time: 45 minutes
Servings: 6

Ingredients

- 2 pounds of lamb shank
- 3 cups of chicken broth
- 1 green onion
- ¼ teaspoon of thyme
- ½ cup of green beans, chopped
- Salt and black pepper
- 2 tablespoons of olive oil

Directions

1. Turn on sauté mode of instant pot and add olive oil.
2. Sear the meat for 3 minutes in oil from both the sides.
3. Add green beans, green onion, and cook for one minute at sautéing mode.
4. Sprinkle salt and black pepper. Pour broth and add thyme to the pot.
5. Turn off the sauté mode and then set the timer to 45 minutes at high pressure.
6. Once timer beeps, release the steam naturally.
7. Open the instant pot and stir the mixture. Then serve.

Nutrition: Calories: 420 kcal Protein: 59.53 g Fat: 18.59 g Carbohydrates: 2.22 g

Vegetables in Half and Half

Preparation Time: 10 minutes
Cooking Time: 8 minutes
Servings: 4

Ingredients

- 2 medium parsnips, peeled and cubed
- 1 fennel bulb, sliced
- 3 cloves garlic, minced
- 1 cup chicken broth
- 1 cup half-and-half
- Salt and pepper, to taste

Directions

1. Add fennel bulbs, parsnip, chicken broth, garlic, salt, and pepper into the instant pot.
2. Lock the lid of the pot. Set timer for 5 minutes at high pressure.
3. Once time beeps, quick release the steam. Turn on the sauté mode and reduce the liquid.
4. Stir occasionally. Next, add half and half and mix well.
5. Stir for 2 more minutes and then serve the dish hot. Enjoy.

Nutrition: Calories: 212 kcal Protein: 16.57 g Fat: 5.37 g Carbohydrates: 25.42 g

Creamy Broccoli and Ham

Preparation Time: 10 minutes

Cooking Time: 10 minutes
Servings: 4

Ingredients

- 20 ounces of broccoli
- 12 ounces of ham, smoked and chopped
- 8 ounces of fat-free cream of mushroom soup
- 1 cup almond milk
- 2 cups of Cheddar cheese, shredded
- Salt and black pepper
- 2 teaspoons of olive oil

Directions

1. Turn on the sauté mode of the instant pot. Add oil and heat it.
2. Then add broccoli and cook for one minute. Next, add ham and season it with salt and pepper. Pour in the cream of mushroom soup and almond milk and lock the lid.
3. Set timer for 4 minutes at high pressure. Once timer beeps, quick release the steam.
4. Reduce the liquid by turning on the sauté mode. Keep stirring.
5. After a few mins, add cheese and cook for 2 minutes at sauté mode. Once it's done serve.

Nutrition: Calories: 209 kcal Protein: 20.75 g Fat: 8.65 g Carbohydrates: 14.87 g

Glazed Carrots and Cauliflower

Preparation Time: 10 minutes
Cooking Time: 5 minutes
Servings: 6

Ingredients

- 1/3 pound of baby carrot
- 1 cauliflower head, small and chopped
- 3/4 cup lime juice
- 3 tablespoons butter/olive oil
- 1/3 cup stevia
- 1/4 teaspoon ground cinnamon
- Salt and black pepper, to taste

Directions

1. Combine all the ingredients in the instant pot. Lock the lid and set the timer to 5 minutes.
2. Open timer beeps, release the steam quickly. Open the instant pot lid. Stir and serve.

Nutrition: Calories: 122 kcal Protein: 2.51 g Fat: 4.91 g Carbohydrates: 23.3 g

Broth-Braised Cabbage

Preparation Time: 10 minutes

Cooking Time: 5 minutes

Servings: 4

Ingredients:

- 1 head of cabbage, sliced
- 1 small onion
- 2 garlic cloves, minced
- 1/3 teaspoon star anise seeds
- 1/4 cup vegetable broth
- 2 slices of diced bacon
- 2 teaspoons of olive oil
- Salt and black pepper, to taste

Directions:

1. Turn on sauté mode of the instant pot. Add oil and heat it.
2. Then add bacon and cook until crisp.
3. Then add small onions and garlic cloves and cook until aroma comes.
4. Add salt, pepper and anise seed. At the end add cabbage and pour the broth.
5. Cook on high for 3 minutes. Then quickly release the steam.
6. Serve and enjoy.

Nutrition: Calories: 135 kcal Protein: 4.2 g Fat: 7.73 g Carbohydrates: 14.81 g

Shredded Bbq Cream Cheese Chicken

Preparation Time: 10 minutes

Cooking Time: 13 minutes

Servings: 4

Ingredients

- 2 pounds of chicken breast
- 1 cup of water
- ½ cup of BBQ sauce, Keto based
- 6 ounces of cream cheese

Directions

1. Pour water in instant pot. Add chicken, and lock the lid.
2. Set timer for 12 minutes at high pressure. Once timer beeps, quick release the steam.
3. Transfer the chicken from the instant pot and place it on the cutting board.
4. Use a fork to shred the chicken meat. Drain water from the instant pot.
5. Transfer the shredded chicken back to the pot.
6. Next, add cream cheese, and BBQ sauce. Stir and combine all the ingredients.
7. Turn on sauté mode and then cook for one minute. Serve and enjoy.

Nutrition: Calories: 525 kcal Protein: 50.81 g Fat: 33.2 g Carbohydrates: 3.67 g

Ranch Dump Style Pork Chops

Preparation Time: 10 minutes

Cooking Time: 12 minutes

Servings: 8

Ingredients

- 4 pounds of pork chops
- 2 ounces of ranch dressing mix
- 18 ounces of cream of chicken soup
- 2 cups of water

Directions

1. Combine the listed ingredients in the instant pot. Lock the lid of the instant pot and set the timer to 12 minutes at high pressure.
2. Once timer beeps, naturally release the steam for 12 minutes. Then quickly release the steam. Open the pot, stir the ingredients and then serve.

Nutrition: Calories: 534 kcal Protein: 59.08 g Fat: 30.17 g Carbohydrates: 2.83 g

Instant Pot Cinnamon Apricot and Pears

Preparation Time: 10 minutes

Cooking Time: 5 minutes

Servings: 3

Ingredients

- ¼ cup of lime juice
- 2 apricot peeled
- 1 teaspoon of cinnamon
- 2 pears, peeled
- Salt, pinch
- 2 scoops of stevia powder

Directions

1. Peel, core, and slice the fruits. Transfer the apricot, cinnamon, pears, salt, and stevia in the instant pot. Pour the lime juice in the instant pot.

2. Lock the lid of the instant pot, and set the timer to 2 minutes at high pressure.

3. Once timer beeps, release the steam quickly. Turn on the sauté mode and reduce the liquid.

4. Serve immediately and enjoy.

Nutrition: Calories: 44 kcal Protein: 0.39 g Fat: 0.07 g Carbohydrates: 12.18 g

Beets Dijon

Preparation Time: 10 minutes
Cooking Time: 14 minutes
Servings: 2

Ingredients

- 1 pound beets, peeled, cubed (1/2-inch)
- 1/3 cup finely chopped onion
- 1/3 cup sour cream
- 2 tablespoons Dijon mustard
- 2–3 teaspoons lemon juice
- Salt and white pepper, to taste

Directions

1. Combine beets, onions, Dijon mustard, lemon juice, salt, and black pepper in a bowl and set aside. Pour water in the instant pot and set trivet inside the pot.

2. Place the heatproof bowl, having beets on a trivet and lock the lid.

3. Set timer to 12 minutes. Once timer beeps, release the steam quickly.

4. Remove the beets bowl from the instant pot. Drain water from pot and turn on sauté mode.

5. Transfer beet to the pot and add sour cream. Cook for 2 minutes and then serve.

Nutrition: Calories: 297 kcal Protein: 9.24 g Fat: 13.24 g Carbohydrates: 38.71 g

Green Bean Casserole

Preparation Time: 10 minutes
Cooking Time: 20 minutes
Servings: 3

Ingredients

- 1 can of cream of mushroom soup

- 1 cup sour cream, full fat
- 12 ounces of green beans, thawed
- Salt and black pepper, to taste
- 2 green onions, chopped
- 1 teaspoon of olive oil
- 1 cup parmesan cheese, grated

Directions

1. Turn on the sauté mode of instant pot and add oil, and green onions. Cook unit aroma comes. Next, add green beans and cook for one minute.

2. Now add cream of mushroom soup. Lock the lid of the instant pot.

3. Set timer for 12 minutes at high. Once timer beeps, do quick release steam.

4. Season the green beans with salt and black pepper and add sour cream.

5. Stir and serve hot with garnish of parmesan cheese.

6. Broil cheese for 5 minutes before serving. Enjoy.

Nutrition: Calories: 44 kcal Protein: 0.39 g Fat: 0.07 g Carbohydrates: 12.18 g

Plain Meat Loaf

Preparation Time: 10 minutes
Cooking Time: 30 minutes
Servings: 6

Ingredients

- 2 pounds beef lean and ground
- ½ cup almond milk
- 2 eggs
- 1/3 cup chopped onion
- 1 teaspoon of Italian seasoning
- Salt and black pepper, to taste

Directions

1. Place a steamer rack inside the instant pot and pour two cups of water.

2. Mix all the listed ingredients in a bowl with hands. Make a large loaf of the mixture.

3. Now place meatloaf over an aluminum foil and wrap the meatloaf in the foil.

4. Place foil on the steaming rack.

5. Lock the lid of the instant pot and set the timer to 30 minutes at high pressure.

6. Once timer beeps, do a natural release for 10 minutes, followed by quick release.

7. Remove the meatloaf from the foil. Transfer it to cutting board, and cut into slices.

8. Serve with your favorite dipping sauce.

Nutrition: Calories: 384 kcal Protein: 43.57 g Fat: 20.28 g

Carbohydrates: 3.83 g

Lemony Dijon Meat Loaf

Preparation Time: 10 minutes

Cooking Time: 35 minutes

Servings: 3-4

Ingredients

- 2 pounds lean ground beef
- 1 cup almond meal
- 2 eggs
- 1 tablespoon lemon, zest, and juice
- 2 teaspoons Dijon mustard
- Seasoning Salt and black pepper, to taste

Directions

1. Pour 1-1/2 cups of water and place trivet inside the instant pot.

2. Mix all the listed ingredients in a mixing bowl. Make a large loaf of the meat mixture.

3. Now place meatloaf over an aluminum foil and wrap the meat in foil.

4. Place foil on the trivet.

5. Lock the lid of the instant Pot and set a timer to 35 minutes at high pressure.

6. Once timer beeps, do a natural release for 15 minutes, followed by quick release.

7. Remove the meatloaf from the foil.

8. Transfer to cutting board, and cut into slices after letting it get cold. Serve.

Nutrition: Calories: 559 kcal Protein: 65.25 g Fat: 30.26 g

Carbohydrates: 2.05 g

Greek-Style Green Beans

Preparation Time: 10 minutes

Cooking Time: 12 minutes

Servings: 3

Ingredients

- 1 pound green beans
- 26 ounces of fresh tomatoes, diced
- 1 onion, chopped
- 2 tablespoons of olive oil
- 2 garlic cloves
- 1/3 cup of water
- Salt and pepper, to taste

Directions

1. Turn on the sauté mode of the instant pot. Add onions and olive oil.

2. Cook onions until translucent. Add garlic and cook until aroma comes.

3. Next, add diced tomatoes and sauté it for 2 minutes.

4. Now, add green beans, salt, and pepper. Add water and lock the lid.

5. Set timer for 10 minutes at high. Once timer beeps, release the steam quickly.

6. Open the pot and stir the ingredients. Serve.

Nutrition: Calories: 132 kcal Protein: 3.97 g Fat: 7.69 g Carbohydrates: 14.94 g

Italian Tofu Scramble

Preparation Time: 15 minutes

Cooking Time: 7 minutes

Servings: 2

Ingredients:

- 1 cup firm silken tofu
- 1 cup chopped cherry tomatoes
- 1 cup mixed chopped squash
- 1tsp mixed herbs
- pinch of salt

Directions:

1. Spray a heat-proof bowl that fits in your Instant Pot with nonstick spray.

2. Chop the tofu finely.

3. Mix with the other ingredients.

4. Pour into the bowl.

5. Place the bowl in your steamer basket.

6. Pour 1 cup of water into your Instant Pot.

7. Lower the basket into your Instant Pot.

8. Seal and cook on low pressure for 7 minutes.

9.   Depressurize quickly.

10.   Stir well and allow to rest, it will finish cooking in its own heat.

Nutrition Calories: 210Carbs: 9Sugar: 4Fat: 3Protein: 18

Kale Sausage Stew

Preparation Time: 15 minutes

Cooking Time: 10 minutes

Servings: 2

Ingredients:

- 1lb cooked chopped sausage
- 1lb shredded kale
- 1 cup vegetable broth
- 1tbsp mixed herbs
- 1tbsp gravy

Recipe:

1.   Mix all the ingredients in your Instant Pot.

2.   Cook on Stew for 10 minutes.

3.   Release the pressure naturally.

Nutrition Calories: 300Carbs: 9Sugar: 1Fat: 20Protein: 30

Tomato and Broccoli

Preparation Time: 15 minutes

Cooking Time: 10 minutes

Servings: 2

Ingredients:

- 1lb chopped broccoli
- 1lb cherry tomato
- 1 cup low sodium broth
- 1tbsp dry basil
- 1 minced onion

Recipe:

1.   Mix all the ingredients in your Instant Pot.

2.   Cook on Stew for 10 minutes.

3.   Release the pressure naturally.

Nutrition Calories: 130Carbs: 6Sugar: 3Fat: 10Protein: 6

MEAT

Roasted Leg Lamb

Preparation Time: 15 minutes
Cooking Time: 2 ½ hours
Serving: 12
Ingredients:
- 1-112 to 144 ounces bone-in lamb leg, trimmed
- 1 cup of chicken broth

Marinade:
- 1/3 cup fresh minced rosemary
- 2 tablespoons of Dijon mustard
- 2 tablespoons of olive oil
- 8 minced garlic cloves
- 1 teaspoon soy sauce reduced-sodium
- 1/2 teaspoon salt
- 1/2 teaspoon pepper

Directions:
1. Preheat your oven to 325degreesF.
2. Combine marinade ingredients and coat the lamb. Refrigerate with cover overnight.
3. Place the lamb on a rack using a shallow roasting pan with the fat side up.
4. Bake without cover for 1 ½ hours.
5. Pour the broth then cover loosely using foil. Bake for another 1 ½ hours or until meat turns to your desired doneness (Medium-rare 135degrees; medium 140degrees; and medium-well 145degrees using kitchen thermometer).
6. Cool lamb for 10 to 15 minutes before slicing.
Nutrition: Calories: 246 |Carbohydrates: 2 g |Fiber: 0 g |Fats: 11 g |Sodium: 320 mg |Protein: 33 g

Lamb Chops Curry

Preparation Time: 10 minutes
Cooking Time: 30 minutes
Serving: 2
Ingredients:
- 4-4 ounces bone-in loin chops of lamb
- 1 tablespoon of canola oil
- 3/4 cup of orange juice
- 2 tablespoons teriyaki sauce reduced-sodium
- 2 teaspoons of grated orange zest
- 1 teaspoon of curry powder
- 1 garlic clove, minced
- 1 teaspoon cornstarch
- 2 tablespoons of cold water

Directions:
1. Brown lamb chops on both sides over canola oil.
2. Combine the next five ingredients and pour over the skillet. Cover and let it simmer for 15 to 20 minutes or until lamb turns tender. Remove from heat and keep warm.
3. Combine the last two ingredients until smooth. Stir into the pan drippings and bring to boil for 2 minutes or until it thickens.
4. Serve with steamed rice if desired.
Nutrition: Calories: 337 |Carbohydrates: 15 g |Fiber: 1 g |Fats: 17 g |Sodium: 402 mg |Protein: 3o g

Pork Cutlets in Cucumber Sauce

Preparation Time: 4 hours 15 minutes
Cooking Time: 15 minutes
Serving: 4 (1 3 oz. slice serving)
Ingredients:
Marinate:
- 16 ounces pork tenderloin, cut into ½-inch thick slices
- 1 small chopped onion
- 2 tablespoons of lemon juice
- 1 tablespoon fresh minced parsley
- 2 minced garlic cloves
- 3/4 teaspoon of dried thyme
- 1/8 teaspoon pepper

Cucumber Sauce:
- 1 small seeded and chopped tomato
- 2/3 cup plain yogurt, reduced-fat
- 1/2 cup seeded cucumber, chopped
- 1 tablespoon onion, finely chopped
- 1/2 teaspoon of lemon juice
- 1/8 teaspoon of garlic powder

Directions:

1. Combine all the marinade ingredients and marinate the chops for 4 hours (or overnight). Cover and refrigerate.
2. Combine all the cucumber sauce ingredients and mix. Cover and refrigerate.
3. Drain and discard marinade. Place chops on a greased broiler pan. Broil for 6 to 8 minutes each side 4-inch from the heat.
4. Serve with cucumber sauce.

Nutrition: Calories: 177 |Carbohydrates: 8 g |Fiber: 1 g |Fats: 5 g |Sodium: 77 mg |Protein: 25 g

Grilled Lamb Chops

Preparation Time: 4 hours 15 minutes
Cooking Time: 15 minutes
Serving: 4 (2 chops serving)
Ingredients:
- 8-3 ounces lamb loin chops

Marinade:
- 1 small sliced onion
- 2 tablespoons of red wine vinegar
- 1 tablespoon of lemon juice
- 1 tablespoon of olive oil
- 2 teaspoons fresh minced rosemary (substitute 3/4 tsp. crushed dried)
- 2 teaspoons of Dijon mustard
- 1 minced garlic clove
- 1/2 teaspoon pepper
- 1/4 teaspoon salt
- 1/4 teaspoon of ground ginger

Directions:
1. Coat the lamb chops with the combined marinade mixture. Cover and refrigerate for 4 hours or overnight.
2. Drain and discard marinade. Lightly oil your grill rack.
3. Grill lamb chops 4 to 7 minutes on each side over medium heat.
4. Grill until it reaches your desired doneness (medium-rare, 135°; medium, 140°medium-well, 145° temperature reading on your kitchen thermometer)

Nutrition: Calories: 164 |Carbohydrates: 0 g |Fiber: 0 g |Fats: 8 g |Sodium: 112 mg |Protein: 21 g

Herb Lamb Chops

Preparation Time: 10 minutes
Cooking Time: 3o minutes
Serving: 4 (2 chops serving)
Ingredients:
- 8-3 ounces lamb loin chops
- 1/2 teaspoon pepper
- 1/4 teaspoon salt

Herb Mixture:
- 3 tablespoons of Dijon mustard
- 1 tablespoon fresh rosemary, minced
- 1 tablespoon fresh thyme, minced
- 3 minced garlic cloves

Directions:
1. Sprinkle chops with salt and pepper.
2. Combine ingredients of herb mixture. Grill chops over a greased grill rack for 6 minutes. Turn and spread the herb mixture on top. Grill for 6-8 minutes more.
3. Follow Step 4 of Grilled Lamb Chops

Nutrition: Calories: 231 |Carbohydrates: 3 g |Fiber: 0 g |Fats: 9 g |Sodium: 493 mg |Protein: 32 g

Beef Moroccan Kebabs

Preparation Time: 8 hours 25 minutes
Cooking Time: 10 minutes
Serving: 8
Ingredients:
- 32 ounces top sirloin steak beef, cut in 1-inch slices

Marinade:
- 1 cup fresh parsley, chopped
- 1 cup fresh cilantro, chopped
- 1/4 cup onion. grated
- 3 tablespoons of lemon juice
- 2 tablespoons of olive oil
- 1 tablespoon of ground cumin
- 1 tablespoon of ground coriander

- 1 tablespoon paprika
- 1 tablespoon of cider vinegar
- 1 tablespoon ketchup
- 2 minced garlic cloves,
- 1 teaspoon fresh gingerroot, minced
- 1 teaspoon Thai style red chili paste
- Dash pepper and salt

Directions:

1. Follow Steps 1 and 2 of Grilled Lamb Chops. Marinate at least 8 hours.

2. Thread beef cubes into skewers, and then follow Steps 3 to 4 of Grilled Lamb Chops.

Nutrition: Calories: 185 |Carbohydrates: 3 g |Fiber: 1 g |Fats: 9 g |Sodium: 91 mg |Protein: 22 g

Pork and Orzo in a Bowl

Preparation Time: 10 minutes
Cooking Time: 30 minutes
Serving: 6

Ingredients:

- 24 ounces pork tenderloin
- 1 teaspoon of coarsely ground pepper
- 2 tablespoons of olive oil
- 3 quarts water
- 1-1/4 cups orzo pasta, uncooked
- 1/4 teaspoon salt
- 1-6 ounces package fresh baby spinach
- 1 cup halved grape tomatoes
- 3/4 cup feta cheese, crumbled

Directions:

1. Rub pepper onto the pork; slice into an inch size cubes. Using a large non-stick skillet, heat oil over medium heat and stir-cook pork for 8 to 10 minutes.

2. Meanwhile, boil water and cook the orzo. Add salt. Keep uncovered and cook for 8 minutes. Add in the spinach and cook until orzo turns tender (about 45 to 60 seconds). Drain.

3. Add tomatoes and heat through. Stir in the orzo and cheese.

Nutrition: Calories: 372 |Carbohydrates: 34 g |Fiber: 3 g |Fats: 11 g |Sodium: 306 mg |Protein: 31 g

Lamb Kebabs

Preparation Time: 8 hours 10 minutes
Cooking Time: 10 minutes
Serving: 4

Ingredients:

Marinade/Basting Sauce

- 1/2 cup of lemon juice
- 2 tablespoons of dried oregano
- 4 teaspoons of olive oil
- 6 minced garlic cloves

Kebabs:

- 16 ounces boneless lamb, cut 1-inch cubes
- 16 cherry tomatoes
- 1 large size green pepper, cut in 1-inch pieces
- 1 large size onion, cut in 1-inch wedges

Directions:

1. Follow directions of Beef Moroccan Kebabs

2. Reserved 1 cup of the sauce for basting while grilling. Alternately, arrange veggies and meat in skewers.

3. Serve

Nutrition: Calories: 226 |Carbohydrates: 13 g |Fiber: 2 g |Fats: 9 g |Sodium: 83 mg |Protein: 25 g

Pork Medallion in Lemon Caper Sauce

Preparation Time: 5 minutes
Cooking Time: 30 minutes
Serving: 4 (3 medallion serving)

Ingredients:

- 1-16 ounces pork tenderloin, cut in 12 slices and flatten ¼-inch thick
- 1/2 cup of all-purpose flour
- 1/2 teaspoon salt
- 1/4 teaspoon pepper
- 1 tablespoon butter
- 1 tablespoon of olive oil

Sauce

- 1 cup chicken broth, reduced-sodium
- 1/4 cup white wine (or ¼ cup reduced-sodium chicken broth)
- 1 minced garlic clove, minced
- 1 tablespoon drained capers

- 1 tablespoon of lemon juice
- 1/2 teaspoon crushed dried rosemary

Directions:

1. Coat pork slices in flour, pepper and salt mixture. Cook pork slices in batches using oil and butter mixture until juices cleared. Remove from skillet and keep warm.

2. Combine first three ingredients in the same pan. Stir to loosen brown bits. Bring to a boil until reduced in half. Stir in the remaining ingredients until heated through. Serve with pork.

Nutrition: Calories: 232 |Carbohydrates: 7 g |Fiber: 0 g |Fats: 10 g |Sodium: 589 mg |Protein: 24 g Diabetic Exchange: 1 1/2 Fat, 1/2 Starch, 3 Lean Meat

Festive Season Stuffed Tenderloin

Preparation Time: 10 minutes
Cooking Time: 45 minutes
Serving: 8 (1/8 of recipe serving)

Ingredients:

- 4 teaspoons of olive oil, divided
- 2 minced shallots
- 1-8 ounce package sliced cremini mushrooms
- 3 minced garlic cloves, divided
- 1 tablespoon fresh thyme, chopped (add extra for garnish)
- 1 1/2 teaspoons fresh parsley, chopped (add extra for garnish)
- 1/4 cup dry sherry (or you can use red wine vinegar)
- 32 to 40 ounces beef tenderloin
- 1/2 cup bread crumbs, fresh whole wheat
- 1 teaspoon salt
- 1/2 teaspoon of black pepper

Directions:

1. Preheat your oven to 425degreesF.

2. Heat 2 tablespoons oil over medium heat and cook shallots for 5 minutes or until tender. Add mushrooms and stir-cook until it softens (about 8 minutes).

3. Stir in the garlic and herbs and cook for a minute more before adding the dry sherry. Reduce the sherry by half then remove and let it cool.

4. Cut the beef lengthwise resembling butterfly wings. Cover with plastic and pound using a mallet until ½-inch thick.

5. Stir in breadcrumbs in your mushroom mixture before spreading evenly onto the beef. Leave a 1-inch space around the edge.

6. Roll the beef jellyroll style and secure with kitchen string at one-inch interval. Place the rolled meat on a rack inside a shallow roasting pan.

7. Combine remaining ingredients and rub over the beef.

8. Roast beef for 35-40 minutes for medium rare or according to your desired doneness.

9. Let it cool 15-20 minutes with loosely tented foil before carving.

10. Serve with extra thyme and parsley.

Nutrition: Calories: 195 |Carbohydrates: 5 g |Fiber: 1 g |Fats: 9 g |Sodium: 381 mg |Protein: 21 g

Roasted Pork with Currant Sauce

Preparation Time: 10 minutes
Cooking Time: 1 hour
Serving: 6 (4 oz. serving)

Ingredients:

- 1 boneless pork loin roast (2 pounds)

Marinade:

- 1-1/2 cups orange juice
- 1/4 cup lemon juice
- 2 teaspoons minced fresh gingerroot
- 1 teaspoon minced garlic
- 1 teaspoon dried oregano
- 1 teaspoon ground cinnamon
- 1/2 teaspoon ground coriander
- 1 small onion, sliced

Currant Sauce:

- 1 shallot, chopped
- 1 teaspoon minced garlic
- 1 tablespoon butter
- 1 tablespoon all-purpose _our

- 1/2 cup reduced-sodium chicken broth
- 1/2 cup red currant jelly

Directions:

1.　Follow Steps 1 and 2 for Grilled Lamb Chops. Reserve 1 cup of the marinade.

2.　Bake 1 hour at 350degreesF or until inserted kitchen thermometer reads 160degrees. Let it cool for 10 minutes before slicing. Set aside.

3.　Sauté shallots and garlic in butter for a minute. Sprinkle flour and stir until blended. Gradually add the remaining ingredients and bring to a boil. Stir-cook for 2 minutes or until thick.

4.　Serve with pork.

Nutrition: Calories: 307 |Carbohydrates: 26 g |Fiber: 0 g |Fats: 9 g |Sodium: 115 mg |Protein: 30 g

Spicy Beef Sloppy Joes

Preparation Time: 20 minutes

Cooking Time: 8 hours

Servings: 12

Ingredients

- Lean ground beef – 2 lb.
- Lower-sodium salsa – 2 ½ cups
- Coarsely chopped fresh mushrooms – 3 cups
- Shredded carrots – 1 ¼ cups
- Finely chopped red and green sweet peppers – 1 ¼ cups
- No-salt added tomato paste – ½ (6-oz.) can
- Garlic – 4 cloves, minced
- Dried basil – 1 tsp. crushed
- Salt – ¾ tsp.
- Dried oregano – ½ tsp. crushed
- Cayenne pepper – ¼ tsp.
- Whole wheat hamburger buns – 12, split and toasted

Directions:

1.　Cook ground beef in a skillet until browned. Drain off fat.

2.　In a slow cooker, add the meat and combine the next 10 ingredients (through cayenne pepper).

3.　Cover and cook on low for 8 to 10 hours or on high for 4 to 5 hours.

4.　Spoon ½-cup of the meat mixture onto each bun.

5.　Serve.

Nutrition: Calories: 278 Fat: 8g Carb: 29g Protein: 20g

Roasted Steak and Tomato Salad

Preparation Time: 20 minutes

Cooking Time: 20 minutes

Servings: 4

Ingredients

- Beef tenderloin steaks – 2 (8 oz.), trimmed
- Cracked black pepper – 1 tsp.
- Kosher salt – ¼ tsp.
- Small tomatoes – 6, halved
- Olive oil – 2 tsps.
- Shredded Parmesan cheese – ¼ cup
- Dried oregano – ½ tsp. crushed
- Torn romaine lettuce – 8 cups
- Artichoke hearts – 1 (14-oz.) can, drained and quartered
- Red onion slivers – 1/3 cup
- Balsamic vinegar – 3 Tbsp.
- Olive oil – 1 Tbsp.

Directions:

1.　Preheat the oven to 400F.

2.　Season the meat with salt and pepper and rub. Let stand for 20 minutes at room temperature.

3.　Arrange tomato halves on a baking sheet (cut side down).

4.　Heat 2 tsps. oil in a skillet. Add meat and cook until well browned on all sides, about 8 minutes. Transfer meat to other side of baking sheet.

5.　Roast for 8 to 10 minutes for medium (145F). Remove meat from oven. Cover with foil and let stand. Move oven rack for broiling.

6.　Turn oven to broil. Turn tomatoes cut sides up. Combine oregano and Parmesan. Sprinkle over tomatoes. Broil 4 to 5 inches from heat for about 2 minutes, or until cheese is melted and golden.

7.　In a bowl, combine onion, artichoke hearts, and lettuce. Drizzle with vinegar and 1 tbsp. oil. Toss to coat.

8.　Arrange on plates. Slice steak and arrange over lettuce with tomato halves.

Nutrition: Calories: 299 Fat: 14g Carb: 16g Protein: 29g

Lamb Fatteh with Asparagus

Preparation Time: 10 minutes

Cooking Time: 20 minutes

Servings: 4

Ingredients

- Olive oil – 1 Tbsp.
- Medium onion – 1, sliced
- Garlic – 4 cloves, minced
- Boneless lamb leg – 12 oz. cut into smaller pieces
- 50% less sodium beef broth – 1 (14.5 oz.) can
- Whole wheat pearl couscous - 1 cup
- Dried oregano – ½ tsp. crushed
- Ground cumin – ½ tsp.
- Salt – ¼ tsp.
- Black pepper – ¼ tsp.
- Thin asparagus spears – 1 lb. sliced into 2-inch pieces
- Chopped red sweet pepper – ¾ cup
- Snipped fresh oregano and lemon wedges

Directions:

1. Heat oil in a skillet. Add onion and cook for 3 minutes.
2. Add garlic and cook for 1 minute.
3. Add lamb and cook until browned on all sides, about 3 to 5 minutes.
4. Stir in the next six ingredients (through black pepper). Bring to a boil. Lower heat and simmer, covered, for 10 minutes. Stirring occasionally.
5. Stir in sweet pepper and asparagus. Cover and simmer until vegetables are crisp-tender, about 3 to 5 minutes.
6. Fluff lamb mixture lightly with a fork. Top with fresh oregano.
7. Serve with lemon wedges.

Nutrition: Calories: 334 Fat: 9g Carb: 39g Protein: 26 g

Beef Goulash Soup

Preparation Time: 30 minutes

Cooking Time: 20 minutes

Servings: 4

Ingredients

- Boneless beef top sirloin steak – 6 oz.
- Olive oil – 1 tsp.
- Chopped onion – ½ cup
- Water – 2 cups
- Beef broth – 1 (14.5 oz.) can
- No-salt-added diced tomatoes – 1 (14.5 oz.) can, undrained
- Thinly sliced carrot – ½ cup
- Unsweetened cocoa powder – 1 tsp.
- Garlic – 1 clove, minced
- Thinly sliced cabbage – 1 cup
- Dried wide noodles – ½ cup
- Paprika – 2 tsps.
- Light sour cream – ¼ cup
- Snipped fresh parsley

Directions:

1. Cut meat into ½-inch cubes. In a saucepan, cook and stir meat in hot oil until browned, for about 6 minutes. Add onion, cook and stir until onion softens, about 3 minutes.
2. Stir in the next six ingredients (through garlic). Bring to a boil. Reduce heat. Simmer, uncovered, for about 15 minutes or until meat is tender.
3. Stir in paprika, noodles, and cabbage. Simmer, uncovered, until noodles are tender but still firm, for about 5 to 7 minutes. Remove from heat.
4. Top each serving with sour cream.
5. Sprinkle with parsley and additional paprika.
6. Serve.

Nutrition: Calories: 188 Fat: 7g Carb: 16g Protein: 14g

Beef-Vegetable Ragout

Preparation Time: 30 minutes

Cooking Time: 8 hours

Servings: 4

Ingredients

- Beef chuck roast – 1 ½ lb.
- Sliced fresh button or cremini mushrooms – 3 cups
- Chopped onion – 1 cup
- Garlic – 4 cloves, minced
- Salt – ½ tsp.

- Black pepper – ½ tsp.
- Quick-cooking tapioca -1/4 cup, crushed
- 50% less-sodium beef broth – 2 (14.5 oz.) cans
- Dry sherry – ½ cup
- Sugar snap pea pods – 4 cups
- Cherry tomatoes – 2 cups, halved
- Hot cooked multigrain noodles – 4 cups

Directions:

1. Cut meat into ¾-inch pieces.

2. Coat a skillet with cooking spray. Cook meat, half at a time, in the hot skillet until browned.

3. Combine the next five ingredients (through pepper) in a slow cooker. Sprinkle with tapioca. Add meat and pour in broth and dry sherry.

4. Cover and cook on low for 8 to 10 hours or high for 4 to 5 hours.

5. If slow cooker is on low, turn to high. Stir in sugar snap peas. Cover and cook for 5 minutes.

6. Stir in cherry tomatoes. Serve meat mixture over hot cooked noodles.

Nutrition: Calories: 208 Fat: 4g Carb: 19g Protein: 24g

Greek Flat Iron Steaks

Preparation Time: 10 minutes
Cooking Time: 15 minutes
Servings: 4

Ingredients

- Lemon – 1
- Boneless beef shoulder top blade steaks (flat iron) – 2 (6 to 8 oz.)
- Salt – ¼ tsp.
- Black pepper – ¼ tsp.
- Dried rosemary – 1 tsp. crushed
- Olive oil – 4 tsp.
- Grape tomatoes – 2 cups, halved
- Garlic – 2 cloves, minced
- Pitted green olives – 1/3 cup, halved
- Crumbled feta cheese – ¼ cup
- Lemon wedges

Directions:

1. Remove 1 tsp. zest from the lemon. Set zest aside. Cut steaks in half and season with salt and pepper. Sprinkle rosemary on both sides of the steaks.

2. Heat 2 tsps. oil in a skillet. Add steaks and cook until medium rare, about 8 to 10 minutes. Turning once. Remove and set aside.

3. Add remaining 2 tsps. oil to the skillet. Add garlic and tomatoes. Cook until tomatoes are soft and burst, for about 3 minutes. Remove from heat. Stir in the lemon zest and olives.

4. Serve steaks with tomato relish.

5. Sprinkle with cheese and serve with the reserved lemon wedges.

Nutrition: Calories: 223 Fat: 14g Carb: 6g Protein: 20g

Spiced Burgers with Cilantro Cucumber Sauce

Preparation Time: 25 minutes
Cooking Time: 15 minutes
Servings: 4

Ingredients

- Plain fat-free Greek yogurt – 1 (5.3 to 6 oz.) container
- Finely chopped cucumber – 2/3 cup
- Snipped fresh cilantro – ¼ cup
- Garlic – 2 cloves, minced
- Salt – 1/8 tsp.
- Black pepper – 1/8 tsp.
- Canned garbanzo beans – ½ cup, rinsed and drained
- Lean ground beef – 1 lb.
- Finely chopped red onion – ¼ cup
- Chopped jalapeno pepper – 2 Tbsps.
- Salt – ½ tsp.
- Ground cumin – ¼ tsp.
- Ground coriander – ¼ tsp.
- Cinnamon – 1/8 tsp.
- Black pepper – 1/8 tsp.
- Radicchio – 1 head, shredded

Directions:

1. To make the sauce: in a bowl, stir together the first six ingredients (through black pepper). Cover and keep in the refrigerator.

2. In a bowl, mash garbanzo beans with a fork. Add the next eight ingredients (through black pepper),

mix well. Form meat mixture into four ¾ inch thick patties.

3.   Grill burgers, covered, over medium 14 to 18 minutes or until done (160F). Turning once.

4.   Toss radicchio with additional fresh cilantro leaves.

5.   Serve burgers on radicchio, top with sauce.

Nutrition: Calories: 258 Fat: 12g Carb: 8g Protein: 29g

Pork Chops with Grape Sauce

Preparation Time: 15 minutes
Cooking Time: 25 minutes
Servings: 4

Ingredients:
- Cooking spray
- 4 pork chops
- ¼ cup onion, sliced
- 1 clove garlic, minced
- ½ cup low-sodium chicken broth
- ¾ cup apple juice
- 1 tablespoon cornstarch
- 1 tablespoon balsamic vinegar
- 1 teaspoon honey
- 1 cup seedless red grapes, sliced in half

Directions:
1.   Spray oil on your pan.
2.   Put it over medium heat.
3.   Add the pork chops to the pan.
4.   Cook for 5 minutes per side.
5.   Remove and set aside.
6.   Add onion and garlic.
7.   Cook for 2 minutes.
8.   Pour in the broth and apple juice.
9.   Bring to a boil.
10.   Reduce heat to simmer.
11.   Put the pork chops back to the skillet.
12.   Simmer for 4 minutes.
13.   In a bowl, mix the cornstarch, vinegar and honey.
14.   Add to the pan.
15.   Cook until the sauce has thickened.
16.   Add the grapes.
17.   Pour sauce over the pork chops before serving.

Nutrition: Calories 188 Fat 4 g Cholesterol 47 mg Sodium 117 mg Carbohydrate 18 g Fiber 1 g Protein 19 g

Roasted Pork & Apples

Preparation Time: 15 minutes
Cooking Time: 30 minutes
Servings: 4

Ingredients:
- Salt and pepper to taste
- ½ teaspoon dried, crushed
- 1 lb. pork tenderloin
- 1 tablespoon canola oil
- 1 onion, sliced into wedges
- 3 cooking apples, sliced into wedges
- 2/3 cup apple cider
- Sprigs fresh sage

Directions:
1.   In a bowl, mix salt, pepper and sage.
2.   Season both sides of pork with this mixture.
3.   Place a pan over medium heat.
4.   Brown both sides.
5.   Transfer to a roasting pan.
6.   Add the onion on top and around the pork.
7.   Drizzle oil on top of the pork and apples.
8.   Roast in the oven at 425 degrees F for 10 minutes.
9.   Add the apples, roast for another 15 minutes.
10.   In a pan, boil the apple cider and then simmer for 10 minutes.
11.   Pour the apple cider sauce over the pork before serving.

Nutrition: Calories 239 Fat 6 g Cholesterol 74 mg Carbohydrate 22 g Fiber 3 g Protein 24 g Potassium 655 mg

Pork with Cranberry Relish

Preparation Time: 30 minutes

Cooking Time: 30 minutes

Servings: 4

Ingredients:

- 12 oz. pork tenderloin, fat trimmed and sliced crosswise
- Salt and pepper to taste
- ¼ cup all-purpose flour
- 2 tablespoons olive oil
- 1 onion, sliced thinly
- ¼ cup dried cranberries
- ¼ cup low-sodium chicken broth
- 1 tablespoon balsamic vinegar

Directions:

1. Flatten each slice of pork using a mallet.
2. In a dish, mix the salt, pepper and flour.
3. Dip each pork slice into the flour mixture.
4. Add oil to a pan over medium high heat.
5. Cook pork for 3 minutes per side or until golden crispy.
6. Transfer to a serving plate and cover with foil.
7. Cook the onion in the pan for 4 minutes.
8. Stir in the rest of the ingredients.
9. Simmer until the sauce has thickened.

Nutrition: Calories 211 Fat 9 g Cholesterol 53 mg Carbohydrate 15 g Fiber 1 g Protein 18 g Potassium 378 mg

Irish Pork Roast

Preparation Time: 40 minutes

Cooking Time: 1 hour

Servings: 8

Ingredients:

- 1 ½ lb. parsnips, peeled and sliced into small pieces
- 1 ½ lb. carrots, sliced into small pieces
- 3 tablespoons olive oil, divided
- 2 teaspoons fresh thyme leaves, divided
- Salt and pepper to taste
- 2 lb. pork loin roast
- 1 teaspoon honey
- 1 cup dry hard cider
- Applesauce

Directions:

1. Preheat your oven to 400 degrees F.
2. Drizzle half of the oil over the parsnips and carrots.
3. Season with half of thyme, salt and pepper.
4. Arrange on a roasting pan.
5. Rub the pork with the remaining oil.
6. Season with the remaining thyme.
7. Season with salt and pepper.
8. Put it on the roasting pan on top of the vegetables.
9. Roast for 65 minutes.
10. Let cool before slicing.
11. Transfer the carrots and parsnips in a bowl and mix with honey.
12. Add the cider.
13. Place in a pan and simmer over low heat until the sauce has thickened.
14. Serve the pork with the vegetables and applesauce.

Nutrition: Calories 272 Fat 8 g Carbohydrate 23 g Fiber 6 g Protein 24 g Potassium 887 mg

Sesame Pork with Mustard Sauce

Preparation Time: 25 minutes

Cooking Time: 25 minutes

Servings: 4

Ingredients:

- 2 tablespoons low-sodium teriyaki sauce
- ¼ cup chili sauce
- 2 cloves garlic, minced
- 2 teaspoons ginger, grated
- 2 pork tenderloins
- 2 teaspoons sesame seeds
- ¼ cup low fat sour cream
- 1 teaspoon Dijon mustard
- Salt to taste
- 1 scallion, chopped

Directions:

1. Preheat your oven to 425 degrees F.

2. Mix the teriyaki sauce, chili sauce, garlic and ginger.
3. Put the pork on a roasting pan.
4. Brush the sauce on both sides of the pork.
5. Bake in the oven for 15 minutes.
6. Brush with more sauce.
7. Top with sesame seeds.
8. Roast for 10 more minutes.
9. Mix the rest of the ingredients.
10. Serve the pork with mustard sauce.

Nutrition: Calories 135 Fat 3 g Carbohydrate 7 g Fiber 1 g Sugars 15 g Protein 20 g Potassium 755 mg

Steak with Mushroom Sauce

Preparation Time: 20 minutes
Cooking Time: 5 minutes
Servings: 4
Ingredients:
- 12 oz. sirloin steak, sliced and trimmed
- 2 teaspoons grilling seasoning
- 2 teaspoons oil
- 6 oz. broccoli, trimmed
- 2 cups frozen peas
- 3 cups fresh mushrooms, sliced
- 1 cup beef broth (unsalted)
- 1 tablespoon mustard
- 2 teaspoons cornstarch
- Salt to taste

Directions:
1. Preheat your oven to 350 degrees F.
2. Season meat with grilling seasoning.
3. In a pan over medium high heat, cook the meat and broccoli for 4 minutes.
4. Sprinkle the peas around the steak.
5. Put the pan inside the oven and bake for 8 minutes.
6. Remove both meat and vegetables from the pan.
7. Add the mushrooms to the pan.
8. Cook for 3 minutes.
9. Mix the broth, mustard, salt and cornstarch.
10. Add to the mushrooms.
11. Cook for 1 minute.

12. Pour sauce over meat and vegetables before serving.

Nutrition: Calories 226 Fat 6 g Cholesterol 51 mg Sodium 356 mg Carbohydrate 16 g Fiber 5 g Protein 26 g

Steak with Tomato & Herbs

Preparation Time: 30 minutes
Cooking Time: 30 minutes
Servings: 2
Ingredients:
- 8 oz. beef loin steak, sliced in half
- Salt and pepper to taste
- Cooking spray
- 1 teaspoon fresh basil, snipped
- ¼ cup green onion, sliced
- ½ cup tomato, chopped

Directions:
1. Season the steak with salt and pepper.
2. Spray oil on your pan.
3. Put the pan over medium high heat.
4. Once hot, add the steaks.
5. Reduce heat to medium.
6. Cook for 10 to 13 minutes for medium, turning once.
7. Add the basil and green onion.
8. Cook for 2 minutes.
9. Add the tomato.
10. Cook for 1 minute.
11. Let cool a little before slicing.

Nutrition: Calories 170 Fat 6 g Cholesterol 66 mg Carbohydrate 3 g Fiber 1 g Sugars 5 g Protein 25 g

Barbecue Beef Brisket

Preparation Time: 25 minutes
Cooking Time: 10 hours
Servings: 10
Ingredients:
- 4 lb. beef brisket (boneless), trimmed and sliced
- 1 bay leaf
- 2 onions, sliced into rings
- ½ teaspoon dried thyme, crushed
- ¼ cup chili sauce

- 1 clove garlic, minced
- Salt and pepper to taste
- 2 tablespoons light brown sugar
- 2 tablespoons cornstarch
- 2 tablespoons cold water

Directions:
1. Put the meat in a slow cooker.
2. Add the bay leaf and onion.
3. In a bowl, mix the thyme, chili sauce, salt, pepper and sugar.
4. Pour the sauce over the meat.
5. Mix well.
6. Seal the pot and cook on low heat for 10 hours.
7. Discard the bay leaf.
8. Pour cooking liquid in a pan.
9. Add the mixed water and cornstarch.
10. Simmer until the sauce has thickened.
11. Pour the sauce over the meat.

Nutrition: Calories 182 Fat 6 g Cholesterol 57 mg Carbohydrate 9 g Fiber 1 g Sugars 4 g Protein 20 g Potassium 383 mg

Beef & Asparagus

Preparation Time: 15 minutes
Cooking Time: 10 minutes
Servings: 4

Ingredients:
- 2 teaspoons olive oil
- 1 lb. lean beef sirloin, trimmed and sliced
- 1 carrot, shredded
- Salt and pepper to taste
- 12 oz. asparagus, trimmed and sliced
- 1 teaspoon dried herbes de Provence, crushed
- ½ cup Marsala
- ¼ teaspoon lemon zest

Directions:
1. Pour oil in a pan over medium heat.
2. Add the beef and carrot.
3. Season with salt and pepper.
4. Cook for 3 minutes.
5. Add the asparagus and herbs.
6. Cook for 2 minutes.
7. Add the Marsala and lemon zest.

8. Cook for 5 minutes, stirring frequently.

Nutrition: Calories 327 Fat 7 g Cholesterol 69 mg Carbohydrate 29 g Fiber 2 g Sugars 3 g Protein 28 g

Italian Beef

Preparation Time: 20 minutes
Cooking Time: 1 hour and 20 minutes
Servings: 4

Ingredients:
- Cooking spray
- 1 lb. beef round steak, trimmed and sliced
- 1 cup onion, chopped
- 2 cloves garlic, minced
- 1 cup green bell pepper, chopped
- ½ cup celery, chopped
- 2 cups mushrooms, sliced
- 14 ½ oz. canned diced tomatoes
- ½ teaspoon dried basil
- ¼ teaspoon dried oregano
- 1/8 teaspoon crushed red pepper
- 2 tablespoons Parmesan cheese, grated

Directions:
1. Spray oil on the pan over medium heat.
2. Cook the meat until brown on both sides.
3. Transfer meat to a plate.
4. Add the onion, garlic, bell pepper, celery and mushroom to the pan.
5. Cook until tender.
6. Add the tomatoes, herbs, and pepper.
7. Put the meat back to the pan.
8. Simmer while covered for 1 hour and 15 minutes.
9. Stir occasionally.
10. Sprinkle Parmesan cheese on top of the dish before serving.

Nutrition: Calories 212 Fat 4 g Cholesterol 51 mg Carbohydrate 14 g Fiber 3 g Protein 30 g Potassium 876 mg

Lamb & Chickpeas

Preparation Time: 30 minutes
Cooking Time: 30 minutes
Servings: 4

Ingredients:

- 1 lb. lamb leg (boneless), trimmed and sliced into small pieces
- 2 tablespoons olive oil
- 1 teaspoon ground coriander
- Salt and pepper to taste
- ½ teaspoon ground cumin
- ¼ teaspoon red pepper, crushed
- ¼ cup fresh mint, chopped
- 2 teaspoons lemon zest
- 2 cloves garlic, minced
- 30 oz. unsalted chickpeas, rinsed and drained
- 1 cup tomatoes, chopped
- 1 cup English cucumber, chopped
- ¼ cup fresh parsley, snipped
- 1 tablespoon red wine vinegar

Directions:

1. Preheat your oven to 375 degrees F.
2. Place the lamb on a baking dish.
3. Toss in half of the following: oil, cumin and coriander.
4. Season with red pepper, salt and pepper.
5. Mix well.
6. Roast for 20 minutes.
7. In a bowl, combine the rest of the ingredients with the remaining seasonings.
8. Add salt and pepper.
9. Serve lamb with chickpea mixture.

Nutrition: Calories 366 Fat 15 g Cholesterol 74 mg Sodium 369 mg Carbohydrate 27 g Fiber 7 g Protein 32 g

Lamb with Broccoli & Carrots

Preparation Time: 20 minutes
Cooking Time: 10 minutes
Servings: 4

Ingredients:

- 2 cloves garlic, minced
- 1 tablespoon fresh ginger, grated
- ¼ teaspoon red pepper, crushed
- 2 tablespoons low-sodium soy sauce
- 1 tablespoon white vinegar
- 1 tablespoon cornstarch
- 12 oz. lamb meat, trimmed and sliced
- 2 teaspoons cooking oil
- 1 lb. broccoli, sliced into florets
- 2 carrots, sliced into strips
- ¾ cup low-sodium beef broth
- 4 green onions, chopped
- 2 cups cooked spaghetti squash pasta

Directions:

1. Combine the garlic, ginger, red pepper, soy sauce, vinegar and cornstarch in a bowl.
2. Add lamb to the marinade.
3. Marinate for 10 minutes.
4. Discard marinade.
5. In a pan over medium heat, add the oil.
6. Add the lamb and cook for 3 minutes.
7. Transfer lamb to a plate.
8. Add the broccoli and carrots.
9. Cook for 1 minute.
10. Pour in the beef broth.
11. Cook for 5 minutes.
12. Put the meat back to the pan.
13. Sprinkle with green onion and serve on top of spaghetti squash.

Nutrition: Calories 205 Fat 6 g Cholesterol 40 mg Carbohydrate 17 g Fiber 4 g Protein 22 g

Braised Lamb with Vegetables

Preparation Time: 30 minutes
Cooking Time: 2 hours and 15 minutes
Servings: 6

Ingredients:

- Salt and pepper to taste
- 2 ½ lb. boneless lamb leg, trimmed and sliced into cubes
- 1 tablespoon olive oil
- 1 onion, chopped
- 1 carrot, chopped
- 14 oz. canned diced tomatoes

- 1 cup low-sodium beef broth
- 1 tablespoon fresh rosemary, chopped
- 4 cloves garlic, minced
- 1 cup pearl onions
- 1 cup baby turnips, peeled and sliced into wedges
- 1 ½ cups baby carrots
- 1 ½ cups peas
- 2 tablespoons fresh parsley, chopped

Directions:

1. Sprinkle salt and pepper on both sides of the lamb.
2. Pour oil in a deep skillet.
3. Cook the lamb for 6 minutes.
4. Transfer lamb to a plate.
5. Add onion and carrot.
6. Cook for 3 minutes.
7. Stir in the tomatoes, broth, rosemary and garlic.
8. Simmer for 5 minutes.
9. Add the lamb back to the skillet.
10. Reduce heat to low.
11. Simmer for 1 hour and 15 minutes.
12. Add the pearl onion, baby carrot and baby turnips.
13. Simmer for 30 minutes.
14. Add the peas.
15. Cook for 1 minute.
16. Garnish with parsley before serving.

Nutrition: Calories 420 Fat 14 g Cholesterol 126 mg Carbohydrate 16 g Fiber 4 g Protein 43 g

Rosemary Lamb

Preparation Time: 15 minutes
Cooking Time: 2 hours
Servings: 14

Ingredients:

- Salt and pepper to taste
- 2 teaspoons fresh rosemary, snipped
- 5 lb. whole leg of lamb, trimmed and cut with slits on all sides
- 3 cloves garlic, slivered
- 1 cup water

Directions:

1. Preheat your oven to 375 degrees F.
2. Mix salt, pepper and rosemary in a bowl.
3. Sprinkle mixture all over the lamb.
4. Insert slivers of garlic into the slits.
5. Put the lamb on a roasting pan.
6. Add water to the pan.
7. Roast for 2 hours.

Nutrition: Calories 136 Fat 4 g Cholesterol 71 mg Sodium 218 mg Protein 23 g Potassium 248 mg

Mediterranean Lamb Meatballs

Preparation Time: 10 minutes
Cooking Time: 20 minutes
Servings: 8

Ingredients:

- 12 oz. roasted red peppers
- 1 ½ cups whole wheat breadcrumbs
- 2 eggs, beaten
- 1/3 cup tomato sauce
- ½ cup fresh basil
- ¼ cup parsley, snipped
- Salt and pepper to taste
- 2 lb. lean ground lamb

Directions:

1. Preheat your oven to 350 degrees F.
2. In a bowl, mix all the ingredients and then form into meatballs.
3. Put the meatballs on a baking pan.
4. Bake in the oven for 20 minutes.

Nutrition: Calories 94 Fat 3 g Cholesterol 35 mg Sodium 170 mg Carbohydrate 2 g Fiber 1 g Protein 14 g

Blackberry Pulled Pork Shoulder

Preparation Time: 15 minutes
Cooking Time: 8–10 hours
Servings: 10–12 servings

Ingredients:

- ¼ cup brown sugar
- ½ tsp. red pepper
- 1 big onion, chopped
- 1 tsp. apple cider vinegar
- 1 tsp. salt
- 2 pints fresh blackberries

- 2 tsp. garlic powder
- 2–3-lb. pork shoulder

Directions:

1. Put the pork shoulder in the Slow Cooker and layer the onion on top.
2. Puree the blackberries and pass them through a sieve or strainer to separate the puree from the seeds.
3. Combine the residual ingredients with the blackberry puree.
4. Pour the blackberry puree over the contents of the Slow Cooker.
5. Cover and Cook on Low for approximately for 8–10 hours.
6. Take out the roast and shred by pulling using two forks. Mix back into the liquid in the Slow Cooker.
7. Serve on buns.

Nutrition Calories 218 Fat 12 gm. Cholesterol 60 mg Sodium 241 mg Potassium 485 gm. Carb 8 gm. Protein 6 gm

Bubble and Squeak

Preparation Time: 15–20 minutes
Cooking Time: 45 minutes
Servings: 8

Ingredients:

- 1/3 cup vinegar, optional
- ½ head cabbage, sliced thin
- 1 onion, diced
- 12 oz. reduced-fat bulk sausage
- 4 moderate potatoes, sliced thin
- cheese of your choice, sliced or grated, optional

Directions:

1. Fry onion and sausage together in a deep iron frying pan until no pink remains in meat. Stir regularly to break up clumps of meat.
2. Mix in potatoes. Keep on cooking over low heat until potatoes begin to become soft. Stir often to prevent sticking and burning, but let potatoes brown.
3. Mix in cut cabbage. Keep on cooking until cabbage wilts and potatoes are soft.
4. Mix in vinegar if you wish. Cook a few minutes to mix flavors.

5. Cover contents of frying pan with cheese if you wish. Allow toss and a few minutes until cheese melts.

Nutrition Calories 185 Fat 6 gm Cholesterol 20 mg Sodium 225 mg Potassium 540 gm Carb 22 gm Fiber 3 gm Protein 9 gm

Cranberry Pork Roast

Preparation Time: 20 minutes
Cooking Time: 8–10 hours
Servings: 9

Ingredients:

- 1/8 tsp. ground cloves
- 1/8 tsp. ground nutmeg
- 1 cup ground, or finely chopped, cranberries
- 1 tsp. grated orange peel
- 2¾-lb. boneless pork roast, trimmed of fat
- 3 Tbsp. honey

Directions:

1. Place roast in Crock Pot.
2. Mix residual ingredients. Pour over roast.
3. Cover. Cook on Low for approximately 8–10 hours.

Nutrition Calories 214 Fat 9 gm Cholesterol 63 mg Sodium 37 mg Carb 7 gm Fiber 1 gm Sugars 7 gm Protein 25 gm

Crock Pork Tenderloin

Preparation Time: 5–15 minutes
Cooking Time: 4 hours
Servings: 6

Ingredients:

- ¾ cup red wine
- 1 cup water
- 1 envelope salt-free onion soup mix
- 2-lb. pork soft loin, cut in half lengthwise, visible fat removed
- 3 Tbsp. light soy sauce
- 6 cloves garlic, peeled and chopped
- freshly ground pepper

Directions:

1. Place pork softloin pieces in Crock Pot. Pour water, wine, and soy sauce over pork.

2.   Turn pork over in liquid several times to totally moisten.

3.   Drizzle with dry onion soup mix. Top with chopped garlic and pepper.

4.   Cover. Cook on Low for approximately 4 hours.

Nutrition Calories 220 Fat 4 gm Cholesterol 115 mg Sodium 370 mg Carb 6 gm Fiber 0 gm Sugars 2 gm Protein 37 gm

Epicurean Pork Chops

Preparation Time: 15–20 minutes
Cooking Time: 60–75 minutes
Servings: 6
Ingredients:
* ¼ tsp. salt
* ½ cup whole wheat panko bread crumbs
* ¾ cup water
* 1 tsp. dried rosemary, crushed
* 1 tsp. ground ginger
* 10½-oz. can lower-sodium, lower-fat cream of chicken soup
* 2 Tbsp. flour
* 2 Tbsp. vegetable oil
* 6 loin pork chops, ½-inch thick
* dash pepper

Directions:
1.   Place oil in good-sized frying pan.
2.   Mix flour, salt, and pepper in shallow but wide dish.
3.   Dredge chops in mixture one at a time.
4.   Place 2 or 3 chops in oil in frying pan at a time, being cautious not to crowd frying pan. Brown chops over moderate to high heat, 3–4 minutes on each side, until a browned crust forms.
5.   As chops brown, place in thoroughly -oil-coated 7×11-inch baking dish.
6.   In vessel, mix soup, water, ginger, and rosemary.
7.   Pour over chops.
8.   Drizzle with half the panko bread crumbs.
9.   Cover. Bake at 350°F for 50–60 minutes, or until chops are soft but not dry.
10.   Uncover. Drizzle with residual panko bread crumbs.

11.   Bake with an open lid 10–15 minutes. Take out from oven and serve.

Nutrition Calories 215 Fat 10 gm Cholesterol 50 mg Sodium 315 mg Potassium 465 gm Carb 11 gm Fiber 1 gm Protein 18 gm

Flawless Pork Chops

Preparation Time: 20 minutes
Cooking Time: 3–4 hours
Servings: 2
Ingredients:
* ¼ cup hot water
* ½ lb. boneless, center loin pork chops, frozen, trimmed of fat
* ¾ tsp. reduced-sodium bouillon granules
* 2 small onions
* 2 Tbsp. prepared mustard with white wine
* fresh ground pepper, to taste
* fresh parsley sprigs, or lemon slices, optional

Directions:
1.   Chop off ends of onions and peel. Chop onions in half crosswise to make 4 thick wheels. Place in bottom of Crock Pot.
2.   Sear both sides of frozen chops in heavy frying pan. Place in cooker on top of onions. Drizzle with pepper.
3.   Dissolve bouillon in hot water. Mix in mustard. Pour into Crock Pot.
4.   Cover. Cook on High heat for approximately 3–4 hours.
5.   Serve topped with fresh parsley sprigs or lemon slices, if desired.

Nutrition Calories Fat 8 gm Cholesterol 51 mg Sodium 392 mg Carb 11 gm Fiber 2 gm Protein 22 gm

Glazed Ham Balls

Preparation Time: 20 minutes
Baking Time: 50 minutes
Servings: 20
Ingredients:
* 1/8 cup chopped onion
* ¼ tsp. pepper, optional
* ½ cup cooked lower-sodium ground ham

- ½ cup egg substitute
- ½ cup ketchup, or milk
- ¾ cup bread crumbs, or crushed saltine crackers
- 1 lb. 50%-reduced-fat bulk sausage
- 1 Tbsp. vinegar
- 22/3 Tbsp. Splenda Brown Sugar Blend
- 2–3 Tbsp. prepared mustard
- 8-oz. can (1 cup) crushed pineapple, undrained

Directions:

1. In a mixing vessel, combine pineapple, Splenda, vinegar, and mustard. Set aside.

2. In a big mixing vessel, completely mix sausage, ham, bread crumbs, egg substitute, ketchup, and onion.

3. Shape into 20 1½-inch balls. Place in thoroughly -oil-coated shallow baking dish.

4. Spoon pineapple mixture over ham balls.

5. Cover. Bake at 350°F for 25 minutes.

6. Uncover. Keep on baking for 25 more minutes.

Nutrition Calories 100 Total Fat 4 gm Cholesterol 15 mg
Sodium 335 mg Carb 8 gm Fiber 0 gm Protein 7 gm

Ham in Cider

Preparation Time: 20 minutes
Cooking Time: 8½–10½ hours
Servings: 8

Ingredients:

- ¼ cup brown sugar substitute to equal ¼ cup sugar
- 1 cup golden raisins
- 1 tsp. ground cloves
- 2 tsp. dry mustard
- 3-lb. boneless, precooked extra-lean, lower-sodium ham, trimmed of fat
- 4 cups sweet cider, or apple juice

Directions:

1. Place ham and cider in Crock Pot.

2. Cover. Cook on Low for approximately 8–10 hours.

3. Take out ham from cider and place in baking pan.

4. Prepare a paste of sugar, mustard, cloves, and a little hot cider. Coat over ham. Pour ½ cup of juice from Crock Pot into baking pan. Mix in raisins.

5. Bake at 375°F for approximately half an hour, until the paste has turned into a glaze.

Nutrition Calories 255 Fat 3 gm Cholesterol 67 mg Sodium 1194 mg Carb 31 gm Fiber 1 gm Protein 27 gm

Ham-Potatoes Green Bean Casserole

Preparation Time: 45 minutes
Cooking Time: half an hour
Servings: 12

Ingredients:

- ½ cup flour
- 1 cup panko bread crumbs
- 1¼ cups grated 50%-reduced fat cheddar cheese
- 2 lbs. fresh green beans with ends nipped off, or 2 16-oz. pkgs. frozen green beans, steamed or microwaved until just-tender
- 3 cups diced lower-sodium cooked ham
- 3 cups fat-free milk
- 3 Tbsp. trans-fat-free tub margarine
- 5 moderate-sized potatoes, cooked and sliced thin

Directions:

1. Melt margarine in saucepan.

2. Mix in flour.

3. Progressively stir in milk. Stir constantly while cooking over low heat until mixture thickens.

4. Put in cheese and stir until it melts.

5. Position potatoes in thoroughly -oil-coated 9×13-inch baking dish.

6. Drain any liquid off green beans. Spread beans over potatoes.

7. Pour half of cheese sauce over beans.

8. Spread ham over sauce.

9. Pour residual sauce over all.

10. Scatter panko crumbs over casserole.

11. Bake at 350°F for approximately half an hour, or until heated through.

Nutrition Calories 235 Fat 6 gm Cholesterol 25 mg Sodium 455 mg Potassium 565 gm Carb 31 gm Fiber 4 gm Protein 16 gm

Kielbasa and Cabbage

Preparation Time: 35 minutes
Cooking Time: 7–8 hours
Servings: 6

Ingredients:

- ½ tsp. pepper
- 2/3 cup dry white wine
- ¾ tsp. caraway seeds
- 1 lb. low-fat Polish kielbasa, cut into 3-inch pieces
- 1 red bell pepper, chopped
- 1 Tbsp. Dijon mustard
- 1½-lb. head green cabbage, shredded
- 2 moderate onions, chopped
- 2 cloves garlic, minced
- 28-oz. can diced no-added-salt tomatoes with juice
- 3 moderate red potatoes, peeled and cubed

Directions:

1. Mix all ingredients in Crock Pot.
2. Cover. Cook on Low for approximately 7–8 hours, or until cabbage is soft.

Nutrition Calories 226 Fat 4 gm Cholesterol 35 mg Sodium 781 mg Carb 34 gm Fiber 7 gm Protein 14 gm

Polish Kraut & Apples

Preparation Time: 25 minutes
Cooking Time: 3–7 hours
Servings: 6

Ingredients:

- 1/8 tsp. pepper
- ½ tsp. caraway seeds, optional
- ¾ cup apple juice, or cider
- 1 lb. fresh, or canned, sauerkraut, divided
- 1 lb. lean low-fat, smoked Polish sausage
- 2 Tbsp. brown sugar substitute to equal 3 Tbsp. sugar
- 3 tart cooking apples, unpeeled, thinly sliced

Directions:

1. Rinse sauerkraut and squeeze dry. Place half in Crock Pot.

2. Chop sausage into 2-inch lengths and add to cooker.
3. Keep on to layer residual ingredients in Crock Pot in order given. Top with residual sauerkraut. Do not stir.
4. Cover. Cook on High heat for approximately 3–3½ hours, or Low 6–7 hours. Stir before serving.

Nutrition Calories 195 Fat 4 gm Cholesterol 35 mg Sodium 945 mg Carb 31 gm Fiber 4 gm Protein 10 gm

Applesauce Meatloaf

Preparation Time: 15 minutes
Baking Time: 40–60 minutes
Servings: 8

Ingredients:

- ¼ cup chopped onion
- ¼ cup egg substitute
- ½ cup unsweetened applesauce
- ¾ cup dry oatmeal
- 1 tsp. salt
- 1½ Tbsp. chili powder
- 2 lbs. 95%-lean ground beef
- dash pepper

Directions:

1. Mix ground beef, dry oatmeal, egg substitute, applesauce, onion, salt, pepper, and chili powder in a good-sized mixing vessel.
2. Shape into a loaf. Place in 5×9-inch oil-coated loaf pan.
3. Bake at 350°F for approximately 40–60 minutes, or until meat thermometer shows 160°F in center of loaf.
4. Let stand 10 minutes before slicing to allow meat to gather its juices and firm up.

Nutrition Calories 200 Total Fat 6 gm Cholesterol 70 mg
Sodium 395 mg Potassium 480 gm Carb 8 gm Fiber 2 gm Protein 26 gm

Beef Burgundy

Preparation Time: 20 minutes
Cooking Time: 2¾–3 hours
Servings: 6

Ingredients:

- ½ lb. fresh mushrooms, sliced, or canned and drained
- ½ tsp. marjoram
- ½ tsp. sugar
- 1 cup chopped green onions
- 2 cloves garlic
- 2 cups burgundy
- 2 lbs. lean stewing beef cubes, trimmed of visible fat
- 6-oz. can tomato paste

Directions:

1. Sauté beef in nonstick Dutch oven with sliced green onions and garlic.
2. Add burgundy. Cover and simmer for approximately 2 hours or until soft but not dry.
3. Mix in marjoram and sliced mushrooms.
4. Cover and simmer for an additional 30 minutes.
5. Put in tomato paste and sugar.
6. Simmer with an open lid until lightly thickened.

Nutrition Calories 220 Fat 6 gm Cholesterol 80 mg Sodium 300 mg Potassium 835 gm Carb 8 gm Fiber 2 gm Protein 32 gm

Beef Burgundy with Bacon

Preparation Time: 25 minutes
Cooking Time: 6¼–8¼ hours
Servings: 6

Ingredients:

- 1/8 tsp. salt
- ¼ cup flour
- ¼ lb. fresh mushrooms, sliced
- ¼ tsp. dried marjoram
- ¼ tsp. dried thyme
- ¼ tsp. pepper
- ½ tsp. seasoning salt
- 1 beef bouillon cube, crushed
- 1 clove garlic, minced
- 1 cup burgundy wine
- 1 slice bacon, cut in squares
- 1 tsp. canola oil
- 2 lbs. sirloin tip or round steak, cubed, trimmed of fat
- 2 Tbsp. cold water
- 2 Tbsp. cornstarch

Directions:

1. Cook bacon in frying pan until browned. Take out bacon.
2. Cover beef with flour and brown on all sides in canola oil.
3. Mix steak, bacon drippings, bacon, seasonings, garlic, bouillon, and wine in Crock Pot.
4. Cover. Cook on Low for approximately 6–8 hours.
5. Put in mushrooms.
6. Combine cornstarch in water. Add to Crock Pot.
7. Cover. Cook on High heat for approximately 15 minutes.
8. Serve over noodles.

Nutrition Calories 202 Fat 7 gm Cholesterol 76 mg Sodium 389 mg Carb 8 gm Fiber 0 gm Protein 25 gm

Beefy Pie

Preparation Time: 15 minutes
Cooking/Baking Time: 50 minutes
Servings: 6

Ingredients:

- ½ cup shredded reduced-fat sharp cheddar cheese, divided
- ¾ cup beef broth (canned, or boxed, or your own homemade)
- ¾ cup fat-free sour cream
- 1 lb. 95%-lean ground beef
- 1¼ lb. red potatoes, unpeeled and cut in chunks
- 2 Tbsp. flour
- 2 Tbsp. ketchup
- 3 cloves garlic
- 4 cups fresh vegetables of your choice (for example, carrots, corn, green beans, peas)

Directions:

1. In saucepan, cook potatoes and garlic in 1½-inch boiling water for approximately 20 minutes, or until potatoes are soft.

2. In the meantime, brown beef in big nonstick frying pan.

3. Mix in flour. Cook 1 minute.

4. Mix in vegetables, broth, and ketchup. Cover. Cook 10 minutes, stirring regularly.

5. Drain cooked potatoes and garlic. Throw them back into their pan.

6. Mix in sour cream. Mash until potatoes are smooth and mixture is thoroughly blended.

7. Stir ¼ cup cheddar cheese into mashed potatoes.

8. Spoon meat mixture into thoroughly -oil-coated 8×8-inch baking dish.

9. Add a layer of mashed potatoes on top.

10. Bake at 375°F for 18 minutes.

11. Top with residual cheddar cheese. Bake 2 minutes more, or until cheese is melted.

Nutrition Calories 310 Fat 7 gm Cholesterol 55 mg Sodium 360 mg Potassium 890 gm Carb 41 gm Fiber 5 gm Sugars 7 gm

Protein 24 gm

Conventional Beef Pot Roast

Preparation time: half an hour
Cooking Time: 10–12 hours
Servings: 8

Ingredients:
- ½ cup boiling water
- ½ tsp. pepper
- 1 moderate onion, sliced
- 1 bouillon cube
- 1 tsp. salt
- 3–4-lb. rump roast, or pot roast, bone removed, and cut into serving-size pieces, trimmed of fat
- 4 moderate carrots, sliced
- 4 moderate potatoes, cubed

Directions:
1. Put vegetables and meat in Crock Pot. Sprinkle with salt and pepper and stir until mixed.

2. Dissolve bouillon cube in water, and then pour over the rest of the ingredients.

3. Cover. Cook on Low for approximately for approximately 10–12 hours.

Nutrition Calories 246 Total Fat 6 gm Cholesterol 73 mg Sodium 485 mgCarb 20 gm Fiber 3 gm Protein 27 gm

Air Fried Beef Schnitzel

Preparation Time: 10 minutes
Cooking Time: 15 minutes
Servings: 1

Ingredients:
- One lean beef schnitzel
- Olive oil: 2 tablespoon
- Breadcrumbs: ¼ cup
- One egg
- One lemon, to serve

Directions:
1. Let the air fryer heat to 180 C.

2. In a big bowl, add breadcrumbs and oil, mix well until forms a crumbly mixture

3. Dip beef steak in whisked egg and coat in breadcrumbs mixture.

4. Place the breaded beef in the air fryer and cook at 180C for 15 minutes or more until fully cooked through.

5. Take out from the air fryer and serve with the side of salad greens and lemon.

Nutrition: Calories 340 Proteins 20g Carbs 14g Fat 10gFiber 7g

Air Fryer Meatloaf

Preparation Time: 10 minutes
Cooking Time: 40 minutes
Servings: 8

Ingredients:
- Ground lean beef: 4 cups
- Bread crumbs: 1 cup (soft and fresh)
- Chopped mushrooms: ½ cup
- Cloves of minced garlic
- Shredded carrots: ½ cup
- Beef broth: ¼ cup
- Chopped onions: ½ cup
- Two eggs beaten

- Ketchup: 3 Tbsp.
- Worcestershire sauce: 1 Tbsp.
- Dijon mustard: 1 Tbsp.

For Glaze
- Honey: ¼ cup
- Ketchup: half cup
- Dijon mustard: 2 tsp

Directions:

1. In a big bowl, add beef broth and breadcrumbs, stir well. And set it aside in a food processor, add garlic, onions, mushrooms, and carrots, and pulse on high until finely chopped

2. In a separate bowl, add soaked breadcrumbs, Dijon mustard, Worcestershire sauce, eggs, lean ground beef, ketchup, and salt. With your hands, combine well and make it into a loaf.

3. Let the air fryer preheat to 390 F.

4. Put Meatloaf in the Air Fryer and let it cook for 45 minutes.

5. In the meantime, add Dijon mustard, ketchup, and brown sugar in a bowl and mix. Glaze this mix over Meatloaf when five minutes are left.

6. Rest the Meatloaf for ten minutes before serving.

Nutrition: Calories 330 Proteins 19g Carbs 16 Fat 9.9 g

Air Fried Steak with Asparagus Bundles

Preparation Time: 20 minutes

Cooking Time: 30 minutes

Servings: 2

Ingredients:
- Olive oil spray
- Flank steak (2 pounds)- cut into 6 pieces
- Kosher salt and black pepper
- Two cloves of minced garlic
- Asparagus: 4 cups
- Tamari sauce: half cup
- Three bell peppers: sliced thinly
- Beef broth: 1/3 cup
- 1 Tbsp. of unsalted butter
- Balsamic vinegar: 1/4 cup

Directions:

1. Sprinkle salt and pepper on steak and rub.

2. In a Ziploc bag, add garlic and Tamari sauce, then add steak, toss well and seal the bag.

3. Let it marinate for one hour to overnight.

4. Equally, place bell peppers and asparagus in the center of the steak.

5. Roll the steak around the vegetables and secure well with toothpicks.

6. Preheat the air fryer.

7. Spray the steak with olive oil spray. And place steaks in the air fryer.

8. Cook for 15 minutes at 400 degrees or more till steaks are cooked

9. Take the steak out from the air fryer and let it rest for five minute

10. Remove steak bundles and allow them to rest for 5 minutes before serving/slicing.

11. In the meantime, add butter, balsamic vinegar, and broth over medium flame. Mix well and reduce it by half. Add salt and pepper to taste.

12. Pour over steaks right before serving.

Nutrition: Calories 47 Proteins 29g Carbs 20g Fat 15g

Air Fryer Hamburgers

Preparation Time: 5 minutes

Cooking Time: 13 minutes

Servings: 4

Ingredients:
- Buns:4
- Lean ground beef chuck: 4 cups
- Salt to taste
- Slices of any cheese: 4 slices
- Black Pepper, to taste

Directions:

1. Let the air fryer preheat to 350 F.

2. In a bowl, add lean ground beef, pepper, and salt. Mix well and form patties.

3. Put them in the air fryer in one layer only, cook for 6 minutes, flip them halfway through. One minute before you take out the patties, add cheese on top.

4. When cheese is melted, take out from the air fryer.

5. Add ketchup, any dressing to your buns, add tomatoes and lettuce and patties.

6.   Serve hot.

Nutrition: Calories: 520kcalCarbohydrates: 22gProtein: 31gFat: 34g

Air Fryer Beef Steak Kabobs with Vegetables

Preparation Time: 30 minutes

Cooking Time: 10 minutes

Servings: 4

Ingredients:

* Light Soy sauce: 2 tbsp.
* Lean beef chuck ribs: 4 cups, cut into one-inch pieces
* Low-fat sour cream: 1/3 cup
* Half onion
* 8 skewers: 6 inch
* One bell peppers

Directions:

1.   In a mixing bowl, add soy sauce and sour cream, mix well. Add the lean beef chunks, coat well, and let it marinate for half an hour or more.

2.   Cut onion, bell pepper into one-inch pieces. In water, soak skewers for ten minutes.

3.   Add onions, bell peppers, and beef on skewers; alternatively, sprinkle with Black Pepper

4.   Let it cook for 10 minutes in a preheated air fryer at 400F, flip halfway through.

5.   Serve with yogurt dipping sauce.

Nutrition: Calories 268 Proteins 20g Carbs 15 Fat 10g

Air Fried Empanadas

Preparation Time: 10 minutes

Cooking Time: 20 minutes

Servings: 2

Ingredients:

* Square gyoza wrappers: eight pieces
* Olive oil: 1 tablespoon
* White onion: 1/4 cup, finely diced
* Mushrooms: 1/4 cup, finely diced
* Half cup lean ground beef
* Chopped garlic: 2 teaspoons
* Paprika: 1/4 teaspoon
* Ground cumin: 1/4 teaspoon

* Six green olives, diced
* Ground cinnamon: 1/8 teaspoon
* Diced tomatoes: half cup
* One egg, lightly beaten

Directions:

1.   In a skillet, over a medium flame, add oil, onions, and beef and cook for 3 minutes, until beef turns brown.

2.   Add mushrooms and cook for six minutes until it starts to brown. Then add paprika, cinnamon, olives, cumin, and garlic and cook for 3 minutes or more.

3.   Add in the chopped tomatoes, and cook for a minute. Turn off the heat; let it cool for five minutes.

4.   Lay gyoza wrappers on a flat surface add one and a half tbsp. of beef filling in each wrapper. Brush edges with water or egg, fold wrappers, and pinch edges.

5.   Put four empanadas in an even layer in an air fryer basket, and cook for 7 minutes at 400°F until nicely browned.

6.   Serve with sauce and salad greens.

Nutrition: Calories 343 Fat 19g Protein 18g Carbohydrate 12.9g

Air Fry Rib-Eye Steak

Preparation Time: 5 minutes

Cooking Time: 14 minutes

Servings: 2

Ingredients:

* Lean rib eye steaks: 2 medium-sized
* Salt & freshly ground black pepper, to taste

Directions:

1.   Let the air fry preheat at 400 F. pat dry steaks with paper towels.

2.   Use any spice blend or just salt and pepper on steaks.

3.   Generously on both sides of the steak.

4.   Put steaks in the air fryer basket. Cook according to the rareness you want. Or cook for 14 minutes and flip after half time.

5.   Take out from the air fryer and let it rest for about 5 minutes.

6.   Serve with micro green salad.

Nutrition: Calories: 470kcal Protein: 45g Fat: 31g Carbs: 23g

Sunday Pot Roast

Preparation Time: 10 minutes

Cooking Time: 105 minutes

Servings: 10

Ingredients:

- 1 (3- to 4-pound / 1.4- to 1.8-kg) beef rump roast
- 2 teaspoons kosher salt, divided
- 2 tablespoons avocado oil
- 1 large onion, coarsely chopped (about 1½ cups)
- 4 large carrots, each cut into 4 pieces
- 1 tablespoon minced garlic
- 3 cups low-sodium beef broth
- 1 teaspoon freshly ground black pepper
- 1 tablespoon dried parsley
- 2 tablespoons all-purpose flour

Directions:

1. Rub the roast all over with 1 teaspoon of the salt.
2. Set the electric pressure cooker to the Sauté setting. When the pot is hot, pour in the avocado oil.
3. Carefully place the roast in the pot and sear it for 6 to 9 minutes on each side. (You want a dark caramelized crust.) Hit Cancel.
4. Transfer the roast from the pot to a plate.
5. In order, put the onion, carrots, and garlic in the pot. Place the roast on top of the vegetables along with any juices that accumulated on the plate.
6. In a medium bowl, whisk together the broth, remaining 1 teaspoon of salt, pepper, and parsley. Pour the broth mixture over the roast.
7. Close and lock the lid of the pressure cooker. Set the valve to sealing.
8. Cook on high pressure for 1 hour and 30 minutes.
9. When the cooking is complete, hit Cancel and allow the pressure to release naturally.
10. Once the pin drops, unlock and remove the lid.
11. Using large slotted spoons transfer the roast and vegetables to a serving platter while you make the gravy.
12. Using a large spoon or fat separator, remove the fat from the juices in the pot. Set the electric pressure cooker to the Sauté setting and bring the liquid to a boil.
13. In a small bowl, whisk together the flour and 4 tablespoons of water to make slurry. Pour the slurry into the pot, whisking occasionally, until the gravy is the thickness you like. Season with salt and pepper, if necessary.
14. Serve the meat and carrots with the gravy.

Nutrition: Calories: 245 Fat: 10g Protein: 33g Carbs: 6g Sugars: 2g Fiber: 1g Sodium: 397mg

Rosemary Lamb Chops

Preparation Time: 25 minutes

Cooking Time: 10 minutes

Servings: 4

Ingredients:

- 1½ pounds (680 g) lamb chops (4 small chops)
- 1 teaspoon kosher salt
- Leaves from 1 (6-inch) rosemary sprig
- 2 tablespoons avocado oil
- 1 shallot, peeled and cut in quarters
- 1 tablespoon tomato paste
- 1 cup beef broth

Directions:

1. Place the lamb chops on a cutting board. Press the salt and rosemary leaves into both sides of the chops. Let rest at room temperature for 15 to 30 minutes.
2. Set the electric pressure cooker to Sauté/More setting. When hot, add the avocado oil.
3. Brown the lamb chops, about 2 minutes per side. (If they don't all fit in a single layer, brown them in batches.)
4. Transfer the chops to a plate. In the pot, combine the shallot, tomato paste, and broth. Cook for about a minute, scraping up the brown bits from the bottom. Hit Cancel.
5. Add the chops and any accumulated juices back to the pot.
6. Close and lock the lid of the pressure cooker. Set the valve to sealing.
7. Cook on high pressure for 2 minutes.
8. When the cooking is complete, hit Cancel and quick release the pressure.
9. Once the pin drops, unlock and remove the lid.

10. Place the lamb chops on plates and serve immediately.

Nutrition: Calories: 233 Fat: 18g Protein: 15g Carbs: 1g Sugars: 1g Fiber: 0g Sodium: 450mg

Roasted Pork Loin

Preparation Time: 5 minutes
Cooking Time: 40 minutes
Servings: 4

Ingredients:
- 1 pound (454 g) pork loin
- 1 tablespoon extra-virgin olive oil, divided
- 2 teaspoons honey
- ¼ teaspoon freshly ground black pepper
- ½ teaspoon dried rosemary
- 2 small gold potatoes, chopped into 2-inch cubes
- 4 (6-inch) carrots, chopped into ½-inch rounds

Directions:
1. Preheat the oven to 350ºF (180ºC).
2. Rub the pork loin with ½ tablespoon of oil and the honey. Season with the pepper and rosemary.
3. In a medium bowl, toss the potatoes and carrots in the remaining ½ tablespoon of oil.
4. Place the pork and the vegetables on a baking sheet in a single layer. Cook for 40 minutes.
5. Remove the baking sheet from the oven and let the pork rest for at least 10 minutes before slicing. Divide the pork and vegetables into four equal portions.

Nutrition: Calories: 343 Fat: 10g Protein: 26g Carbs: 26g
Sugars: 6g Fiber: 4g Sodium: 109mg

Steak Fajita Bake

Preparation Time: 10 minutes
Cooking Time: 15 minutes
Servings: 4

Ingredients:
- 1 green bell pepper
- 1 yellow bell pepper
- 1 red bell pepper
- 1 small white onion

- 10 ounces (283 g) sirloin steak, trimmed of visible fat
- 2 tablespoons avocado oil
- ½ teaspoon ground cumin
- ¼ teaspoon chili powder
- ¼ teaspoon garlic powder
- 4 (6-inch) 100% whole-wheat tortillas

Directions:
1. Preheat the oven to 400ºF (205ºC).
2. Cut the green bell pepper, yellow bell pepper, red bell pepper, onion, and steak into ½-inch-thick slices, and put them on a large baking sheet.
3. In a small bowl, combine the oil, cumin, chili powder, and garlic powder, and then drizzle the mixture over the meat and vegetables to fully coat them.
4. Arrange the steak and vegetables in a single layer, and bake for 10 to 15 minutes, or until the steak is cooked through.
5. Divide the steak and vegetables equally between the tortillas.

Nutrition: Calories: 349 Fat: 18g Protein: 19g Carbs: 28g Sugars: 5g Fiber: 5g Sodium: 197mg

Beef Burrito Bowl

Preparation Time: 5 minutes
Cooking Time: 15minutes
Servings: 4

Ingredients:
- 1 pound (454 g) 93% lean ground beef
- 1 cup canned low-sodium black beans, drained and rinsed
- ¼ teaspoon ground cumin
- ¼ teaspoon chili powder
- ¼ teaspoon garlic powder
- ¼ teaspoon onion powder
- ¼ teaspoon salt
- 1 head romaine or preferred lettuce, shredded
- 2 medium tomatoes, chopped
- 1 cup shredded Cheddar cheese or packaged cheese blend

Directions:
1. Heat a large skillet over medium-low heat. Put the beef, beans, cumin, chili powder, garlic powder,

onion powder, and salt into the skillet, and cook for 8 to 10 minutes, until cooked through. Stir occasionally.

2.   Divide the lettuce evenly between four bowls. Add one-quarter of the beef mixture to each bowl and top with one-quarter of the tomatoes and cheese.

Nutrition: Calories: 351 Fat: 18g Protein: 35g Carbs: 14g Sugars: 4g Fiber: 6g Sodium: 424mg

Zoodles Carbonara

Preparation Time: 10 minutes

Cooking Time: 25 minutes

Servings: 4

Ingredients:

- 6 slices bacon, cut into pieces
- 1 red onion, finely chopped
- 3 zucchini, cut into noodles
- 1 cup peas
- ½ teaspoon sea salt
- 3 garlic cloves, minced
- 3 large eggs, beaten
- 1 tablespoon heavy cream
- Pinch red pepper flakes
- ½ cup grated Parmesan cheese (optional, for garnish)

Directions:

1.   In a large skillet over medium-high heat, cook the bacon until browned, about 5 minutes. With a slotted spoon, transfer the bacon to a plate.

2.   Add the onion to the bacon fat in the pan and cook, stirring, until soft, 3 to 5 minutes. Add the zucchini, peas, and salt. Cook, stirring, until the zucchini softens, about 3 minutes. Add the garlic and cook, stirring constantly, for 5 minutes.

3.   In a small bowl, whisk together the eggs, cream, and red pepper flakes. Add to the vegetables.

4.   Remove the pan from the stove top and stir for 3 minutes, allowing the heat of the pan to cook the eggs without setting them.

5.   Return the bacon to the pan and stir to mix.

6.   Serve topped with Parmesan cheese, if desired.

Nutrition: Calories: 326 Fat: 24g Protein: 14g Carbs: 15g

Sugars: 2g Fiber: 4g Sodium: 555mg

Pork and Apple Skillet

Preparation Time: 10 minutes

Cooking Time: 20 minutes

Servings: 4

Ingredients:

- 1 pound (454 g) ground pork
- 1 red onion, thinly sliced
- 2 apples, peeled, cored, and thinly sliced
- 2 cups shredded cabbage
- 1 teaspoon dried thyme
- 2 garlic cloves, minced
- ¼ cup apple cider vinegar
- 1 tablespoon Dijon mustard
- ½ teaspoon sea salt
- 1/8 teaspoon freshly ground black pepper

Directions:

1.   In a large skillet over medium-high heat, cook the ground pork, crumbling it with a spoon, until browned, about 5 minutes. Use a slotted spoon to transfer the pork to a plate.

2.   Add the onion, apples, cabbage, and thyme to the fat in the pan. Cook, stirring occasionally, until the vegetables are soft, about 5 minutes.

3.   Add the garlic and cook, stirring constantly, for 5 minutes.

4.   Return the pork to the pan.

5.   In a small bowl, whisk together the vinegar, mustard, salt, and pepper. Add to the pan. Bring to a simmer. Cook, stirring, until the sauce thickens, about 2 minutes.

Nutrition: Calories: 364 Fat: 24g Protein: 20g Carbs: 19g

Fiber: 4g Sodium: 260mg

Broccoli Beef Stir-Fry

Preparation Time: 10 minutes
Cooking Time: 15 minutes
Servings: 4

Ingredients:

- 2 tablespoons extra-virgin olive oil
- 1 pound (454 g) sirloin steak, cut into ¼-inch-thick strips
- 2 cups broccoli florets
- 1 garlic clove, minced
- 1 teaspoon peeled and grated fresh ginger
- 2 tablespoons reduced-sodium soy sauce
- ¼ cup beef broth
- ½ teaspoon Chinese hot mustard
- Pinch red pepper flakes

Directions:

1. In a large skillet over medium-high heat, heat the olive oil until it shimmers. Add the beef. Cook, stirring, until it browns, 3 to 5 minutes. With a slotted spoon, remove the beef from the oil and set it aside on a plate.
2. Add the broccoli to the oil. Cook, stirring, until it is crisp-tender, about 4 minutes.
3. Add the garlic and ginger and cook, stirring constantly, for 30 seconds.
4. Return the beef to the pan, along with any juices that have collected.
5. In a small bowl, whisk together the soy sauce, broth, mustard, and red pepper flakes.
6. Add the soy sauce mixture to the skillet and cook, stirring, until everything warms through, about 3 minutes.

Nutrition: Calories: 227 Fat: 11g Protein: 27g Carbs: 5g Sugars: 0g Fiber: 1g Sodium: 375mg

Beef and Pepper Fajita Bowls

Preparation Time: 10 minutes
Cooking Time: 15 minutes
Servings: 4

Ingredients:

- 4 tablespoons extra-virgin olive oil, divided
- 1 head cauliflower, riced
- 1 pound (454 g) sirloin steak, cut into ¼-inch-thick strips
- 1 red bell pepper, seeded and sliced
- 1 onion, thinly sliced
- 2 garlic cloves, minced
- Juice of 2 limes
- 1 teaspoon chili powder

Directions:

1. In a large skillet over medium-high heat, heat 2 tablespoons of olive oil until it shimmers. Add the cauliflower. Cook, stirring occasionally, until it softens, about 3 minutes. Set aside.
2. Wipe out the skillet with a paper towel. Add the remaining 2 tablespoons of oil to the skillet, and heat it on medium-high until it shimmers. Add the steak and cook, stirring occasionally, until it browns, about 3 minutes. Use a slotted spoon to remove the steak from the oil in the pan and set aside.
3. Add the bell pepper and onion to the pan. Cook, stirring occasionally, until they start to brown, about 5 minutes.
4. Add the garlic and cook, stirring constantly, for 30 seconds.
5. Return the beef along with any juices that have collected and the cauliflower to the pan. Add the lime juice and chili powder. Cook, stirring, until everything is warmed through, 2 to 3 minutes.

Nutrition: Calories: 310 Fat: 18g Protein: 27g Carbs: 13g Sugars: 2g Fiber: 3g Sodium: 93mg

Pork Chop Diane

Preparation Time: 10 minutes
Cooking Time: 20 minutes
Servings: 4

Ingredients:

- ¼ cup low-sodium chicken broth
- 1 tablespoon freshly squeezed lemon juice
- 2 teaspoons Worcestershire sauce
- 2 teaspoons Dijon mustard
- 4 (5-ounce / 142-g) boneless pork top loin chops, about 1 inch thick
- Sea salt and freshly ground black pepper, to taste

- 1 teaspoon extra-virgin olive oil
- 1 teaspoon lemon zest
- 1 teaspoon butter
- 2 teaspoons chopped fresh chives

Directions:

1. In a small bowl, stir together the chicken broth, lemon juice, Worcestershire sauce, and Dijon mustard and set it aside.

2. Season the pork chops lightly with salt and pepper.

3. Place a large skillet over medium-high heat and add the olive oil.

4. Cook the pork chops, turning once, until they are no longer pink, about 8 minutes per side.

5. Transfer the chops to a plate and set it aside.

6. Pour the broth mixture into the skillet and cook until warmed through and thickened, about 2 minutes.

7. Whisk in the lemon zest, butter, and chives.

8. Serve the chops with a generous spoonful of sauce.

Nutrition: Calories: 200 Fat: 8g Protein: 30g Carbs: 1g Sugars: 1g Fiber: 0gSodium: 394mg

Chipotle Chili Pork Chops

Preparation Time: 5 minutes

Cooking Time: 20 minutes

Servings: 4

Ingredients:

- Juice and zest of 1 lime
- 1 tablespoon extra-virgin olive oil
- 1 tablespoon chipotle chili powder
- 2 teaspoons minced garlic
- 1 teaspoon ground cinnamon
- Pinch sea salt
- 4 (5-ounce / 142-g) pork chops, about 1 inch thick
- Lime wedges, for garnish

Directions:

1. Combine the lime juice and zest, oil, chipotle chili powder, garlic, cinnamon, and salt in a resealable plastic bag. Add the pork chops. Remove as much air as possible and seal the bag.

2. Marinate the chops in the refrigerator for at least 4 hours, and up to 24 hours, turning them several times.

3. Preheat the oven to 400ºF (205ºC) and set a rack on a baking sheet. Let the chops rest at room temperature for 15 minutes, then arrange them on the rack and discard the remaining marinade.

4. Roast the chops until cooked through, turning once, about 10 minutes per side.

5. Serve with lime wedges.

Nutrition: Calories: 204 Fat: 9g Protein: 30g Carbs: 1g Sugars: 1g Fiber: 0g Sodium: 317mg

Lime-Parsley Lamb Cutlets

Preparation Time: 10 minutes

Cooking Time: 10 minutes

Servings: 4

Ingredients:

- ¼ cup extra-virgin olive oil
- ¼ cup freshly squeezed lime juice
- 2 tablespoons lime zest
- 2 tablespoons chopped fresh parsley
- Pinch sea salt
- Pinch freshly ground black pepper
- 12 lamb cutlets (about 1½ pounds / 680 g total)

Directions:

1. In a medium bowl, whisk together the oil, lime juice, zest, parsley, salt, and pepper.

2. Transfer the marinade to a resealable plastic bag.

3. Add the cutlets to the bag and remove as much air as possible before sealing.

4. Marinate the lamb in the refrigerator for about 4 hours, turning the bag several times.

5. Preheat the oven to broil.

6. Remove the chops from the bag and arrange them on an aluminum foil-lined baking sheet. Discard the marinade.

7. Broil the chops for 4 minutes per side for medium doneness.

8. Let the chops rest for 5 minutes before serving.

Nutrition: Calories: 413 Fat: 29g Protein: 31g Carbs: 1g Sugars: 0g Fiber: 0g Sodium: 100mg

Traditional Beef Stroganoff

Preparation Time: 10 minutes
Cooking Time: 30 minutes
Servings: 4

Ingredients:

- 1 teaspoon extra-virgin olive oil
- 1 pound (454 g) top sirloin, cut into thin strips
- 1 cup sliced button mushrooms
- ½ sweet onion, finely chopped
- 1 teaspoon minced garlic
- 1 tablespoon whole-wheat flour
- ½ cup low-sodium beef broth
- ¼ cup dry sherry
- ½ cup fat-free sour cream
- 1 tablespoon chopped fresh parsley
- Sea salt and freshly ground black pepper, to taste

Directions:

1. Place a large skillet over medium-high heat and add the oil.
2. Sauté the beef until browned, about 10 minutes, then remove the beef with a slotted spoon to a plate and set it aside.
3. Add the mushrooms, onion, and garlic to the skillet and sauté until lightly browned, about 5 minutes.
4. Whisk in the flour and then whisk in the beef broth and sherry.
5. Return the sirloin to the skillet and bring the mixture to a boil.
6. Reduce the heat to low and simmer until the beef is tender, about 10 minutes.
7. Stir in the sour cream and parsley. Season with salt and pepper.

Nutrition: Calories: 257 Fat: 14g Protein: 26g Carbs: 6g Sugars: 1g Fiber: 1g Sodium: 141mg

Smothered Sirloin

Preparation Time: 15 minutes
Cooking Time: 30 minutes
Servings: 5

Ingredients:

- 1 pound (454 g) beef round sirloin tip
- 1 teaspoon freshly ground black pepper
- 1 teaspoon celery seeds
- 2 tablespoons extra-virgin olive oil
- 1 medium yellow onion, chopped
- ¼ cup chickpea flour
- 2 cups chicken broth, divided
- 2 celery stalks, thinly sliced
- 1 medium red bell pepper, chopped
- 2 garlic cloves, minced
- 2 tablespoons whole-wheat flour
- Generous pinch cayenne pepper
- Chopped fresh chives, for garnish (optional)
- Smoked paprika, for garnish (optional)

Directions:

1. In a bowl, season the steak on both sides with the black pepper and celery seeds.
2. Select the Sauté setting on an electric pressure cooker, and combine the olive oil and onions. Cook for 3 to 5 minutes, stirring, or until the onions are browned but not burned.
3. Slowly add the chickpea flour, 1 tablespoon at a time, while stirring.
4. Add 1 cup of broth, ¼ cup at a time, as needed.
5. Stir in the celery, bell pepper, and garlic and cook for 3 to 5 minutes, or until softened.
6. Lay the beef on top of vegetables, and pour the remaining 1 cup of broth on top.
7. Close and lock the lid and set the pressure valve to sealing.
8. Change to the Manual setting, and cook for 20 minutes.
9. Once cooking is complete, quick-release the pressure. Carefully remove the lid.
10. Remove the steak and vegetables from the pressure cooker, reserving the leftover liquid for the gravy base.
11. To make the gravy, add the whole-wheat flour and cayenne to the liquid in the pressure cooker, mixing continuously until thickened.
12. To serve, spoon the gravy over the steak and garnish with the chives (if using) and paprika (if using).

Nutrition: Calories: 253 Fat: 13g Protein: 22g Carbs: 10g Sugars: 3g Fiber: 2g Sodium: 86mg

Loaded Cottage Pie

Preparation Time: 15 minutes

Cooking Time: 60 minutes

Servings: 6-8

Ingredients:

- 4 large russet potatoes, peeled and halved
- 3 tablespoons extra-virgin olive oil, divided
- 1 small onion, chopped
- 1 bunch collard greens, stemmed and thinly sliced
- 2 carrots, peeled and chopped
- 2 medium tomatoes, chopped
- 1 garlic clove, minced
- 1 pound (454 g) 90 percent lean ground beef
- ½ cup chicken broth
- 1 teaspoon Worcestershire sauce
- 1 teaspoon celery seeds
- 1 teaspoon smoked paprika
- ½ teaspoon dried chives
- ½ teaspoon ground mustard
- ½ teaspoon cayenne pepper

Directions:

1. Preheat the oven to 400ºF (205ºC).
2. Bring a large pot of water to a boil.
3. Add the potatoes, and boil for 15 to 20 minutes, or until fork-tender.
4. Transfer the potatoes to a large bowl and mash with 1 tablespoon of olive oil.
5. In a large cast iron skillet, heat the remaining 2 tablespoons of olive oil.
6. Add the onion, collard greens, carrots, tomatoes, and garlic and sauté, stirring often, for 7 to 10 minutes, or until the vegetables are softened.
7. Add the beef, broth, Worcestershire sauce, celery seeds, and smoked paprika.
8. Spread the meat and vegetable mixture evenly onto the bottom of a casserole dish. Sprinkle the chives, ground mustard, and cayenne on top of the mixture. Spread the mashed potatoes evenly over the top.
9. Transfer the casserole dish to the oven, and bake for 30 minutes, or until the top is light golden brown.

Nutrition: Calories: 440 Fat: 17g Protein: 27g Carbs: 48g Sugars: 6g Fiber: 9g Sodium: 107mg

Fresh Pot Pork Butt

Preparation Time: 10 minutes

Cooking Time: 45 minutes

Servings: 8

Ingredients:

- 2 tablespoons extra-virgin olive oil
- ¼ cup apple cider vinegar
- 1 tablespoon freshly ground black pepper
- 1 tablespoon dried oregano
- 1 small yellow onion, minced
- 2 scallions, white and green parts, minced
- 1 celery stalk, minced
- Juice of 1 lime
- 2 pounds (907 g) boneless pork butt
- 4 garlic cloves, sliced
- 1 cup chicken broth

Directions:

1. In a medium bowl, combine the oil, vinegar, pepper, oregano, onion, scallions, celery, and lime juice. Mix well until a paste is formed.
2. Score the pork with 1-inch-deep cuts in a diamond pattern on both sides. Push the garlic into the slits.
3. Massage the paste all over meat. Cover and refrigerate overnight or for at least 4 hours.
4. Select the Sauté setting on an electric pressure cooker. Cook the meat for 2 minutes on each side.
5. Add the broth, close and lock the lid, and set the pressure valve to sealing.
6. Change to the Manual setting, and cook for 20 minutes.
7. Once cooking is complete, allow the pressure to release naturally. Carefully remove the lid.
8. Remove the pork from the pressure cooker, and serve with Ranch Dressing.

Nutrition: Calories: 287 Fat: 22g Protein: 20g Carbs: 1g Sugars: 1g Fiber: 1g Sodium: 88mg

Cherry-Glazed Lamb Chops

Preparation Time: 10 minutes

Cooking Time: 20 minutes

Servings: 4

Ingredients:

- 4 (4-ounce / 113-g) lamb chops
- 1½ teaspoons chopped fresh rosemary
- ¼ teaspoon salt
- ¼ teaspoon freshly ground black pepper
- 1 cup frozen cherries, thawed
- ¼ cup dry red wine
- 2 tablespoons orange juice
- 1 teaspoon extra-virgin olive oil

Directions:

1. Season the lamb chops with the rosemary, salt, and pepper.
2. In a small saucepan over medium-low heat, combine the cherries, red wine, and orange juice, and simmer, stirring regularly, until the sauce thickens, 8 to 10 minutes.
3. Heat a large skillet over medium-high heat. When the pan is hot, add the olive oil to lightly coat the bottom.
4. Cook the lamb chops for 3 to 4 minutes on each side until well-browned yet medium rare.
5. Serve, topped with the cherry glaze.

Nutrition: Calories: 355Fat: 27.1gProtein: 19.8gCarbs: 5.9gFiber: 1.0gSugar: 4.0g Sodium: 200mg

Autumn Pork Chops

Preparation Time: 15 minutes

Cooking Time: 30 minutes

Servings: 4

Ingredients:

- ¼ cup apple cider vinegar
- 2 tablespoons granulated sweetener
- 4 (4-ounce / 113-g) pork chops, about 1 inch thick
- Sea salt and freshly ground black pepper, to taste
- 1 tablespoon extra-virgin olive oil
- ½ red cabbage, finely shredded

- 1 sweet onion, thinly sliced
- 1 apple, peeled, cored, and sliced
- 1 teaspoon chopped fresh thyme

Directions:

1. In a small bowl, whisk together the vinegar and sweetener. Set it aside.
2. Season the pork with salt and pepper.
3. Place a large skillet over medium-high heat and add the olive oil.
4. Cook the pork chops until no longer pink, turning once, about 8 minutes per side.
5. Transfer the chops to a plate and set aside.
6. Add the cabbage and onion to the skillet and sauté until the vegetables have softened, about 5 minutes.
7. Add the vinegar mixture and the apple slices to the skillet and bring the mixture to a boil.
8. Reduce the heat to low and simmer, covered, for 5 additional minutes.
9. Return the pork chops to the skillet, along with any accumulated juices and thyme, cover, and cook for 5 more minutes.

Nutrition: Calories: 224Fat: 8.1gProtein: 26.1gCarbs: 12.1gFiber: 3.1gSugar: 8.0gSodium: 293mg

Roasted Pork Loin with Carrots

Preparation Time: 5 minutes

Cooking Time: 40 minutes

Servings: 4

Ingredients:

- 1 pound (454 g) pork loin
- 1 tablespoon extra-virgin olive oil, divided
- 2 teaspoons honey
- ¼ teaspoon freshly ground black pepper
- ½ teaspoon dried rosemary
- 4 (6-inch) carrots, chopped into ½-inch rounds

Directions:

1. Preheat the oven to 350ºF (180ºC).
2. Rub the pork loin with ½ tablespoon of oil and the honey. Season with the pepper and rosemary.
3. In a medium bowl, toss the carrots in the remaining ½ tablespoon of oil.
4. Place the pork and the carrots on a baking sheet in a single layer. Cook for 40 minutes.

5. Remove the baking sheet from the oven and let the pork rest for at least 10 minutes before slicing. Divide the pork and carrots into four equal portions.

Nutrition: Calories: 344Fat: 10.1gProtein: 26.1gCarbs: 25.9gFiber: 3.9gSugar: 6.0gSodium: 110mg

Herbed Meatballs

Preparation Time: 10 minutes
Cooking Time: 15 minutes
Servings: 4

Ingredients:

- ½ pound (227 g) lean ground pork
- ½ pound (227 g) lean ground beef
- 1 sweet onion, finely chopped
- ¼ cup bread crumbs
- 2 tablespoons chopped fresh basil
- 2 teaspoons minced garlic
- 1 egg
- Pinch sea salt
- Pinch freshly ground black pepper

Directions:

1. Preheat the oven to 350ºF (180ºC).
2. Line a baking tray with parchment paper and set it aside.
3. In a large bowl, mix together the pork, beef, onion, bread crumbs, basil, garlic, egg, salt, and pepper until very well mixed.
4. Roll the meat mixture into 2-inch meatballs.
5. Transfer the meatballs to the baking sheet and bake until they are browned and cooked through, about 15 minutes.
6. Serve the meatballs with your favorite marinara sauce and some steamed green beans.

Nutrition: Calories: 333Fat: 19.1gProtein: 24.1gCarbs: 12.9gFiber: 0.9gSugar: 2.9gSodium: 189mg

Roasted Beef with Shallot Sauce

Preparation Time: 10 minutes
Cooking Time: 100 minutes
Servings: 4

Ingredients:

- 1½ pounds (680 g) top rump beef roast
- Sea salt and freshly ground black pepper, to taste
- 3 teaspoons extra-virgin olive oil, divided
- 3 shallots, minced
- 2 teaspoons minced garlic
- 1 tablespoon green peppercorns
- 2 tablespoons dry sherry
- 2 tablespoons all-purpose flour
- 1 cup sodium-free beef broth

Directions:

1. Heat the oven to 300ºF (150ºC).
2. Season the roast with salt and pepper.
3. Place a large skillet over medium-high heat and add 2 teaspoons of olive oil.
4. Brown the beef on all sides, about 10 minutes in total, and transfer the roast to a baking dish.
5. Roast until desired doneness, about 1½ hours for medium. When the roast has been in the oven for 1 hour, start the sauce.
6. In a medium saucepan over medium-high heat, sauté the shallots in the remaining 1 teaspoon of olive oil until translucent, about 4 minutes.
7. Stir in the garlic and peppercorns, and cook for another minute. Whisk in the sherry to deglaze the pan.
8. Whisk in the flour to form a thick paste, cooking for 1 minute and stirring constantly.
9. Pour in the beef broth and whisk until the sauce is thick and glossy, about 4 minutes. Season the sauce with salt and pepper.
10. Serve the beef with a generous spoonful of sauce.

Nutrition: Calories: 331Fat: 18.1gProtein: 36.1gCarbs: 3.9gFiber: 0gSugar: 1.0gSodium: 208mg

Beef Stroganoff

Preparation Time: 10 minutes
Cooking Time: 30 minutes
Servings: 4

Ingredients:

- 1 teaspoon extra-virgin olive oil
- 1 pound (454 g) top sirloin, cut into thin strips
- 1 cup sliced button mushrooms
- ½ sweet onion, finely chopped
- 1 teaspoon minced garlic

- 1 tablespoon whole-wheat flour
- ½ cup low-sodium beef broth
- ¼ cup dry sherry
- ½ cup fat-free sour cream
- 1 tablespoon chopped fresh parsley
- Sea salt and freshly ground black pepper, to taste

Directions:

1. Place a large skillet over medium-high heat and add the oil.
2. Sauté the beef until browned, about 10 minutes, then remove the beef with a slotted spoon to a plate and set it aside.
3. Add the mushrooms, onion, and garlic to the skillet and sauté until lightly browned, about 5 minutes.
4. Whisk in the flour and then whisk in the beef broth and sherry.
5. Return the sirloin to the skillet and bring the mixture to a boil.
6. Reduce the heat to low and simmer until the beef is tender, about 10 minutes.
7. Stir in the sour cream and parsley. Season with salt and pepper.

Nutrition: Calories: 258Fat: 14.1gProtein: 26.1gCarbs: 6.1gFiber: 1.1gSugar: 1.0g Sodium: 142mg

Pulled Pork Sandwiches with Apricot Jelly

Preparation Time: 5 minutes
Cooking Time: 15 minutes
Servings: 4

Ingredients:

- Avocado oil cooking spray
- 8 ounces (227 g) store-bought pulled pork
- ½ cup chopped green bell pepper
- 2 slices provolone cheese
- 4 whole-wheat sandwich thins
- 2½ tablespoons apricot jelly

Directions:

1. Heat the pulled pork according to the package instructions.
2. Heat a medium skillet over medium-low heat. When hot, coat the cooking surface with cooking spray.

3. Put the bell pepper in the skillet and cook for 5 minutes. Transfer to a small bowl and set aside.
4. Meanwhile, tear each slice of cheese into 2 strips, and halves the sandwich thins so you have a top and bottom.
5. Reduce the heat to low, and place the sandwich thins in the skillet cut-side down to toast, about 2 minutes.
6. Remove the sandwich thins from the skillet. Spread one-quarter of the jelly on the bottom half of each sandwich thin, and then place one-quarter of the cheese, pulled pork, and pepper on top. Cover with the top half of the sandwich thin.

Nutrition: Calories: 250 Fat: 8.1gProtein: 16.1gCarbs: 34.1gFiber: 6.1gSugar: 8.0gSodium: 510mg

Beef and Mushroom Cauliflower Wraps

Preparation Time: 5 minutes
Cooking Time: 20 minutes
Servings: 4

Ingredients:

- Avocado oil cooking spray
- ½ cup chopped white onion
- 1 cup chopped portobello mushrooms
- 1 pound (454 g) 93% lean ground beef
- ½ teaspoon garlic powder
- Pinch salt
- 1 (10-ounce / 283-g) bag frozen cauliflower rice
- 12 iceberg lettuce leaves
- ¾ cup shredded Cheddar cheese

Directions:

1. Heat a large skillet over medium heat. When hot, coat the cooking surface with cooking spray and add the onion and mushrooms. Cook for 5 minutes, stirring occasionally.
2. Add the beef, garlic powder, and salt, stirring and breaking apart the meat as needed. Cook for 5 minutes.
3. Stir in the frozen cauliflower rice and increase the heat to medium-high. Cook for 5 minutes more, or until the water evaporates.
4. For each portion, use three lettuce leaves. Spoon one-quarter of the filling onto the lettuce leaves, and top

with one-quarter of the cheese. Then, working from the side closest to you, roll up the lettuce to close the wrap. Repeat with the remaining lettuce leaves and filling.
Nutrition: Calories: 290Fat: 15.1gProtein: 31.1gCarbs: 7.1gFiber: 3.1gSugar: 4.0g Sodium: 265mg

Zucchini Carbonara

Preparation Time: 10 minutes
Cooking Time: 25 minutes
Servings: 4
Ingredients:
- 6 slices bacon, cut into pieces
- 1 red onion, finely chopped
- 3 zucchini, cut into noodles
- 1 cup peas
- ½ teaspoon sea salt
- 3 garlic cloves, minced
- 3 large eggs, beaten
- 1 tablespoon heavy cream
- Pinch red pepper flakes
- ½ cup grated Parmesan cheese (optional, for garnish)

Directions:
1. In a large skillet over medium-high heat, cook the bacon until browned, about 5 minutes. With a slotted spoon, transfer the bacon to a plate.
2. Add the onion to the bacon fat in the pan and cook, stirring, until soft, 3 to 5 minutes. Add the zucchini, peas, and salt. Cook, stirring, until the zucchini softens, about 3 minutes. Add the garlic and cook, stirring constantly, for 5 minutes.
3. In a small bowl, whisk together the eggs, cream, and red pepper flakes. Add to the vegetables.
4. Remove the pan from the stove top and stir for 3 minutes, allowing the heat of the pan to cook the eggs without setting them.
5. Return the bacon to the pan and stir to mix.
6. Serve topped with Parmesan cheese, if desired.
Nutrition: Calories: 327Fat: 24.1gProtein: 14.1gCarbs: 14.9gFiber: 3.9gSugar: 11.0g Sodium: 556mg

Steak and Broccoli Bowls

Preparation Time: 10 minutes
Cooking Time: 15 minutes
Servings: 4
Ingredients:
- 2 tablespoons extra-virgin olive oil
- 1 pound (454 g) sirloin steak, cut into ¼-inch-thick strips
- 2 cups broccoli florets
- 1 garlic clove, minced
- 1 teaspoon peeled and grated fresh ginger
- 2 tablespoons reduced-sodium soy sauce
- ¼ cup beef broth
- ½ teaspoon Chinese hot mustard
- Pinch red pepper flakes

Directions:
1. In a large skillet over medium-high heat, heat the olive oil until it shimmers. Add the beef. Cook, stirring, until it browns, 3 to 5 minutes. With a slotted spoon, remove the beef from the oil and set it aside on a plate.
2. Add the broccoli to the oil. Cook, stirring, until it is crisp-tender, about 4 minutes.
3. Add the garlic and ginger and cook, stirring constantly, for 30 seconds.
4. Return the beef to the pan, along with any juices that have collected.
5. In a small bowl, whisk together the soy sauce, broth, mustard, and red pepper flakes.
6. Add the soy sauce mixture to the skillet and cook, stirring, until everything warms through, about 3 minutes.
Nutrition: Calories: 230Fat: 11.1gProtein: 27.1gCarbs: 4.9gFiber: 1.0gSugar: 3.0g Sodium: 376mg

Cauliflower and Beef Fajita

Preparation Time: 10 minutes
Cooking Time: 15 minutes
Servings: 4
Ingredients:
- 4 tablespoons extra-virgin olive oil, divided
- 1 head cauliflower, riced
- 1 pound (454 g) sirloin steak, cut into ¼-inch-thick strips

- 1 red bell pepper, seeded and sliced
- 1 onion, thinly sliced
- 2 garlic cloves, minced
- Juice of 2 limes
- 1 teaspoon chili powder

Directions:

1. In a large skillet over medium-high heat, heat 2 tablespoons of olive oil until it shimmers. Add the cauliflower. Cook, stirring occasionally, until it softens, about 3 minutes. Set aside.

2. Wipe out the skillet with a paper towel. Add the remaining 2 tablespoons of oil to the skillet, and heat it on medium-high until it shimmers. Add the steak and cook, stirring occasionally, until it browns, about 3 minutes. Use a slotted spoon to remove the steak from the oil in the pan and set aside.

3. Add the bell pepper and onion to the pan. Cook, stirring occasionally, until they start to brown, about 5 minutes.

4. Add the garlic and cook, stirring constantly, for 30 seconds.

5. Return the beef along with any juices that have collected and the cauliflower to the pan. Add the lime juice and chili powder. Cook, stirring, until everything is warmed through, 2 to 3 minutes.

Nutrition: Calories: 311Fat: 18.1gProtein: 27.1gCarbs: 13.1g Fiber: 2.9gSugar: 10.0gSodium: 94mg

Lamb Kofta with Cucumber Salad

Preparation Time: 10 minutes
Cooking Time: 15 minutes
Servings: 4

Ingredients:

- ¼ cup red wine vinegar
- Pinch red pepper flakes
- 1 teaspoon sea salt, divided
- 2 cucumbers, peeled and chopped
- ½ red onion, finely chopped
- 1 pound (454 g) ground lamb
- 2 teaspoons ground coriander
- 1 teaspoon ground cumin
- 3 garlic cloves, minced
- 1 tablespoon fresh mint, chopped

Directions:

1. Preheat the oven to 375°F (190°C). Line a rimmed baking sheet with parchment paper.

2. In a medium bowl, whisk together the vinegar, red pepper flakes, and ½ teaspoon of salt. Add the cucumbers and onion and toss to combine. Set aside.

3. In a large bowl, mix the lamb, coriander, cumin, garlic, mint, and remaining ½ teaspoon of salt. Form the mixture into 1-inch meatballs and place them on the prepared baking sheet.

4. Bake until the lamb reaches 140°F (60°C) internally, about 15 minutes.

5. Serve with the salad on the side.

Nutrition: Calories: 346Fat: 27.1gProtein: 20.1gCarbs: 6.9gFiber: 1.1gSugar: 5.0gSodium: 363mg

Mustard Pork Chops

Preparation Time: 5 minutes
Cooking Time: 25 minutes
Servings: 4

Ingredients:

- ¼ cup Dijon mustard
- 1 tablespoon pure maple syrup
- 2 tablespoons rice vinegar
- 4 bone-in, thin-cut pork chops

Directions:

1. Preheat the oven to 400°F (205°C).

2. In a small saucepan, combine the mustard, maple syrup, and rice vinegar. Stir to mix and bring to a simmer over medium heat. Cook for about 2 minutes until just slightly thickened.

3. In a baking dish, place the pork chops and spoon the sauce over them, flipping to coat.

4. Bake, uncovered, for 18 to 22 minutes until the juices run clear.

Nutrition: Calories: 258Fat: 7.1gProtein: 39.1gCarbs: 6.9g Fiber: 0gSugar: 4.0gSodium: 465mg

Parmesan Golden Pork Chops

Preparation Time: 10 minutes

Cooking Time: 25 minutes

Servings: 4

Ingredients:

- Nonstick cooking spray
- 4 bone-in, thin-cut pork chops
- 2 tablespoons butter
- ½ cup grated Parmesan cheese
- 3 garlic cloves, minced
- ¼ teaspoon salt
- ¼ teaspoon dried thyme
- Freshly ground black pepper, to taste

Directions:

1. Preheat the oven to 400ºF (205ºC). Line a baking sheet with parchment paper and spray with nonstick cooking spray.

2. Arrange the pork chops on the prepared baking sheet so they do not overlap.

3. In a small bowl, combine the butter, cheese, garlic, salt, thyme, and pepper. Press 2 tablespoons of the cheese mixture onto the top of each pork chop.

4. Bake for 18 to 22 minutes until the pork is cooked through and its juices run clear. Set the broiler to high, then broil for 1 to 2 minutes to brown the tops.

Nutrition: Calories: 333 Fat: 16.1gProtein: 44.1gCarbs: 1.1gFiber: 0gSugar: 0gSodium: 441mg

Mango Pork Tenderloin

Preparation Time: 10 minutes

Cooking Time: 20 minutes

Servings: 4

Ingredients:

- 1 pound (454 g) boneless pork tenderloin, trimmed of fat
- 1 teaspoon chopped fresh rosemary
- 1 teaspoon chopped fresh thyme
- ¼ teaspoon salt, divided
- ¼ teaspoon freshly ground black pepper, divided
- 1 teaspoon extra-virgin olive oil
- 1 tablespoon honey
- 2 tablespoons white wine vinegar

- 2 tablespoons dry cooking wine
- 1 tablespoon minced fresh ginger
- 1 cup diced mango

Directions:

1. Preheat the oven to 400ºF (205ºC).

2. Season the tenderloin with the rosemary, thyme, 1/8 teaspoon of salt, and 1/8 teaspoon of pepper.

3. Heat the olive oil in an oven-safe skillet over medium-high heat, and sear the tenderloin until browned on all sides, about 5 minutes total.

4. Transfer the skillet to the oven and roast for 12 to 15 minutes until the pork is cooked through, the juices run clear, and the internal temperature reaches 145ºF (63ºC). Transfer to a cutting board to rest for 5 minutes.

5. In a small bowl, combine the honey, vinegar, cooking wine, and ginger. In to the same skillet, pour the honey mixture and simmer for 1 minute. Add the mango and toss to coat. Transfer to a blender and purée until smooth. Season with the remaining 1/8 teaspoon of salt and 1/8 teaspoon of pepper.

6. Slice the pork into rounds and serve with the mango sauce.

Nutrition: Calories: 183 Fat: 4.1gProtein: 24.1gCarbs: 11.9gFiber: 1.1gSugar: 10.0gSodium: 241mg

Steak Sandwich

Preparation Time: 10 minutes

Cooking Time: 10 minutes

Servings: 4

Ingredients:

- 2 tablespoons balsamic vinegar
- 2 teaspoons freshly squeezed lemon juice
- 1 teaspoon fresh parsley, chopped
- 2 teaspoons fresh oregano, chopped
- 2 teaspoons garlic, minced
- 2 tablespoons olive oil
- 1 pound (454 g) flank steak, trimmed of fat
- 4 whole-wheat pitas
- 1 tomato, chopped
- 1 ounce (28 g) low-sodium feta cheese
- 2 cups lettuce, shredded
- 1 red onion, thinly sliced

Directions:

1. Combine the balsamic vinegar, lemon juice, parsley, oregano, garlic, and olive oil in a bowl.

2. Dunk the steak in the bowl to coat well, then wrap the bowl in plastic and refrigerate for at least 1 hour.

3. Preheat the oven to 450°F (235°C).

4. Remove the bowl from the refrigerator. Discard the marinade and arrange the steak on a baking sheet lined with aluminum foil.

5. Broil in the preheated oven for 10 minutes for medium. Flip the steak halfway through the cooking time.

6. Remove the steak from the oven and allow to cool for 10 minutes. Slice the steak into strips.

7. Assemble the pitas with steak, tomato, feta cheese, lettuce, and onion to make the sandwich, and serve warm.

Nutrition: Calories: 345Fat: 15.8gProtein: 28.1gCarbs: 21.9gFiber: 3.1gCarbs: 18.8gSodium: 295mg

Easy Beef Roast with Green Peppercorn Sauce

Preparation Time: 10 minutes

Cooking Time: 100 minutes

Servings: 4

Ingredients:

*   1½ pounds (680 g) top rump beef roast
*   Salt and freshly ground black pepper, to taste
*   3 teaspoons olive oil, divided
*   3 shallots, diced
*   1 tablespoon green peppercorns
*   2 teaspoons garlic, minced
*   2 tablespoons dry sherry
*   2 tablespoons all-purpose flour
*   1 cup low-sodium beef broth

Directions:

1. Preheat the oven to 300°F (150°C).

2. On a clean work surface, rub the beef with salt and black pepper.

3. Heat 2 teaspoons olive oil in an oven-safe skillet over medium-high heat until shimmering.

4. Add the beef to the skillet and cook for 10 minutes until well browned on both sides. Flip the beef halfway through the cooking time.

5. Roast in the preheated oven for 1 hour and 30 minutes or until the beef reaches the desired doneness.

6. Meanwhile, heat the remaining olive oil in a saucepan over medium-high heat.

7. Add the shallots to the saucepan and sauté for 4 minutes or until translucent.

8. Add the peppercorns and garlic to the pan and sauté for 1 minute until fragrant.

9. Pour the sherry into the pan for deglazing, and then fold in the flour and stir until the mixture has a thick consistency. Cook for an additional minute. Keep stirring during the cooking.

10. Add the beef broth to the pan and stir until the sauce is thick and smooth, then sprinkle with salt and black pepper.

11. Remove the beef from the oven and serve with the peppercorn sauce on top.

Nutrition: Calories: 332Fat: 17.8gProtein: 36.1gCarbs: 3.9gFiber: 0gSugar: 1.1gSodium: 205mg

Coffeed and Herbed Steak

Preparation Time: 10 minutes

Cooking Time: 10 minutes

Servings: 4

Ingredients:

*   ¼ cup whole coffee beans
*   2 teaspoons fresh rosemary, chopped
*   2 teaspoons fresh thyme, chopped
*   2 teaspoons garlic, minced
*   1 teaspoon freshly ground black pepper
*   2 tablespoons apple cider vinegar
*   2 tablespoons olive oil
*   1 pound (454 g) flank steak, trimmed of fat

Directions:

1. Put the coffee beans, rosemary, thyme, garlic, and black pepper in a food processor. Pulse until well ground and combined.

2. Pour the mixture in a large bowl, then pour the vinegar and olive oil in the bowl. Stir to mix well.

3.   Dunk the steak in the mixture, then wrap the bowl in plastic and refrigerate to marinate for 2 hours.

4.   Preheat the broiler to MEDIUM.

5.   Remove the bowl from the refrigerator, and discard the marinade.

6.   Place the marinated steak on a baking sheet lined with aluminum foil.

7.   Broil in the preheated broiler for 10 minutes or until the steak reaches your desired doneness. Flip the steak halfway through the cooking time.

Nutrition: Calories: 316Fat: 19.8gProtein: 31.1gCarbs: 0gFiber: 0gSugar: 0gSodium: 78mg

Pork Loin, Carrot, and Gold Tomato Roast

Preparation Time: 5 minutes

Cooking Time: 40 minutes

Servings: 4

Ingredients:

- 1 pound (454 g) pork loin
- 2 teaspoons honey
- ½ teaspoon dried rosemary
- ¼ teaspoon freshly ground black pepper
- 1 tablespoon extra-virgin olive oil, divided
- 4 (6-inch) carrots, chopped into ½-inch rounds
- 2 small gold potatoes, chopped into 2-inch cubes

Directions:

1.   Preheat the oven to 350ºF (180ºC).

2.   On a clean work surface, rub the pork with honey, rosemary, black pepper, and½ tablespoon of olive oil. Brush the carrots and gold potatoes with remaining olive oil.

3.   Place the pork, carrots, and potatoes in s single layer on a baking sheet.

4.   Roast in the preheated oven for 40 minutes or until the pork is lightly browned and the vegetables are soft.

5.   Remove them from the oven. Allow to cool for 10 minutes before serving.

Nutrition: Calories: 346Fat: 9.9gProtein: 26.1gCarbs: 25.9gFiber: 4.1gSugar: 5.9gSodium: 107mg

Sloppy Joes

Preparation Time: 10 minutes

Cooking Time: 15 minutes

Servings: 4

Ingredients:

- 1 tablespoon extra-virgin olive oil
- 1 pound (454 g) 93% lean ground beef
- 1 medium red bell pepper, chopped
- ½ medium yellow onion, chopped
- 2 tablespoons low-sodium Worcestershire sauce
- 1 (15-ounce / 425-g) can low-sodium tomato sauce
- 2 tablespoons low-sodium, sugar-free ketchup
- 4 whole-wheat sandwich thins, cut in half
- 1 cup cabbage, shredded

Directions:

1.   Heat the olive oil in a nonstick skillet over medium heat until shimmering.

2.   Add the beef, bell pepper, and onion to the skillet and sauté for 8 minutes or until the beef is browned and the onion is translucent.

3.   Pour the Worcestershire sauce, tomato sauce, and ketchup in the skillet. Turn up the heat to medium-high and simmer for 5 minutes.

4.   Assemble the sandwich thin halves with beef mixture and cabbage to make the sloppy Joes, then serve warm.

Nutrition: Calories: 329Fat: 8.9gProtein: 31.2gCarbs: 35.9gFiber: 7.9gSugar: 10.9gSodium: 271mg

Mushroom, Beef, and Cauliflower Rice in Lettuce

Preparation Time: 5 minutes

Cooking Time: 20 minutes

Servings: 4

Ingredients:

- 1 tablespoon avocado oil
- 1 cup portobello mushrooms, chopped
- ½ cup white onion, chopped
- 1 pound (454 g) 93% lean ground beef
- ½ teaspoon garlic powder
- Salt, to taste

- 1 (10-ounce / 284-g) bag frozen cauliflower rice
- ¾ cup Cheddar cheese, shredded
- 12 iceberg lettuce leaves

Directions:

1. Heath the avocado oil in a nonstick skillet over medium heat.

2. Add the mushrooms and onion to the skillet and sauté for 5 minutes until the mushrooms are soft and the onion starts to become translucent.

3. Add the beef, garlic powder, and salt to the skillet and sauté for another 5 minutes to brown the beef.

4. Increase the heat to medium-high, and then add the cauliflower rice and sauté for an additional 5 minutes.

5. Divide the mixture and cheese on all lettuce leaves with a spoon, then roll up the lettuce to seal the wrap and serve warm.

Nutrition: Calories: 289Fat: 14.8gProtein: 31.2gCarbs: 6.9gFiber: 3.1gSugar: 3.8gSodium: 262mg

SNACK

Ketogenic Madeleine

Preparation Time: 10 minutes
Cooking Time: 15 minutes
Servings: 12

Ingredients
- 2 Large pastured eggs
- ¾ Cup of almond flour
- 1 and ½ Tablespoons of Swerve
- ¼ Cup of cooled, melted coconut oil
- 1 Teaspoon of vanilla extract
- 1 Teaspoon of almond extract
- 1 Teaspoon of lemon zest
- ¼ Teaspoon of salt

Directions
1. Preheat your oven to a temperature of about 350 F.
2. Combine the eggs with the salt and whisk on a high speed for about 5 minutes.
3. Slowly add in the Swerve and keep mixing on high for 2 additional minutes.
4. Stir in the almond flour until it is very well-incorporated; then add in the vanilla and the almond extracts.
5. Add in the melted coconut oil and stir all your ingredients together.
6. Pour the obtained batter into equal parts in a greased Madeleine tray.
7. Bake your Ketogenic Madeleine for about 13 minutes or until the edges start to have a brown color.
8. Flip the Madeleines out of the baking tray.
9. Serve and enjoy your madeleines!

Nutrition: Calories: 87 Fat: 8.1gCarbohydrates: 3gFiber: 2g Protein: 8g

Keto Waffles

Preparation Time: 20 minutes
Cooking Time: 30 minutes
Servings: 3

Ingredients:
For the Ketogenic waffles:

- 8 Oz of cream cheese
- 5 Large pastured eggs
- 1/3 Cup of coconut flour
- ½ Teaspoon of Xanthan gum
- 1 Pinch of salt
- ½ Teaspoon of vanilla extract
- 2 Tablespoons of Swerve
- ¼ Teaspoon of baking soda
- 1/3 Cup of almond milk

Optional ingredients:
- ½ Teaspoon of cinnamon pie spice
- ¼ Teaspoon of almond extract

To prepare the low-carb Maple Syrup:
- 1 Cup of water
- 1 Tablespoon of Maple flavor
- ¾ Cup of powdered Swerve
- 1 Tablespoon of almond butter
- ½ Teaspoon of Xanthan gum

Directions
For the waffles:
1. Make sure all your ingredients are exactly at room temperature.
2. Place all your ingredients for the waffles from cream cheese to pastured eggs, coconut flour, Xanthan gum, salt, vanilla extract, the Swerve, the baking soda and the almond milk except for the almond milk with the help of a processor.
3. Blend your ingredients until it becomes smooth and creamy; then transfer the batter to a bowl.
4. Add the almond milk and mix your ingredients with a spatula.
5. Heat a waffle maker to a temperature of high.
6. Spray your waffle maker with coconut oil and add about ¼ of the batter in it evenly with a spatula into your waffle iron.
7. Close your waffle and cook until you get the color you want.
8. Carefully remove the waffles to a platter.

For the Ketogenic Maple Syrup:

1. Place 1 and ¼ cups of water, the swerve and the maple in a small pan and bring to a boil over a low heat; then let simmer for about 10 minutes.

2. Add the coconut oil.

3. Sprinkle the Xanthan gum over the top of the waffle and use an immersion blender to blend smoothly.

4. Serve and enjoy your delicious waffles!

Nutrition: Calories: 316 Fat: 26gCarbohydrates: 7gFiber: 3g Protein: 11g

Ketogenic pretzels

Preparation Time: 10 minutes

Cooking Time: 20 minutes

Servings: 7-8

Ingredients:

- 1 and ½ cups of pre-shredded mozzarella
- 2 Tablespoons of full fat cream cheese
- 1 Large egg
- ¾ Cup of almond flour+ 2 tablespoons of ground almonds or almond meal
- ½ Teaspoon of baking powder
- 1 Pinch of coarse sea salt

Directions:

1. Heat your oven to a temperature of about 180 C/356 F.

2. Melt the cream cheese and the mozzarella cheese and stir over a low heat until the cheeses are perfectly melted.

3. If you choose to microwave the cheese, just do that for about 1 minute no more and if you want to do it on the stove, turn off the heat as soon as the cheese is completely melted.

4. Add the large egg to the prepared warm dough; then stir until your ingredients are very well combined. If the egg is cold; you will need to gently heat it.

5. Add in the ground almonds or the almond flour and the baking powder and stir until your ingredients are very well combined.

6. Take one pinch of the dough of cheese and toll it or stretch it in your hands until it is about 18 to 20 cm of length; if your dough is sticky, you can oil your hands to avoid that.

7. Now, form pretzels from the cheese dough and nicely shape it; then place it over a baking sheet.

8. Sprinkle with a little bit of salt and bake for about 17 minutes.

9. Serve and enjoy your pretzels!

Nutrition: Calories: 113 Fat: 8.4gCarbohydrates: 2.5gFiber: 0.8g Protein: 8.7g

Cheesy Taco bites

Preparation Time: 5 minutes

Cooking Time: 10 minutes

Servings: 12

Ingredients

- 2 Cups of Packaged Shredded Cheddar Cheese
- 2 Tablespoon of Chili Powder
- 2 Tablespoons of Cumin
- 1 Teaspoon of Salt
- 8 Teaspoons of coconut cream for garnishing
- Use Pico de Gallo for garnishing as well

Directions:

1. Preheat your oven to a temperature of about 350 F.

2. Over a baking sheet lined with a parchment paper, place 1 tablespoon piles of cheese and make sure to a space of 2 inches between each.

3. Place the baking sheet in your oven and bake for about 5 minutes.

4. Remove from the oven and let the cheese cool down for about 1 minute; then carefully lift up and press each into the cups of a mini muffin tin.

5. Make sure to press the edges of the cheese to form the shape of muffins mini.

6. Let the cheese cool completely; then remove it.

7. While you continue to bake the cheese and create your cups.

8. Fill the cheese cups with the coconut cream, then top with the Pico de Gallo.

9. Serve and enjoy your delicious snack!

Nutrition: Calories: 73 Fat: 5gCarbohydrates: 3gFiber: 1g Protein: 4g

Nut squares

Preparation Time: 30 minutes
Cooking Time: 10 minutes
Servings: 10

Ingredients:

- 2 Cups of almonds, pumpkin seeds, sunflower seeds and walnuts
- ½ Cup of desiccated coconut
- 1 Tablespoon of chia seeds
- ¼ Teaspoon of salt
- 2 Tablespoons of coconut oil
- 1 Teaspoon of vanilla extract
- 3 Tablespoons of almond or peanut butter
- 1/3 Cup of Sukrin Gold Fiber Syrup

Directions:

1. Line a square baking tin with a baking paper; then lightly grease it with cooking spray
2. Chop all the nuts roughly; then slightly grease it too, you can also leave them as whole
3. Mix the nuts in a large bowl; then combine them in a large bowl with the coconut, the chia seeds and the salt
4. In a microwave-proof bowl; add the coconut oil; then add the vanilla, the coconut butter or oil, the almond butter and the fiber syrup and microwave the mixture for about 30 seconds
5. Stir your ingredients together very well; then pour the melted mixture right on top of the nuts
6. Press the mixture into your prepared baking tin with the help of the back of a measuring cup and push very well
7. Freeze your treat for about 1 hour before cutting it
8. Cut your frozen nut batter into small cubes or squares of the same size
9. Serve and enjoy!

Nutrition: Calories: 268 Fat: 22gCarbohydrates: 14gFiber: 1g Protein: 7g

Coconut snack bars

Preparation Time: 30 minutes
Cooking Time: 0 minutes

Servings: 13

Ingredients:

- 2 Cups of coconut flakes
- ¾ Cup of melted coconut oil
- 1 and ½ cups of macadamia nuts
- 1 large scoop of vanilla protein powder
- ¼ Cup of unsweetened dark chocolate chips

Directions:

1. Gather the coconut flakes with the melted coconut oil, the macadamia nuts, the vanilla protein powder and the dark chocolate chips in a large bowl and mix very well.
2. Line an 8×8 baking tray with a parchment paper.
3. Process the macadamia nuts with the coconut oil in a food processor until it becomes smooth.
4. Pour the batter into a pan and freeze it for about 30 minutes.
5. Cut the frozen batter into bars with a sharp knife into your preferred size.
6. Serve and enjoy your Ketogenic treat or store it and serve it whenever you want.

Nutrition: Calories: 213.7 Fat: 20gCarbohydrates: 6gFiber: 2 g Protein: 4g

Flax seed Crackers

Preparation Time: 8 minutes
Cooking Time: 10 minutes
Servings: 25

Ingredients:

- 2 and 1/2 cups of almond flour
- ½ Cup of coconut flour
- 1 Teaspoon of ground flaxseed meal
- ½ Teaspoon of dried rosemary, chopped
- ½ Teaspoon of onion powder
- ¼ Teaspoon of kosher salt
- 3 large organic eggs
- 1 Tablespoon of extra-virgin olive oil

Directions:

1. Preheat your oven to a temperature of about 325 F.
2. Line a baking sheet with a parchment paper.
3. In a large bowl; combine the flours with the rosemary, the flax meal, the salt and the onion powder and mix.
4. Crack in the eggs and add the oil; then mix very well and combine your ingredients very well.

5.   Keep mixing until you get the shape of a large ball for about 1 minute.

6.   Cut the dough into the 2 pieces of parchment paper and roll it to a thickness of about ¼".

7.   Cut the dough into squares and transfer it to the prepared baking sheet.

8.   Bake your dough for about 13 to 15 minutes; then let cool for about 15 minutes.

9.   Serve and enjoy your crackers or store in a container.

Nutrition: Calories: 150.2 Fat: 13gCarbohydrates: 5.4g Fiber: 2.6g Protein: 7g

Almond flour crackers

Preparation Time: 7 minutes

Cooking Time: 12 minutes

Servings: 15

Ingredients:
- 2 Cups of Blanched almond flour
- ½ Teaspoon of sea salt
- 1 Beaten large Egg

Directions:

1.   Preheat your oven to a temperature of about 350 F.

2.   Line a baking sheet with a parchment paper; then combine the almond flour and the salt in a large bowl; then crack in the egg and mix very well until you form a large ball of dough.

3.   Place your dough between two large pieces of prepared parchment paper; then use a rolling pin to roll the dough into a rectangular shape.

4.   Cut the dough into rectangles; then prick it with a fork and place it over the prepared and lined baking sheet.

5.   Bake your crackers for about 8 to 12 minutes.

6.   Let the crackers cool for about 10 minutes.

7.   Store the crackers in a container; or serve and enjoy them right away!

Nutrition Calories: 120 Fat: 6gCarbohydrates: 14gFiber: 2g Protein: 3g

Keto donuts

Preparation Time: 5 minutes

Cooking Time: 0 minutes

Servings: 4

Ingredients:

For the donut ingredients:
- ½ Cup of sifted almond flour
- 3 to 4 tablespoons of coconut milk
- 2 Large eggs
- 2 to 3 tablespoons granulated of stevia
- 1 Teaspoon of Keto-friendly baking powder
- 1 Heap teaspoon of apple cider vinegar
- 1 Pinch of salt
- 1 and ½ Tablespoon of sifted cacao powder
- 3 Teaspoons of Ceylon cinnamon
- 1 Teaspoon of powdered vanilla bean
- 1 Tablespoon of grass-fed ghee
- 2 Tablespoons of Coconut oil for greasing

For the Icing Ingredients:
- 4 Tablespoons of melted coconut butter with 1 to 2 teaspoons of coconut oil
- Optional garnishing ingredients: edible rose petals, or shredded cacao

Directions:

1.   Preheat the oven to a temperature of about 350 degrees.

2.   Grease a donut tray with the coconut oil.

3.   Stir all together the sifted almond flour with the coconut milk, eggs, the granulated of stevia, the Keto-friendly baking powder, the apple cider vinegar, the salt, the sifted cocoa powder, the Ceylon cinnamon, the powdered vanilla bean and the grass-fed ghee.

4.   Mix your donut ingredients until they are evenly combined.

5.   Divide the obtained batter into the donut moulds making sure to fill each to ¾ full.

6.   Bake for about 8 minutes; then remove the tray from the oven and carefully transfer it to a wire rack.

7.   Serve and enjoy your donut or top it with the icing and the garnish of your choice.

8.   Serve and enjoy your delicious treat!

Nutrition Calories: 122 Fat: 6.8gCarbohydrates: 13.5gFiber: 2.3g Protein: 3g

DESSERT

Strawberry Sherbet

Preparation Time: 3 hours
Cooking Time: 0 minutes
Servings: 5

Ingredients

- 3/4 cup white sugar
- 1/4 cup milk
- 1/4 cup lime juice
- 2 quarts fresh strawberries, mashed
- 1 egg white

Directions

1. Mix sugar, milk, and lime juice together in a bowl. Mix in mashed strawberries.
2. Beat egg white in a glass, metal, or ceramic bowl until stiff peaks form. Fold into the strawberry-lime mixture. Pour the mixture right into a freezer-safe container. Cover with plastic wrap.
3. Freeze until almost firm, about 2 hours. Remove from freezer and stir thoroughly to split up chunks. Go back to the freezer for 3 hours, stirring once every hour. Freeze until firm, 8 hours to overnight.

Nutrition: Calories: 205 kcal Protein: 5.13 gFat: 15.54 g Carbohydrates: 14.49 g

Honeysuckle Pineapple

Preparation Time: 10 minutes
Cooking Time: 10 minutes
Servings: 6

Ingredients

- 4 slices fresh pineapples
- 1 1/2 tablespoons honey
- 2 tablespoons cherry brandy
- 1 teaspoon lemon juice

Directions

1. To Marinate: Combine honey, brandy and lemon juice in a nonporous glass dish or bowl. Mix together and add pineapple; coat well with marinade mixture. Cover dish and marinate in refrigerator for 1 hour.

2. Preheat grill to medium heat and lightly oil grate.
3. Remove pineapple from dish or bowl, discarding any leftover marinade. Place pineapple wedges directly on rack or in a basket and grill for about 10 minutes, turning, until pineapple is hot and caramelized.

Nutrition: Calories: 37 kcal Protein: 0.18 g Fat: 0.03 g Carbohydrates: 9.74 g

Sneaky Mommy's Chocolate Zucchini Cake

Preparation Time: 10 minutes
Cooking Time: 45 minutes
Servings: 5

Ingredients

- 2 1/2 cups whole wheat flour
- 1/4 cup unsweetened cocoa powder
- 1 teaspoon baking soda
- 1 teaspoon cinnamon
- 1/2 teaspoon baking powder
- 1/2 teaspoon ground cloves
- 2 large eggs
- 1 cup sugar
- 1/2 cup unsweetened applesauce
- 1/2 cup vegetable oil
- 3/4 cup apple juice concentrate, thawed
- 1 teaspoon vanilla extract
- 1/2 cup milk
- 2 cups shredded, unpeeled zucchini
- 1/2 cup shredded carrot
- 1 cup chopped raisins
- 1/3 cup chopped dates

Directions

1. Preheat oven to 350 degrees F (175 degrees C). Grease a 9x13 inch baking dish. Whisk together the flour, cocoa powder, baking soda, cinnamon, baking powder and cloves in a bowl; reserves.
2. Beat together the eggs, sugar, applesauce, vegetable oil, apple juice concentrate, and vanilla extract in a mixing bowl until smooth. Stir in the dry mixture

alternately with the milk, then add the zucchini, carrot, raisins, and dates; stir until just moistened. Pour into the prepared baking dish.

3. Bake in the preheated oven until a toothpick inserted into the center of the cake comes out clean, 35 to 45 minutes. Cool in the pan set over a wire rack.

Nutrition: Calories: 37 kcal Protein: 0.18 g Fat: 0.03 g Carbohydrates: 9.74 g

Honeydew Blueberry Soup

Preparation Time: 5 minutes
Cooking Time: 0 minutes
Servings: 6
Ingredients

- 1 honeydew melon
- 1 -pint blueberries
- 6 cookie (2-5/8"dia) s oatmeal cookies

Directions

1. Cut the melon from the rind and into chunks. Puree until smooth in a food processor or blender. Pour into a large bowl and stir blueberries into pureed melon. Chill until quite cold.

2. To serve, ladle soup into individual bowls and crumble an oatmeal cookie over each serving.

Nutrition: Calories: 38 kcal Protein: 0.44 g Fat: 1.44 g Carbohydrates: 5.89 g

Sugarless Applesauce Cake

Preparation Time: 15 minutes
Cooking Time: 1 hour
Servings: 5
Ingredients

- 2 cups all-purpose flour
- 1 teaspoon baking powder
- 1 teaspoon baking soda
- 1/2 teaspoon ground cinnamon
- 1/2 teaspoon ground nutmeg
- 1/2 teaspoon salt
- 1 1/2 cups unsweetened applesauce
- 3/4 cup brown sugar twin
- 2 large eggs
- 1 teaspoon vanilla extract
- 1/2 cup raisins

Directions

1. Preheat oven to 350 degrees F (175 degrees C). Spray an 8x4 inch loaf pan with cooking spray.

2. Sift together flour, baking powder, baking soda, cinnamon, nutmeg and salt. Set aside.

3. Beat the eggs until light and add sugar twin. Add applesauce and vanilla.

4. Add flour mixture and beat until smooth. Fold in raisins.

5. Pour batter into loaf pan. Bake at 350 degrees F (175 degrees C) for about an hour, or until a toothpick inserted into cake comes out clean.

Nutrition: Calories: 298 kcal Protein: 6.39 g Fat: 2.46 g Carbohydrates: 62.56 g

Chilled Cantaloupe Soup

Preparation Time: 1 hour
Cooking Time: 0 minutes
Servings: 6
Ingredients

- 1 cantaloupe - peeled, seeded and cubed
- 2 cups orange juice
- 1 tablespoon fresh lime juice
- 1/4 teaspoon ground cinnamon

Directions

1. Peel, seed, and cube the cantaloupe.

2. Place cantaloupe and 1/2 cup orange juice in a blender or food processor; cover, and process until smooth. Transfer to large bowl. Stir in lime juice, cinnamon, and remaining orange juice. Cover, and refrigerate for at least one hour. Garnish with mint if desired.

Nutrition: Calories: 42 kcal Protein: 0.6 g Fat: 0.11 g Carbohydrates: 10.07 g

Warm Apple Cinnamon Cobbler

Preparation Time: 20 minutes
Cooking Time: 30 minutes
Servings: 6
Ingredients

- 4 medium (2-3/4"dia) s apples - peeled, cored and sliced
- 1 cup water

- 2 teaspoons ground cinnamon
- 2 tablespoons cornstarch
- 1/4 cup fructose (fruit sugar)
- 1 cup whole wheat pastry flour
- 1 teaspoon baking powder
- 1/4 cup canola oil
- 1 tablespoon honey
- 1/2 cup low-fat buttermilk

Directions

1. Preheat oven to 375 degrees F (190 degrees C).
2. In a sizable saucepan over medium heat, incorporate the apples, water, cinnamon, cornstarch and fructose. Cook until apples are soft and mixture is thickened, about ten minutes.
3. Pour the apple mixture right into a casserole dish.
4. Prepare biscuit dough by combining the whole-wheat pastry flour and baking powder. Add the oil and stir until well mixed. Add the honey and buttermilk; stir with a fork until flour mixture is moist. Add additional milk if necessary.
5. Drop biscuit dough by tablespoons along with apples. Bake for 20 minutes or until biscuits are golden brown. Serve warm.

Nutrition: Calories: 216 kcal Protein: 6.01 g Fat: 12 gCarbohydrates: 23.34 g

Strawberry Champagne Soup

Preparation Time: 2 hours
Cooking Time: 0 minutes
Servings: 8

Ingredients

- 10 cups quartered strawberries
- 1/2 cup white sugar
- teaspoon 1/8 salt
- 2 cups champagne

Directions

1. Place the strawberries into a blender, and sprinkle with sugar and salt. Process until smooth. Cover, and chill for 2 hours. Stir in champagne just before serving.

Nutrition: Calories: 105 | Carbohydrate: 16.6g | Protein: 5.5g | Fat: 2.1g | Sugars: 3.9g | Dietary Fiber: 3.6g | Cholesterol: 0mg | Sodium: 1451mg |Potassium: 317mg

Sugar Free Spice Cookie

Preparation Time: 10 minutes
Cooking Time: 10 minutes
Servings: 8

Ingredients

- 2 1/2 cups water
- 2/3 cup shortening
- 2 cups raisins
- 1 1/2 tablespoons ground cinnamon
- 1 teaspoon ground nutmeg
- 4 large eggs
- 1 teaspoon salt
- 2 teaspoons baking soda
- 1 1/2 tablespoons liquid artificial sweetener
- 1/4 cup water
- 2 teaspoons baking powder
- 4 cups all-purpose flour

Directions

1. Preheat oven to 350 degrees F (175 degrees C). Grease a cookie sheet.
2. In a tiny saucepan, bring the 11/4 cup of water, raisins, shortening, cinnamon, and nutmeg to a boil. Remove from heat, beat in eggs, individually. Dissolve salt, soda, and liquid sweetener into the remaining 2 tablespoons of water; add alternately to the egg mixture, with the flour and baking powder.
3. Drop cookies by teaspoonfuls onto the prepared cookie sheet. Bake for 8 to ten minutes in the preheated oven. Cool on wire racks.

Nutrition: Calories: 194 kcal Protein: 1.43 g Fat: 19.56 g Carbohydrates: 4.27 g

Fresh Strawberry Granita

Preparation Time: 1 hour
Cooking Time: 0 minutes
Servings: 8

Ingredients

- 2 pounds ripe strawberries, hulled and halved
- 1/3 cup white sugar, or to taste

- 1 cup water
- 1/2 teaspoon lemon juice
- 1/4 teaspoon balsamic vinegar
- 1 tiny pinch salt

Directions

1.   Rinse strawberries with cold water; let drain. Transfer berries to a blender and add sugar, water, lemon juice, balsamic vinegar, and salt.

2.   Pulse several times to get the mixture moving, then blend until smooth, about 1 minute. Pour into a large baking dish. Puree should only be about 3/8 -inch deep in the dish.

3.   Place dish uncovered in the freezer until mixture barely begins to freeze around the edges, about 45 minutes. Mixture will still be slushy in the center.

4.   Lightly stir the crystals from the edge of the granita mixture into the center, using a fork, and mix thoroughly. Close freezer and chill until granita are nearly frozen, 30 to 40 more minutes. Mix lightly with a fork as before, scraping the crystals loose. Repeat freezing and stirring with the fork 3 to 4 times until the granita is light, crystals are separate, and granita looks dry and fluffy.

5.   Portion the granita into small serving bowls to serve.

Nutrition: Calories: 55 kcal Protein: 1 g Fat: 1.93 g Carbohydrates: 9.8 g

Pumpkin Pie for Dieters

Preparation Time: 1 hour chilling time
Cooking Time: 0 minutes
Servings: 6

Ingredients

- 1 (15-ounce) can pumpkin puree
- 1/2 cup skim milk
- 1 (1-ounce) package instant sugar-free vanilla pudding mix
- 1 teaspoon pumpkin pie spice
- 1 (8-ounce) container fat free frozen whipped topping

Directions

1.   In a medium bowl, mix together the pumpkin, milk, and instant pudding mix. Stir in the pumpkin pie spice, and fold in half of the whipped topping.

2.   Pour into an 8-inch pie plate, and spread remaining whipped topping over the top. Chill for 1 hour, or until set.

Nutrition: Calories: 76 kcal Protein: 0.66 g Fat: 0.15 gCarbohydrates: 18.17 g

Lime abalemon Glaciate

Preparation Time: 5 minutes
Cooking Time: 0 minutes
Servings: 2

Ingredients

- 1 1/2 cups crushed ice
- 1 ripe banana
- 1/2 lime, juiced
- 1/2 lemon, juiced
- 1 tablespoon shredded coconut, as garnish
- 2 cherries pitted cherries, as garnish

Directions

1.   Blend the ice and banana together in a blender set to Low until mixed, adding the lime juice and lemon juice as it blends to keep the ice from freezing to the side of the blender.

2.   Serve in a tall glass and garnish with coconut or a cherry.

Nutrition: Calories: 293 kcal Protein: 3.89 g Fat: 15.56 g Carbohydrates: 36.27 g

Healthy and Tasty Strawberry Sherbet

Preparation Time: 1 hour plus chilling time
Cooking Time: 0 minutes
Servings: 2

Ingredients

- 2 cups frozen strawberries
- 2 tablespoons white sugar
- 1 teaspoon lemon juice

Directions

1.   Place strawberries in a food processor and blend until smooth, about 30 seconds. Blend in sugar and lemon juice, about 10 seconds more.

2.   Freeze sherbet until solid, about 1 hour.

Nutrition: Calories: 53 kcal Protein: 1.06 g Fat: 1.02 g Carbohydrates: 11.62 g

Apple Cinnamon Cake

Preparation Time: 10 minutes
Cooking Time: 35 minutes
Servings: 4

Ingredients
- 2/3 cup flour
- 1/2 cup whole wheat flour
- 1 teaspoon baking soda
- 1 teaspoon cinnamon
- 1/4 teaspoon salt
- 1 1/2 cups peeled cored and finely chopped apples
- 1/4 cup fat-free liquid egg product
- 1/2 cup Splenda + 1/4 cup brown sugar
- 1/2 cup chopped walnuts or 1/2 cup pecans
- 1/4 cup applesauce
- 1 tablespoon flour
- 1 tablespoon whole wheat flour
- 1/2 teaspoon cinnamon
- 1 tablespoon butter
- 1/4 cup walnuts or 1/4 cup pecans

Directions
1. Lightly coat a 9-inch baking pan with cooking spray; set aside.
2. In a medium bowl combine the 2/3 cup flour, 1/2 cup whole flour, soda, 1 teaspoon cinnamon, and salt, set aside.
3. In a large mixing bowl toss together the chopped apple and egg product; stir in the 3/4 cup sugar, the 1/4 cup nuts and applesauce. Add flour mixture and stir until just combined.
4. Pour batter into prepared pan.
To Make Topping:
1. Stir together the brown sugar the remaining flour, whole wheat flour and cinnamon; Cut in butter until crumbly, stir in remaining nuts, sprinkle topping over batter in pan.
2. Bake in 350F oven 30 to 35 minutes or until a toothpick comes out clean; cool in pan for 10 minutes, serve warm.

Nutrition: 217 Calories; 7g fat; 37g Carbohydrates; 3g Protein; per 1/10 of recipe

Chocolate Apple Cake

Preparation Time: 10 minutes
Cooking Time: 3 minutes
Servings: 4
Preparation Time:
Cooking Time:
Servings:

Ingredients
- 3/4 cup whole wheat flour
- 3/4 cup flour
- 1 teaspoon baking soda
- 1/4 cup cocoa
- 1/2 teaspoon salt
- 1 cup water
- 1/4 cup applesauce
- 1 teaspoon lemon juice
- 1 teaspoon vanilla
- 1 apple, chopped and peeled (1 cup)
- 3/4 cup Splenda
- 1/2 teaspoon cinnamon

Directions
1. Oven to 350F°.
2. Spray a square pan with nonstick spray, I used a glass pan. Combine first 5 ingredients in bowl.
3. In another bowl, combine water, oil, lemon juice, vanilla. Add to dry ingredients, stir until just combined.
4. Toss apples with sugar and cinnamon, fold into batter. Pour into prepared pan.
5. Bake for 30-35 minutes or until done.

Nutrition: 141 Calories; 1g fat; 32g Carbohydrates; 3g Protein; per 1/9 of recipe

Walnut Apple Cake

Preparation Time: 10 minutes
Cooking Time: 3 minutes
Servings: 4

Ingredients
- 1 1/2 cups low-fat buttermilk
- 1 cup organic rolled oats
- 1/2 cup applesauce
- 2 beaten eggs (or 1/2 cup Eggbeaters)
- 1/4 cup honey or 1/4 cup Splenda granular

- 1 cup whole wheat flour
- 1/2 cup unbleached self-rising flour
- 1 1/4 teaspoons baking powder
- 3/4 teaspoon ground cinnamon (or to taste)
- 1/4 cup roughly chopped walnuts
- 2 tablespoons sultanas

Directions

1. Combine the buttermilk and rolled oats in a bowl and set aside for 15-20 minutes until the oats have softened.

2. While the buttermilk and oats are standing, pre-heat your oven to 350°f and line a standard baking tin with greaseproof paper.

3. Beat the eggs and add to the oatmeal mix along with the applesauce.

4. If using honey add to wet ingredients. It using Splenda add to dry ingredients.

5. Mix the dry ingredients together, stirring to combine and add to the wet, mixing well.

6. Transfer the solid batter into the prepared baking tin. Using a wooden spoon, spread the batter to even it out.

7. Sprinkle the cake with roughly chopped walnuts and sultanas and let it sit for 20 minutes before baking.

8. Bake cake for approximately 1 hour or until a skewer inserted into the cake comes out clean.

Nutrition: 141 Calories; 1g fat; 32g Carbohydrates; 3g Protein; per 1/9 of recipe

Apple Pie

Preparation Time: 10 minutes
Cooking Time: 3 minutes
Servings: 4

Ingredients

- 1 cup dry rolled oats
- 1/4 cup whole-wheat pastry flour
- 1/4 cup ground almonds
- 2 tablespoons brown sugar, packed
- 3 tablespoons canola oil
- 1 tablespoon water

Filling

- 6 cups sliced and peeled tart apples (about 4 large apples)

- 1/3 cup frozen apple juice concentrate
- 2 tablespoons quick-cooking tapioca
- 1 teaspoon cinnamon

Directions

1. To prepare pie crust, mix dry ingredients together in a large mixing bowl. In a separate bowl, mix oil and water together with whisk. Add oil and water mixture to dry ingredients. Mix until dough holds together. Add a bit more water if needed. Press dough into a 9-inch pie plate. Set aside until filling is prepared.

2. To prepare filling, combine all ingredients in a large bowl. Let stand for 15 minutes. Stir and then spoon into prepared pie crust.

3. Bake at 425 F for 15 minutes. Reduce heat to 350 F and bake 40 minutes, or until apples are tender.

Nutrition: 204 calories; 8 g fat;29 g carbohydrates; 4 g protein; per cookie

Cranberry Pound Cake

Preparation Time: 10 minutes
Cooking Time: 40 minutes
Servings: 4

Ingredients

- 2 cups all-purpose flour
- 1 1/4 teaspoons baking powder
- 1/2 teaspoon baking soda
- 3 tablespoons butter, softened
- 1/2 cup Splenda Sugar Blend for Baking
- 2 eggs
- 1/4 teaspoon orange extract (optional)
- 2/3 cup plain nonfat yogurt
- 2 cups fresh cranberries
- 1/4 cup water or 1/4 cup orange juice
- 1 1/2 teaspoons orange zest, finely grated

Directions

1. Preheat oven to 350F. Prepare Bundt or tube pan with a light coat of cooking spray.

2. In a medium bowl, sift together the flour, baking soda and baking powder.

3. In a large bowl, cream the butter with an electric mixer. Add Splenda blend and beat until pale, light and fluffy. Add the eggs, one at a time, mixing after each

addition for a total of two or three minutes. If want more orange flavor, mix in the orange extract at this step.

4. Mix together the yogurt and water or orange juice.

5. Add in the cranberries, folding in to distribute throughout the batter.

6. Pour batter into the prepare tube pan and bake for 40 minutes or until an inserted toothpick comes out clean.

7. Cool cake in pan for 10 minutes until turning onto cake rack or plate.

Nutrition: 161 Calories; 4g fat; 27g Carbohydrates; 4g Protein; per 1/12 of recipe

Chocolate Fudge Nut Cake

Preparation Time: 10 minutes

Cooking Time: 35 minutes

Servings: 4

Ingredients

- ½ cup whole-wheat pastry flour
- ½ cup all-purpose flour
- 1/3 cup sugar or 3 tablespoons Splenda Sugar Blend for Baking
- ¼ cup unsweetened cocoa powder, sifted
- 1½ teaspoons baking powder
- ½ teaspoon salt
- 1 large egg
- ½ cup 1% milk
- 2 tablespoons canola oil
- 2 teaspoons vanilla extract
- ¾ cup semisweet chocolate chips
- 11/3 cups hot brewed coffee
- 2/3 cup packed light brown sugar, or Splenda Granular
- ¼ cup chopped walnuts, or pecans, toasted
- Confectioners' sugar, for dusting

Directions

1. Preheat oven to 350°F. Coat a 1½- to 2-quart baking dish with cooking spray. Whisk whole-wheat flour, all-purpose flour, sugar or Splenda Sugar Blend, cocoa, baking powder and salt in a large bowl.

2. Whisk egg, milk, oil and vanilla in a glass measuring cup. Add to the flour mixture; stir with a rubber spatula until just combined.

3. Fold in chocolate chips, if using. Scrape the batter into the prepared baking dish. Mix hot coffee and brown sugar or Splenda Granular in the measuring cup and pour over the batter.

4. Sprinkle with nuts.

5. Bake the pudding cake until the top springs back when touched lightly, 30 to 35 minutes. Let cool for at least 10 minutes. Dust with confectioners' sugar and serve hot or warm.

Nutrition: 162 Calories; 22g Carbohydrates; 7g Fat; 4g Protein; per 1/8 of recipe

Crustless Pumpkin Pie

Preparation Time: 10 minutes

Cooking Time: 0 minutes

Servings: 4

Ingredients

- 1 (15 ounce) can pumpkin puree
- 1/2 cup skim milk
- 1 (1 ounce) package instant sugar-free vanilla pudding mix
- 1 teaspoon pumpkin pie spice
- 1 (8 ounce) container fat free frozen whipped topping

Directions

1. In a medium bowl, mix together the pumpkin, milk, and instant pudding mix. Stir in the pumpkin pie spice, and fold in half of the whipped topping.

2. Pour into an 8-inch pie plate, and spread remaining whipped topping over the top. Chill for 1 hour, or until set.

Nutrition: 110 Calories; 0g fat; 23g Carbohydrates; 1.5g Protein; per 1/6 of recipe

Applesauce Raisin Cake

Preparation Time: 10 minutes
Cooking Time: 1 hour
Servings: 4

Ingredients

- 2 cups all-purpose flour
- 1 teaspoon baking powder
- 1 teaspoon baking soda
- 1/2 teaspoon ground cinnamon
- 1/2 teaspoon ground nutmeg
- 1/2 teaspoon salt
- 1 1/2 cups unsweetened applesauce
- 3/4 cup brown sugar twin
- 2 eggs
- 1 teaspoon vanilla extract
- 1/2 cup raisins

Directions

1. Preheat oven to 350 degrees F (175 degrees C). Spray an 8x4 inch loaf pan with cooking spray.
2. Sift together flour, baking powder, baking soda, cinnamon, nutmeg and salt. Set aside.
3. Beat the eggs until light and add sugar twin. Add applesauce and vanilla.
4. Add flour mixture and beat until smooth. Fold in raisins.
5. Pour batter into loaf pan. Bake at 350 F (175 degrees C) for about an hour, or until a toothpick inserted into cake comes out clean.

Nutrition: 125 Calories; 1g fat; 26g Carbohydrates; 3g Protein; per 1/12 of recipe

Easy Peanut Butter Squares

Preparation Time: 10 minutes
Cooking Time: 2 minutes
Servings: 4

Ingredients

- 1 box butterscotch pudding jello (sugar and fat free mix)
- 6 1 oz. squares baker's white chocolate
- 1/2 cup peanut butter (smooth, with salt)
- 3 cups Stevia (Powdered measures like sugar)
- 1/4 cup mixed nuts, dry roasted, chopped

- 1/3 cup water

Directions

1. Line an 8" square pan with foil, leaving ends sticking out to use as handles later.
2. In a microwave bowl combine 6 oz. white Bakers chocolate, 1/2 cup peanut butter and 1/3 cup water. Cook on high 1 1/2 minutes and stir, repeat until smooth.
3. Add dry pudding mix, whisk 2 minutes. Gradually stir in Stevia. Spread in the bottom of 8" square pan. Top with chopped nuts, pressing down to secure.
4. Refrigerate 2 hours, lift from foil edges and flip onto cutting board.

Nutrition: 93 calories; 6 g fat; 7 g carbohydrates; 2 g protein

Chocolate Walnut Brownies

Preparation Time: 10 minutes
Cooking Time: 30 minutes
Servings: 4

Ingredients

- 1/2 cup margarine
- 1/4 cup unsweetened cocoa powder
- 2 eggs
- 1 cup granular sucrolose sweetener
- 1/4 teaspoon baking powder
- 1/2 teaspoon vanilla
- 3/4 cup all-purpose flour
- 1/8 teaspoon salt
- 1/4 cup 2% milk
- 1/2 cup chopped walnuts

Directions

1. Preheat oven to 350 degrees F (175 degrees C). Grease and flour an 8x8 inch pan.
2. In a small saucepan over medium heat, melt margarine and cocoa together, stirring occasionally until smooth. Remove from heat and set aside to cool. In a large bowl, beat eggs until frothy. Stir in the sucrolose sweetener. Combine the flour, baking powder and salt; stir into the egg mixture then mix in the vanilla, cocoa and margarine.

3. Finally stir in the 1/4 cup of milk and the walnuts. Pour into the prepared pan.

4. Bake for 25 to 30 minutes in the preheated oven, until a toothpick inserted into the center, comes out clean.

Nutrition: 129 calories; 4g fat; 24g carbohydrates; 2g protein; per 1/12 of recipe

Banana Peanut Butter Cookies

Preparation Time: 10 minutes
Cooking Time: 14 minutes
Servings: 6

Ingredients

- 1 1/2 cups all-purpose flour
- 2 teaspoons baking powder
- 1/2 teaspoon baking soda
- 1/8 teaspoon cream of tartar
- 1/8 teaspoon salt
- 1/2 cup all natural peanut butter
- 1/2 cup unsalted butter
- 1 large egg
- 1 ripe medium banana, mashed
- 1/2 cup Splenda Brown Sugar Substitute
- 1/4 cup Splenda
- 2 teaspoons vanilla

Directions

1. Preheat oven to 350°F.
2. Sift together the first five dry ingredients.
3. In a large mixer bowl, cream together the peanut butter and unsalted butter until fluffy. At low speed, mix in the egg, pureed banana, Splenda, and vanilla.
4. With the mixer at low speed, slowly add the sifted dry ingredients until fully mixed.
5. Shape dough into one-inch balls. Place on ungreased cookie sheet 1" (2.5cm) apart. Flatten cookies with the palm of your hand.
6. Bake for 12 – 14 minutes or until bottoms are golden brown.
7. Remove cookies from cookie sheets to wire rack, and cool completely.

Nutrition: 46 calories; 3g fat; 5g carbohydrates; 1g protein; per cookie

Pumpkin Cinnamon Cookies

Preparation Time: 10 minutes
Cooking Time: 5 minutes
Servings: 14

Ingredients

- 3/4 cup Splenda Granular
- 1 cup rolled oats
- 1 cup whole wheat flour
- 1/2 cup soy flour
- 1 3/4 teaspoons baking soda
- 1/2 teaspoon baking powder
- 1/2 teaspoon salt
- 2 teaspoons ground cinnamon
- 1 teaspoon ground nutmeg
- 1/2 cup pumpkin puree
- 1 tablespoon canola oil
- 2 teaspoons water
- 2 egg whites
- 1 teaspoon molasses
- 1 tablespoon flax seeds (optional)

Directions

1. Preheat oven to 350 F.
2. In a large bowl, whisk together Splenda, oats, wheat flour, soy flour, baking soda, baking powder, salt, cinnamon, and nutmeg. Stir in pumpkin, canola oil, water, egg whites, and molasses. Stir in flax seeds, if desired. Roll into 14 large balls, and flatten on a baking sheet.
3. Bake for 5 minutes in preheated oven. Careful not to over bake or the cookies will be too dry.

Nutrition: 85 calories; 2g fat; 13g carbohydrates; 4g protein

Almond Cookies

Preparation Time: 10 minutes
Cooking Time: 20 minutes
Servings: 30 cookies

Ingredients

- 1 1/2 cups almond flour
- 1/2 cup flax seed meal
- 1/4 cup artificial sweetener
- 2 ounces walnuts, chopped

- 1 teaspoon baking powder
- 4 egg whites
- 1 ounce butter, softened

Directions

1. Preheat oven to 350°F. Combine and mix all dry ingredients.

2. Add softened butter and rub into dry ingredients until even and produces a slightly grainy texture. Add egg whites and mix well.

3. Using a leveled tablespoon, add dough onto parchment paper. Press each cookie down with a fork.

4. Bake 18-20 minutes. Remove and cool on a wire rack.

Nutrition: per cookie 31 calories3g fat1g carbohydrates1g protein

Buckwheat Chocolate Cake

Preparation Time: 10 minutes
Cooking Time: 20 minutes
Servings: 6

Ingredients

- 7 oz. unsweetened 100 % dark chocolate
- 2 tablespoons butter
- 4 whole eggs
- 1 egg yolk
- Swerve, to taste
- 1 oz. cornflour
- 1 oz. buckwheat flour
- 1/4 cup coconut milk

Directions

1. Adjust the oven to 360 degrees F. Grease four ramekin with oil.

2. Heat chocolate with butter in a saucepan until it melts. Keep it aside.

3. Whisk eggs with sweetener and egg yolk in a mixer.

4. Stir in buckwheat flour and corn flour. Mix until smooth.

5. Heat coconut milk in a saucepan then pours it into egg mixture with continuous stirring.

6. Add in chocolate melts then divide the batter into the ramekins.

7. Bake for 15 minutes.

8. Serve.

Nutrition: 148 calories4.7 g fat176 mg cholesterol36 mg sodium12.5 g carbohydrates0.5 g dietary fiber4.5 g sugars1.4 g protein

Meringue Custard dessert

Preparation Time: 10 minutes
Cooking Time: 20 minutes
Servings: 2

Ingredients

- Vanilla custard
- 2 cup canned coconut milk
- 1 teaspoon vanilla extract
- 4 egg yolk
- 1 cup swerve sweetener
- Poached Meringue
- 4 egg white
- 2 tablespoons swerve

Garnish

- 2 tablespoons sliced almonds
- 1/4 cup raspberries fresh or defrost

Directions

Vanilla Custard

1. Heat milk mixed with vanilla in a saucepan until it boils.

2. Separate egg yolk from egg whites.

3. Beat egg yolk with sugar-free sweetener in an electric mixer until fluffy.

4. Pour in lukewarm vanilla milk and mix well.

5. Heat the combined mixture in a saucepan and cook for 10 minutes on low heat until it thickens.

6. Refrigerate the custard until further used.

7. Prepare the meringue

8. Beat egg white with sweetener in an electric mixer until foamy.

9. Boil 1-liter water in a saucepan and add egg white mixture scoop by scoop.

10. Let it poach for 30 seconds on both sides.

11. Serve the custard with meringue, melted chocolate, caramel, almonds, and raspberries.

Nutrition: 274 calories0.7 g fat 31 mg cholesterol21 mg sodium22.5 g carbohydrates0.3 g dietary fiber0.4 g protein

Avocado Brownies

Preparation Time: 10 minutes

Cooking Time: 40 minutes

Servings: 4

Ingredients

- 3 oz. unsweetened dark chocolate bites
- 2 teaspoons virgin coconut oil
- 1 cup ripe avocado flesh
- 2 eggs
- 1/2 cup erythritol
- 1/2 cup almond meal
- 1/2 cup unsweetened cocoa powder
- 1/2 teaspoon baking soda
- 1/4 teaspoon salt
- 1 teaspoon vanilla extract

Directions

1. Adjust the oven to 350F. Layer a 24x24 cm brownie pan with a parchment sheet.
2. Melt chocolate bites with coconut oil in a saucepan.
3. Blend avocado flesh, almond meal, eggs, erythritol, cocoa powder, salt, baking soda, vanilla extract and melted chocolate in a blender.
4. Pour the avocado batter into the square pan. Spread it evenly.
5. Bake for 30 minutes.
6. Cool and slice the brownies.
7. Serve.

Nutrition: 265 calories0.6 g fat 145 mg cholesterol311 mg sodium15.5 g carbohydrates0.3 g dietary fiber3.2 g total sugars0.4 g protein

Lemon Curd Pie

Preparation Time: 10 minutes

Cooking Time: 20 minutes

Servings: 6

Ingredients

- 1 coconut flour pie crust dough
- 1/2 cup lemon juice
- 2 eggs
- 2 egg yolk
- 1/2 cup coconut oil
- 1/4 cup erythritol
- 2 egg white

Directions

1. Beat egg yolks with eggs, lemon juice and sweetener in a saucepan.
2. Heat this mixture then add coconut oil with occasional stirring.
3. Increase the heat and cook until it all thickens.
4. Remove the egg yolks mixture from the heat then allow to cool for 15 minutes.
5. Spread the crust in a pie pan and fill with its lemon curd.
6. Refrigerate for 2 hours.
7. Serve

Nutrition: 138 calories2.7 g fat 22 mg cholesterol43 mg sodium11.5 g carbohydrates0.4 g dietary fiber2.3 g total sugars1.6 g protein

Peanut Butter Chocolate Brownie

Preparation Time: 10 minutes

Cooking Time: 10 minutes

Servings: 1

Ingredients

- 2 tablespoon almond meal
- 2 tablespoon almond milk
- 1 tablespoon crunchy peanut butter
- 1 tablespoon unsweetened cocoa powder
- 1 teaspoon erythritol powder
- or 1/4 teaspoon stevia powder
- 1 teaspoon sugar-free chocolate chips

Directions

1. Mix almond flour with sweetener, milk and cocoa powder in a mug.
2. Stir in peanut butter and chocolate chips.
3. Microwave it for 40 seconds on high heat.
4. Serve immediately.

Nutrition: 218 calories3.3 g fat 21 mg cholesterol34 mg sodium

19.5 g carbohydrates0 g dietary fiber0.5 g total sugars7.4 g protein

Roasted Cashew Cookies

Preparation Time: minutes
Cooking Time: minutes
Servings: Servings: 4

Ingredients

- 2 cup unsweetened desiccated coconut
- 2 tablespoon coconut flour
- 3/4 cup cashews nut, roasted
- ¼ cup extra virgin coconut oil, melted
- 2 eggs
- 1/4 cup sugar-free chocolate chips
- 1/4 cup Swerve
- 1 tablespoon vanilla extract

Directions

1. Adjust the oven 320 degrees F.
2. Layer a cookie sheet with a parchment sheet. Keep it aside.
3. Blend everything in a blender leaving just chocolate chips.
4. Fold in chocolate chips and make 8 cookies out of this dough.
5. Place the cookies in the cookie sheet and bake for 20 minutes.
6. Serve

Nutrition: 211 calories1.7 g fat 212 mg cholesterol53 mg sodium 17.5 g carbohydrates 0.6 g dietary fiber0.5 g total sugars 6.1 g protein

Creamy Chocolate mousse

Preparation Time: 10 minutes
Cooking Time: 10 minutes
Servings: 2

Ingredients

- 3 egg whites
- 1 cup coconut cream full cream canned
- 4 tablespoon unsweetened cocoa powder
- 2 tablespoons swerve

Directions

1. Separate egg yolks from egg whites.
2. Beat egg whites in an electric mixer for 2 minutes.
3. Add xylitol and mix well.

4. Slow stir in coconut cream, and cocoa powder.
5. Refrigerate the mousse for 2 hours.
6. Garnish with coconut flakes.
7. Serve.

Nutrition: 121 calories1.5 g fat 322 mg cholesterol143 mg sodium12.5 g carbohydrates0 g dietary fiber0.5 g total sugars
7.4 g protein

Coconut Bounty Bars

Preparation Time: 10 minutes
Cooking Time: 10 minutes
Servings: 4

Ingredients

- 2 cups unsweetened desiccated coconut
- 1/2 cup coconut cream canned
- 1/3 cup erythritol
- 1/3 cup extra virgin coconut oil

Chocolate coating

- 6 oz. sugar-free chocolate chips
- 2 teaspoon extra virgin coconut oil
- 1-2 stevia drops -to taste

Directions

1. Layer a 10 inches square pan with a plastic wrap.
2. Blend everything in a blender except chocolate coating.
3. Mix well until the dough is smooth.
4. Wrap the dough with the plastic wrap and freeze for 10 minutes.
5. Cut the dough into 20 bars.
6. Melt chocolate chips with stevia drops in the microwave by heating for 30 secs.
7. Dip each bar into the chocolate melt.
8. Freeze the bars for 10 minutes.
9. Serve.

Nutrition: 281 calories 9.7 g fat 228 mg cholesterol160 mg sodium 0.5 g carbohydrates 0 g dietary fiber 0.5 g total sugars
7.4 g protein

Blueberry Almond Tart

Preparation Time: 10 minutes
Cooking Time: 25 minutes
Servings: 4

Ingredients

- Walnuts Almond Crust
- 1 cup walnuts
- 6 tablespoon almond meal
- 2 tablespoon coconut oil
- 1 egg white
- Vanilla extract 2-3 drops

Filling

- 1 cup frozen blueberries
- 2 tablespoon chia seeds

Directions

Walnuts Almond Crust

1. Grind everything in a food processor and turn the dough into a ball.
2. Wrap this ball with a plastic wrap and roll it into a crust.
3. Place this almond crust in the pie mound.

Filling

1. Mix chia seeds with blueberries in a bowl.
2. Pour this mixture into the crust.
3. Make a criss-cross design on top using some remaining dough crust.
4. Bake for 25 minutes. Serve.

Nutrition: 221 calories0.7 g fat28 mg cholesterol16 mg sodium
21.5 g carbohydrates0 g dietary fiber3.2 g total sugars0.4 g protein.

Chia Coco Pudding

Preparation Time: 10 minutes
Cooking Time: 0 minutes
Servings: 2

Ingredients

- 1/3 cup Chia Seeds
- 1/4 cup. unsweetened cocoa powder
- Stevia, to taste
- 1/3 cup Raw Cacao (Nibs)
- 2 1/2 cup Sugar-free Chocolate Almond Milk

Directions

1. Mix chia seeds, stevia, cocoa nibs, cocoa powder and milk in a bowl.
2. Cover chia seeds mixture and put it in the refrigerator for 4 hours.
3. Garnish with cocoa nibs, berries, and coconut cream.
4. Serve.

Nutrition: 253 calories10.2 g fat 312 mg cholesterol11 mg sodium17.5 g carbohydrates0.4 g dietary fiber12.5 g total sugars0.4 g protein

No-Added Sugar Strawberry Shortcake

Cooking Time: 10 minutes
Preparation Time: 15 minutes
Servings: 1

Ingredients

- 1 cup of skim milk
- 1 packet of artificial sweetener
- 6 cups of sliced fresh strawberries
- refrigerated butter-flavored cooking spray
- 1 -1/4 cups of low-fat biscuit and baking mix
- 12 tablespoons of fat-free, no sugar added frozen whipped topping, thawed

Directions

1. Preheat the oven to 400 degrees F.
2. Coat a nonstick baking sheet lightly using cooking spray.
3. Combine the milk, biscuit mix, and sweetener in a bowl, mixing until just combined.
4. Roll dough out on a floured surface into a circle 1/3-inch thick.
5. Cut out 6 biscuits using a 2-inch biscuit cutter, reusing scraps as needed.
6. On your prepared baking sheet, place the biscuits.
7. Spray the tops of the biscuits lightly using cooking spray and bake until nicely browned and done, for about 10 minutes.
8. Split the biscuits in half horizontally, placing half in each of 12 dessert dishes.
9. Top each with 1/2 cup of strawberries and 1 tablespoon of whipped topping.
10. Serve immediately and enjoy it.

Nutrition Fat: 1g Protein: 2g Fiber: 2g Sodium: 159mg Sugar: 0g

Carrot Cake

Preparation Time: 20 minutes

Cooking Time: 45 minutes

Servings: 1

Ingredients

- cooking spray
- 2 teaspoons of baking powder
- 1/2 teaspoon of baking soda
- 1/4 teaspoon of salt
- 1 teaspoon of ground cinnamon
- 1/2 teaspoon of ground nutmeg
- 2 large egg whites, at room temperature
- 1/2 cup of plain non-fat yogurt
- 3 tablespoons of canola oil
- 3/4 cup of unsweetened applesauce
- 1/3 cup of dark brown sugar, packed
- 2 teaspoons of vanilla extract
- 2-1/2 cups of all-purpose flour
- 4 ounces of unsweetened crushed pineapple with juice
- 1/4 cup of dark raisins
- 1/4 cup of sugar substitute

Directions

1.   Preheat the oven to 400 degrees F. Position the top rack in the center of the oven. Coat a 9-inch cake pan lightly using cooking spray. Dust with flour, then tap out excess. Whisk together yogurt, oil, egg whites, brown sugar, applesauce, vanilla, pineapple with juice in a large bowl.

2.   Sift together the baking powder, salt (if using), baking soda, flour, nutmeg, and cinnamon in a bowl.

3.   Add to egg-applesauce mixture gradually, stirring until the cake batter. Spoon the batter into the prepared pan, smoothing the top using the back of a spoon. Bake until a toothpick inserted in the center comes out clean, for about 30 to 40 minutes.

4.   Cool in the pan on a rack for 10-min.

5.   Slide a thin knife just around the edges to loosen the cake from the pan. Invert onto a rack to cool.

6.   Transfer cake into a serving platter when ready to serve.

7.   Serve and enjoy.

Nutrition: Calories: 103kcal Carbs: 19g Fat: 2g Protein: 3g Fiber: 1g Sodium: 123mg

Brownie Sundae Pie

Preparation Time: 15 minutes

Cooking Time: 20 minutes

Servings: 1

Ingredients

- 1/2 teaspoon of baking powder
- 1/8 teaspoon of salt
- 1/2 cup of reduced-calories frozen whipped topping, thawed
- 1/2 cups of sliced bananas
- 2 tablespoons of chopped walnuts
- cooking spray
- 2/3 cup of sugar
- 6 tablespoons of reduced-calorie margarine, melted
- 1 large egg
- 1 teaspoon of vanilla extract
- 1/2 cup of all-purpose flour
- 1/3 cup of unsweetened cocoa powder
- 1 -1/2 cups of non-fat vanilla frozen yogurt (optional)

Directions

1.   Preheat oven to 350 degrees F.

2.   Spray a 9-inch pie pan with cooking spray.

3.   Combine the margarine, sugar, vanilla, and egg until well blended in a large bowl.

4.   Stir in the cocoa, flour, salt, and baking powder until well incorporated.

5.   Spread in the prepared pan. Bake for about 20 minutes.

6.   Cool on a wire rack completely.

7.   Spoon the whipped topping decoratively around the edges of the pie just before serving.

8.   Garnish with walnuts and banana slices.

9.   Cut the pie into 8 wedges. Serve with non-fat frozen vanilla yogurt if you want. Enjoy.

Lemon Meringue Pie

Preparation Time: 30 minutes

Cooking Time: 15 minutes

Servings: 1

Ingredients

- 1 cup of Sugar Twin® Spoonable
- 1 teaspoon of grated lemon zest
- 3 large eggs, separated
- 2 drops of yellow food coloring (optional)
- 1 9-inch fresh or frozen pie shell, baked and cooled
- 1/4 teaspoon of cream of tartar
- 1/2 pure vanilla extract
- 1/2 cup of cornstarch
- 1/4 teaspoon of cream of tartar
- 1/4 teaspoon of salt
- 1-1/2 cups of water
- 1/2 cup of fresh lemon juice
- 2 tablespoons of margarine

Directions

1. Combine cream of tartar, salt, cornstarch, 1 cup of SugarTwin in a nonstick medium saucepan. Whisk in lemon juice and water.
2. Cook over medium heat and stir until the mixture boils. Reduce heat to medium-low. Go ahead with cooking and stirring for a minute.
3. Remove from heat. Stir in lemon zest and margarine; set it aside.
4. Whisk together egg yolks until lemon-colored in a medium bowl.
5. Whisk at least half of the hot cornstarch mixture into eggs. Stir this mixture into the rest of the mixture in saucepan, blending well.
6. Return pan to medium-low heat. Cook, stirring, for about 2 minutes.
7. Slightly cool and pour filling into a baked pie crust—Preheat oven to 350 degrees F.

Making the Meringue:

1. Combine egg whites and 1/4 teaspoon of cream of tartar in a small bowl.
2. Beat with an electric mixer until froth on high-speed. Add vanilla. Gradually add SugarTwin, and one tablespoon at a time. Beat until it stiff peaks form.
3. Evenly spread over lemon filling, sealing well around the edge of the crust.
4. Swirl peaks by lifting up some of the meringue with the back of a spoon if you want.
5. Bake until meringue is golden brown, for about 15 minutes.
6. Cool before serving.
7. Refrigerate leftover for no more than two days.
8. Serve and enjoy.

Nutrition: Calories 153kcal Carbs: 14g Fat: 9g Protein: 3g Fiber: 0g Sodium: 152mg

Banana Chocolate Parfaits

Preparation Time: 10 minutes

Cooking Time: 0 minutes

Servings: 1

Ingredients

- 1 cup of plain low-fat yogurt
- 1/4 cup of reduced-fat frozen dairy whipped topping
- unsweetened cocoa powder
- 1 tablespoon of chopped walnuts (optional)
- 1 0.8-ounce box of sugar-free chocolate pudding mix
- 2 medium bananas
- 1 teaspoon of fresh lemon juice
- 4 fresh raspberries (for garnish)

Directions

1. Fold in yogurt.
2. Cut each banana into six pieces on the diagonal.
3. Sprinkle with lemon juice.
4. Place two bananas quarters in each of 4 parfait glasses.
5. Top with 1/4 of the pudding mix.
6. Top each with one tablespoon of whipped topping.
7. Sift a little cocoa powder on top of each serving using a fine sieve.
8. Sprinkle with walnuts.
9. Add a raspberry too if you want. Enjoy.

Sliced Baked Apples

Preparation Time: 5 minutes
Cooking Time: 30 minutes
Servings: 1
Nutrition

Ingredients

- 1/3 cup of unsweetened apple juice
- 1/3 cup of dry white wine
- 1/3 cup of water
- 2 tablespoons of grated orange zest
- 4 medium-size, 6 ounces each, baking apples
- ground cinnamon to taste
- 1 tablespoon of ground walnuts

Directions

1. Preheat oven to 375 degrees F.
2. Simmer the apple juice, water, and wine with the orange zest in a small pot, for about 10 minutes.
3. Meanwhile, core the apples and remove peel from the top 1/3 of each apple.
4. Remove and discard the seed and core using a small spoon.
5. In a small baking dish, place them just big enough for the apples.
6. Pout apple juice mixture around the apples. Sprinkle cinnamon on each of the apples.
7. Bake until the apples are cooked through, for about 20 minutes, but still, hold their shape.
8. Place each of the apples in a small dessert dish.
9. Top with one tablespoon of the cooking liquid with 1/4 of the walnuts.
10. Serve warm and enjoy.

Chocolate Chip Cookies

Preparation Time: 10 minutes
Cooking Time: 10 minutes
Servings: 1

Ingredients

- 1/2 cup (1 stick) of softened margarine or butter
- 1/4 cup of sugar
- 3 tablespoons of cocoa powder
- 1/2 teaspoon of baking soda
- 1/8 teaspoon of salt
- 2 tablespoons of skim milk
- sugar substitute equal to 1/2 cup of sugar
- 1 large egg
- 1 teaspoon of vanilla extract
- 1 cup of flour
- 1/3 cup of semi-sweet chocolate chips

Directions

1. Preheat oven to 375 degrees F.
2. Beat sugar, butter, and sugar substitute in a medium bowl, until well blended.
3. Add vanilla and egg; then beat until combined.
4. Sift together cocoa powder, flour, salt, and baking soda.
5. Alternately add flour and milk mixture to butter and sugar mixture, beating until well blended between additions.
6. Stir in chocolate chips.
7. Drop by teaspoonful onto the ungreased cookie sheet. Press flat and bake until set, for about 7 minutes.
8. Remove from cookie sheet to wire rack.
9. Cool completely, serve, and enjoy.

Nutrition: Calories: 50kcal Carbs: 5g Fat: 3g Protein: 1g Fiber: 0g Sodium: 50mg Calcium: 0mg

Baked Pita Chips

Preparation Time: 5 minutes
Cooking Time: 5 minutes
Servings: 1

Ingredients

- 6 6-inch pita bread
- cooking spray
- Mrs. Dash or various spices to taste

Directions

1. Preheat oven to 375 degrees F.
2. Cut each pita bread into 6 wedges with a sharp knife.
3. Pull apart each triangle to separate it into 2 pieces gently, getting 12 triangles per pita bread.
4. In a single layer, lay the triangles on a large non-stick baking sheet. You can use parchment paper if you want.
5. Coat triangles with cooking spray lightly and sprinkle on spices.

6. Bake until pita starts to color, for about 7 minutes.

7. Turn pita over and continue to bake until golden brown and crisp, for about 5 minutes.

8. Store in an airtight container.

9. Serve and enjoy.

Nutrition: Calories: 83kcal Carbs: 17g Fat: 5.2g Protein: 3g Fiber: 1g Sodium: 161mg

Oatmeal Raisin Cookies

Preparation Time: 20 minutes
Cooking Time: 10 minutes
Servings: 1

Ingredients

- 1/4 teaspoon of ground cinnamon
- 1/8 teaspoon of salt
- 1/2 cup of margarine (at room temperature)
- 3/4 cup of light brown sugar
- 2 tablespoons of granulated sugar
- 1 large egg
- cooking spray
- 1 cup of unbleached all-purpose flour
- 1/2 teaspoon of baking soda
- 2 tablespoons of 1% milk
- 1/2 teaspoon of vanilla extract
- 1-1/2 cups of rolled oats
- 1/2 cup of dark raisins

Directions

1. Preheat oven to 350 degrees F.

2. Coat a large cookie sheet using cooking spray.

3. Sift together baking soda, flour, salt, and cinnamon into a bowl. Set it aside.

4. Cream the margarine and sugars until fluffy and light using an electric mixer.

5. Add the milk, egg, and vanilla. Beat well.

6. Add the flour mixture gradually, 1/4 cup at a time, beating after each addition until the flour is incorporated.

7. By hand, stir in rolled raisins and rolled oats.

8. Drop by rounded teaspoonful onto prepared cookie sheet at least 2-inches apart.

9. Bake for about 10 minutes, until golden brown.

10. Transfer cookies to rack to cool.

11. Serve and enjoy.

Nutrition: Calories: 155kcal Carbs: 24g Fat: 6g Protein: 2g
Fiber: 1g Sodium: 119mg

Vanilla and Chocolate Swirl Cookies

Preparation Time: 3 hours 38 minutes
Cooking Time: 8 minutes
Servings: 1

Ingredients

- 1-1/2 cups of unbleached all-purpose flour
- 1/2 teaspoon of baking powder
- 1/4 cup of skim milk, warmed to room temperature
- 1 teaspoon of unsweetened cocoa powder
- 1/8 teaspoon of vanilla extract
- 1/2 cup of margarine, softened
- 2 tablespoons of sugar
- 2 teaspoons of vanilla extract
- 6 tablespoons of liquid egg substitute
- cooking spray

Directions

1. Cream the margarine, vanilla, sugar, and egg substitute.

2. Add baking powder, flour, and three tablespoons of the milk; stir to mix thoroughly.

3. Divide dough into 2 parts. Add cocoa to one part, stirring until it's well blended. Add vanilla extract to the other half.

4. Chill both halves for at least 60 minutes.

5. Working on a floured surface, roll out each part to a rectangle about 3-inches wide and 18 inches long.

6. On top of the white part, place the chocolate part, pressing together tightly with a rolling pin.

7. Use the remaining milk to brush the chocolate dough. Roll up like a jelly roll to make a log for about 1 to ½-inches in diameter.

8. Wrap in waxed paper. Chill for about 2 hours, until firm.

9. Preheat oven to 375 degrees F when you're ready to bake.

10. Slice cookies for about 1/8 inch thick. Place on a non-stick cookie sheet that has been coated with cooking spray.

11. Bake until lightly browned, for about 8 minutes. Transfer to a wire rack to cool.

12. Serve and enjoy.

Nutrition: Calories: 85kcal Carbs: 9g Fat: 5g Protein: 2g Fiber: 0g Sodium: 73mg

Raspberry Thumbprint Cookie

Preparation Time: 20 minutes
Cooking Time: 10 minutes
Servings: 1

Ingredients

- 1 large egg white
- 1 teaspoon of vanilla extract
- 1/4 cup of margarine, softened
- 3 tablespoons of sugar
- 1-1/2 cups of sifted all-purpose flour
- cooking spray
- 3 tablespoons of no-sugar-added raspberry fruit spread

Directions

1. Preheat oven to 350 degrees F.
2. Cream margarine and sugar until fluffy and light in a large bowl.
3. Add vanilla and egg white. Beat well.
4. Stir in flour in 3 parts, stirring well each time until the flour is well-incorporated.
5. Form dough into a ball using your hands. Wrap in plastic wrap. Then chill for about 30 minutes.
6. Shape down into 1-inch balls, and place 2 inches apart on a cookie sheet that has been coated with cooking spray.
7. Press a hole in the center of each cookie using your thumb.
8. Bake until golden for about 10 minutes.
9. Cool completely on wire racks.
10. Spoon half a teaspoon of the raspberry fruit spread into the center of each cookie.
11. Serve and enjoy.

Nutrition: Calories:85 kcal Carbs: 1g Fat: 3gProtein: 1g Fiber: 0g Sodium: 43mg

Cranberry Scones

Preparation Time: 10 minutes
Cooking Time: 15 minutes
Servings: 1

Ingredients

- 1-1/2 cups of all-purpose flour
- 1/4 cup of egg substitute
- 1 tablespoon of sugar
- 1/4 teaspoon of ground nutmeg
- 1/2 teaspoon of ground cinnamon
- cooking spray
- 1/4 cup of dried cranberries, raisins, or currants
- 2 tablespoons of brandy or orange juice
- 1 cup of rolled oats (or quick oats)
- 3 tablespoons of reduced-fat margarine, melted
- 2-1/2 teaspoons of baking powder
- 3/4 cups skim milk

Directions

1. Preheat oven to 400 degrees F.
2. Use cooking spray to spray a nonstick cookie sheet.
3. Place the raisins, cranberries, or currants in a small bowl with the orange juice or brandy. Allow macerating for about 15 minutes. Drain and set aside, discarding any excess orange juice or brandy.
4. Combine the rest of the ingredients in a large bowl, mixing lightly until just moistened - make sure you don't over mix it.
5. Flour your hands, and form dough into two 8-inch circles for about half-inch thick.
6. Place on prepared cookie sheet for about 4-inches apart.
7. Dip a sharp knife into flour. Cut each round into 8 pie-shaped wedges.
8. Separate the scones about half an inch from each other.
9. Bake until nicely browned, for about 12 to 15 minutes.
10. Cool on a rack and store in an airtight plastic wrap until ready to serve. Enjoy.

Nutrition: Calories: 91kcal Carbs: 15g Fat: 2g Protein: 3g Fiber: 1g Sodium: 103mg

Frozen Lemon & Blueberry

Preparation time: 10 minutes

Cooking time: 30 minutes

Servings: 4

Ingredients:

- 6 cup fresh blueberries
- 8 sprigs fresh thyme
- ¾ cup light brown sugar
- 1 teaspoon lemon zest
- ¼ cup lemon juice
- 2 cups water

Directions:

1. Add blueberries, thyme and sugar in a pan over medium heat.
2. Cook for 6 to 8 minutes.
3. Transfer mixture to a blender.
4. Remove thyme sprigs.
5. Stir in the remaining ingredients.
6. Pulse until smooth.
7. Strain mixture and freeze for 1 hour.

Nutrition: Calories 78 Fat 0 g Carbohydrate 20 g Protein 3 g

Pumpkin & Banana Ice Cream

Preparation time: 10 minutes

Cooking time: 30 minutes

Servings: 4

Ingredients:

- 15 oz. pumpkin puree
- 4 bananas, sliced and frozen
- 1 teaspoon pumpkin pie spice
- Chopped pecans

Directions:

1. Add pumpkin puree, bananas and pumpkin pie spice in a food processor.
2. Pulse until smooth.
3. Chill in the refrigerator.
4. Garnish with pecans.

Nutrition: Calories 71 Fat 0.4 g Carbohydrate 18 g Protein 1.2 g

Coconut Chia Pudding

Preparation time: 10 minutes

Cooking time: 0 minutes

Servings: 6

Ingredients:

- 2 ¼ cup canned coconut milk
- 1 teaspoon vanilla extract
- Pinch salt
- ½ cup chia seeds

Directions:

1. Combine the coconut milk, vanilla, and salt in a bowl.
2. Stir well and sweeten with stevia to taste.
3. Whisk in the chia seeds and chill overnight.
4. Spoon into bowls and serve with chopped nuts or fruit.

Nutrition: 300 calories 27.5g fat 6g protein 14.5g carbs 10g fiber 4.5g net carbs

Strawberries in Honey Yogurt Dip

Preparation time: 10 minutes

Cooking time: 0 minutes

Servings: 4

Ingredients:

- 1 cup plain yogurt, low-fat
- 1 tablespoon of orange juice
- 1 to 2 teaspoons of honey
- Ground cinnamon
- 1 quart of fresh strawberries (remove stems)

Directions:

1. Combine first four ingredients to make a sauce.
2. Pour over strawberries and serve.

Nutrition: Calories: 88 Carbohydrates: 16 g Fiber: 4 g Fats: 1 g
Sodium: 41 mg Protein: 4 g

Mortadella & Bacon Balls

Preparation time: 10 minutes

Cooking time: 30 minutes

Servings: 2

Ingredients:

- 4 ounces Mortadella sausage
- 4 bacon slices, cooked and crumbled
- 2 tbsp almonds, chopped

- ½ tsp Dijon mustard
- 3 ounces' cream cheese

Directions:

1. Combine the mortadella and almonds in the bowl of your food processor. Pulse until smooth. Whisk the cream cheese and mustard in another bowl. Make balls out of the mortadella mixture.

2. Make a thin cream cheese layer over. Coat with bacon, arrange on a plate and chill before serving.

Nutrition: Calories 547 Fat: 51g Carbs: 3.4g Protein: 21.5g

Tiramisu Shots

Preparation Time: 5 minutes

Cooking Time: 10 minutes

Servings: 4

Ingredients:

- 1 pack silken tofu
- 1 oz. dark chocolate, finely chopped
- ¼ cup sugar substitute
- 1 teaspoon lemon juice
- ¼ cup brewed espresso
- Pinch salt
- 24 slices angel food cake
- Cocoa powder (unsweetened)

Directions:

1. Add tofu, chocolate, sugar substitute, lemon juice, espresso and salt in a food processor.

2. Pulse until smooth.

3. Add angel food cake pieces into shot glasses.

4. Drizzle with the cocoa powder.

5. Pour the tofu mixture on top.

6. Top with the remaining angel food cake pieces.

7. Chill for 30 minutes and serve.

Nutrition: 75 Calories 12g Carbohydrate 2.9g Protein

Ice Cream Brownie Cake

Preparation Time: 5 minutes

Cooking Time: 10 minutes

Servings: 4

Ingredients:

- Cooking spray
- 12 oz. no-sugar brownie mix

- ¼ cup oil
- 2 egg whites
- 3 tablespoons water
- 2 cups sugar-free ice cream

Directions:

1. Preheat your oven to 325 degrees F.

2. Spray your baking pan with oil.

3. Mix brownie mix, oil, egg whites and water in a bowl.

4. Pour into the baking pan.

5. Bake for 25 minutes.

6. Let cool.

7. Freeze brownie for 2 hours.

8. Spread ice cream over the brownie.

9. Freeze for 8 hours.

Nutrition: 198 Calories 33g Carbohydrate 3g Protein

Peanut Butter Cups

Preparation Time: 5 minutes

Cooking Time: 10 minutes

Servings: 4

Ingredients:

- 1 packet plain gelatin
- ¼ cup sugar substitute
- 2 cups nonfat cream
- ½ teaspoon vanilla
- ¼ cup low-fat peanut butter
- 2 tablespoons unsalted peanuts, chopped

Directions:

1. Mix gelatin, sugar substitute and cream in a pan.

2. Let sit for 5 minutes.

3. Place over medium heat and cook until gelatin has been dissolved.

4. Stir in vanilla and peanut butter.

5. Pour into custard cups. Chill for 3 hours.

6. Top with the peanuts and serve.

Nutrition: 171 Calories 21g Carbohydrate 6.8g Protein

Fruit Pizza

Preparation Time: 5 minutes

Cooking Time: 10 minutes

Servings: 4

Ingredients:

- 1 teaspoon maple syrup
- ¼ teaspoon vanilla extract
- ½ cup coconut milk yogurt
- 2 round slices watermelon
- ½ cup blackberries, sliced
- ½ cup strawberries, sliced
- 2 tablespoons coconut flakes (unsweetened)

Directions:

1. Mix maple syrup, vanilla and yogurt in a bowl.
2. Spread the mixture on top of the watermelon slice.
3. Top with the berries and coconut flakes.

Nutrition: 70 Calories 14.6g Carbohydrate 1.2g Protein

Choco Peppermint Cake

Preparation Time: 5 minutes

Cooking Time: 10 minutes

Servings: 4

Ingredients:

- Cooking spray
- 1/3 cup oil
- 15 oz. package chocolate cake mix
- 3 eggs, beaten
- 1 cup water
- ¼ teaspoon peppermint extract

Directions:

1. Spray slow cooker with oil.
2. Mix all the ingredients in a bowl.
3. Use an electric mixer on medium speed setting to mix ingredients for 2 minutes.
4. Pour mixture into the slow cooker.
5. Cover the pot and cook on low for 3 hours.
6. Let cool before slicing and serving.

Nutrition: 185 Calories 27g Carbohydrate 3.8g Protein

Roasted Mango

Preparation Time: 5 minutes

Cooking Time: 10 minutes

Servings: 4

Ingredients:

- 2 mangoes, sliced
- 2 teaspoons crystallized ginger, chopped
- 2 teaspoons orange zest
- 2 tablespoons coconut flakes (unsweetened)

Directions:

1. Preheat your oven to 350 degrees F.
2. Add mango slices in custard cups.
3. Top with the ginger, orange zest and coconut flakes.
4. Bake in the oven for 10 minutes.

Nutrition: 89 Calories 20g Carbohydrate 0.8g Protein

Roasted Plums

Preparation Time: 5 minutes

Cooking Time: 10 minutes

Servings: 4

Ingredients:

- Cooking spray
- 6 plums, sliced
- ½ cup pineapple juice (unsweetened)
- 1 tablespoon brown sugar
- 2 tablespoons brown sugar
- ¼ teaspoon ground cardamom
- ½ teaspoon ground cinnamon
- 1/8 teaspoon ground cumin

Directions:

1. Combine all the ingredients in a baking pan.
2. Roast in the oven at 450 degrees F for 20 minutes.

Nutrition: 102 Calories 18.7g Carbohydrate 2g Protein

Figs with Honey & Yogurt

Preparation Time: 5 minutes

Cooking Time: 10 minutes

Servings: 4

Ingredients:

- ½ teaspoon vanilla
- 8 oz. nonfat yogurt
- 2 figs, sliced
- 1 tablespoon walnuts, chopped and toasted

- 2 teaspoons honey

Directions:
1. Stir vanilla into yogurt.
2. Mix well.
3. Top with the figs and sprinkle with walnuts.
4. Drizzle with honey and serve.

Nutrition: 157 Calories 24g Carbohydrate 7g Protein

Flourless Chocolate Cake

Preparation Time: 10 minutes
Cooking Time: 45 minutes
Servings: 6

Ingredients:
- ½ Cup of stevia
- 12 Ounces of unsweetened baking chocolate
- 2/3 Cup of ghee
- 1/3 Cup of warm water
- ¼ Teaspoon of salt
- 4 Large pastured eggs
- 2 Cups of boiling water

Directions:
1. Line the bottom of a 9-inch pan of a spring form with a parchment paper.
2. Heat the water in a small pot; then add the salt and the stevia over the water until wait until the mixture becomes completely dissolved.
3. Melt the baking chocolate into a double boiler or simply microwave it for about 30 seconds.
4. Mix the melted chocolate and the butter in a large bowl with an electric mixer.
5. Beat in your hot mixture; then crack in the egg and whisk after adding each of the eggs.
6. Pour the obtained mixture into your prepared spring form tray.
7. Wrap the spring form tray with a foil paper.
8. Place the spring form tray in a large cake tray and add boiling water right to the outside; make sure the depth doesn't exceed 1 inch.
9. Bake the cake into the water bath for about 45 minutes at a temperature of about 350 F.
10. Remove the tray from the boiling water and transfer to a wire to cool.

11. Let the cake chill for an overnight in the refrigerator.

Nutrition 295 Calories 6g Carbohydrates 4g Fiber

Raspberry Cake with White Chocolate Sauce

Preparation Time: 15 minutes
Cooking Time: 60 minutes
Servings: 5

Ingredients:
- 5 Ounces of melted cacao butter
- 2 Ounces of grass-fed ghee
- ½ Cup of coconut cream
- 1 Cup of green banana flour
- 3 Teaspoons of pure vanilla
- 4 Large eggs
- ½ Cup of as Lakanto Monk Fruit
- 1 Teaspoon of baking powder
- 2 Teaspoons of apple cider vinegar
- 2 Cup of raspberries

For white chocolate sauce:
- 3 and ½ ounces of cacao butter
- ½ Cup of coconut cream
- 2 Teaspoons of pure vanilla extract
- 1 Pinch of salt

Directions:
1. Preheat your oven to a temperature of about 280 degrees Fahrenheit.
2. Combine the green banana flour with the pure vanilla extract, the baking powder, the coconut cream, the eggs, the cider vinegar and the monk fruit and mix very well.
3. Leave the raspberries aside and line a cake loaf tin with a baking paper.
4. Pour in the batter into the baking tray and scatter the raspberries over the top of the cake.
5. Place the tray in your oven and bake it for about 60 minutes; in the meantime, prepare the sauce by Directions for sauce:
6. Combine the cacao cream, the vanilla extract, the cacao butter and the salt in a saucepan over a low heat.

7. Mix all your ingredients with a fork to make sure the cacao butter mixes very well with the cream.

8. Remove from the heat and set aside to cool a little bit; but don't let it harden.

9. Drizzle with the chocolate sauce.

10. Scatter the cake with more raspberries.

11. Slice your cake; then serve and enjoy it!

Nutrition 323 Calories 9.9g Carbohydrates 4g Fiber

Lava Cake

Preparation Time: 10 minutes

Cooking Time: 10 minutes

Servings: 2

Ingredients:

- 2 Oz of dark chocolate; you should at least use chocolate of 85% cocoa solids
- 1 Tablespoon of super-fine almond flour
- 2 Oz of unsalted almond butter
- 2 Large eggs

Directions:

1. Heat your oven to a temperature of about 350 Fahrenheit.

2. Grease 2 heat proof ramekins with almond butter.

3. Now, melt the chocolate and the almond butter and stir very well.

4. Beat the eggs very well with a mixer.

5. Add the eggs to the chocolate and the butter mixture and mix very well with almond flour and the swerve; then stir.

6. Pour the dough into 2 ramekins.

7. Bake for about 9 to 10 minutes.

8. Turn the cakes over plates and serve with pomegranate seeds!

Nutrition 459 Calories 3.5g Carbohydrates 0.8g Fiber

Cheese Cake

Preparation Time: 15 minutes

Cooking Time: 50 minutes

Servings: 6

Ingredients:

For Almond Flour Cheesecake Crust:

- 2 Cups of Blanched almond flour

- 1/3 Cup of almond Butter
- 3 Tablespoons of Erythritol (powdered or granular)
- 1 Teaspoon of Vanilla extract

For Keto Cheesecake Filling:

- 32 Oz of softened Cream cheese
- 1 and ¼ cups of powdered erythritol
- 3 Large Eggs
- 1 Tablespoon of Lemon juice
- 1 Teaspoon of Vanilla extract

Directions:

1. Preheat your oven to a temperature of about 350 degrees F.

2. Grease a spring form pan of 9" with cooking spray or just line its bottom with a parchment paper.

3. In order to make the cheesecake rust, stir in the melted butter, the almond flour, the vanilla extract and the erythritol in a large bowl.

4. The dough will get will be a bit crumbly; so, press it into the bottom of your prepared tray.

5. Bake for about 12 minutes; then let cool for about 10 minutes.

6. In the meantime, beat the softened cream cheese and the powdered sweetener at a low speed until it becomes smooth.

7. Crack in the eggs and beat them in at a low to medium speed until it becomes fluffy. Make sure to add one a time.

8. Add in the lemon juice and the vanilla extract and mix at a low to medium speed with a mixer.

9. Pour your filling into your pan right on top of the crust. You can use a spatula to smooth the top of the cake.

10. Bake for about 45 to 50 minutes.

11. Remove the baked cheesecake from your oven and run a knife around its edge.

12. Let the cake cool for about 4 hours in the refrigerator.

13. Serve and enjoy your delicious cheese cake!

Nutrition 325 Calories 6g Carbohydrates 1g Fiber

Cake with Whipped Cream Icing

Preparation Time: 20 minutes

Cooking Time: 25 minutes

Servings: 7

Ingredients:

- ¾ Cup Coconut flour
- ¾ Cup of Swerve Sweetener
- ½ Cup of Cocoa powder
- 2 Teaspoons of Baking powder
- 6 Large Eggs
- 2/3 Cup of Heavy Whipping Cream
- ½ Cup of Melted almond Butter

For whipped Cream Icing:

- 1 Cup of Heavy Whipping Cream
- ¼ Cup of Swerve Sweetener
- 1 Teaspoon of Vanilla extract
- 1/3 Cup of Sifted Cocoa Powder

Directions:

1. Preheat your oven to a temperature of about 350 F.

2. Grease an 8x8 cake tray with cooking spray.

3. Add the coconut flour, the Swerve sweetener; the cocoa powder, the baking powder, the eggs, the melted butter; and combine very well with an electric or a hand mixer.

4. Pour your batter into the cake tray and bake for about 25 minutes.

5. Remove the cake tray from the oven and let cool for about 5 minutes.

6. For the Icing

7. Whip the cream until it becomes fluffy; then add in the Swerve, the vanilla and the cocoa powder.

8. Add the Swerve, the vanilla and the cocoa powder; then continue mixing until your ingredients are very well combined.

9. Frost your baked cake with the icing!

Nutrition 357 Calories 11g Carbohydrates 2g Fiber

Walnut-Fruit Cake

Preparation Time: 15 minutes

Cooking Time: 20 minutes

Servings: 7

Ingredients:

- 1/2 Cup of almond butter (softened)
- ¼ Cup of so Nourished granulated erythritol
- 1 Tablespoon of ground cinnamon
- ½ Teaspoon of ground nutmeg
- ¼ Teaspoon of ground cloves
- 4 Large pastured eggs
- 1 Teaspoon of vanilla extract
- ½ Teaspoon of almond extract
- 2 Cups of almond flour
- ½ Cup of chopped walnuts
- ¼ Cup of dried of unsweetened cranberries
- ¼ Cup of seedless raisins

Directions:

1. Preheat your oven to a temperature of about 350 F and grease an 8-inch baking tin of round shape with coconut oil.

2. Beat the granulated erythritol on a high speed until it becomes fluffy.

3. Add the cinnamon, the nutmeg, and the cloves; then blend your ingredients until they become smooth.

4. Crack in the eggs and beat very well by adding one at a time, plus the almond extract and the vanilla.

5. Whisk in the almond flour until it forms a smooth batter then fold in the nuts and the fruit.

6. Spread your mixture into your prepared baking pan and bake it for about 20 minutes.

7. Remove the cake from the oven and let cool for about 5 minutes.

8. Dust the cake with the powdered erythritol.

Nutrition 250 Calories 12g Carbohydrates 2g Fiber

Healthy Chocolate Ice Cream

Preparation Time: 5 minutes

Cooking Time: 0 minutes

Servings: 4

Ingredients:

- 3 large frozen bananas
- ½ cup cocoa powder
- Sweetener to taste
- 1 tsp. vanilla extract

Directions:

1. Place the frozen bananas in a food processor and blitz until smooth.

2. Add the vanilla extract and cocoa powder into the processor and blitz very quickly for 10 seconds.

3. Taste the ice cream and add sweetener if desired.

4. Serve immediately as soft-serve ice cream or freeze in a container for more solid ice cream if preferred.

Nutrition Calories 118 Carbs 23g Carbs 17g Fat 1g Protein 4g Sodium 3mg

Low Carb Greek Yogurt Ice Cream

Preparation Time: 5 minutes

Cooking Time: 0 minutes

Servings: 1

Ingredients:

- ¼ cup fat-free Greek yogurt
- 1 scoop vanilla protein powder
- ½ cup unsweetened almond milk
- 1 tsp. vanilla extract
- Sweetener to taste

Directions:

1. Put all the ingredients into a blender and pulse, until the mixture is well blended.

2. Add around 2 tablespoons of sweetener, according to your taste.

3. You can use an ice cream maker if you have one. Alternatively, place the mixture into a container and freeze. Stir the mixture every ten minutes until you have the right consistency which will take around 2 hours.

4. You can serve the ice cream straight away or keep it in the freezer for up to a week.

5. Ideal served with your favorite fresh berries and a sprinkling of chopped nuts.

Nutrition Calories 127 Carbs 8g Carbs 6g Fat 4g Protein 15g Sodium 22mg

Skinny Sue's Strawberries n' Cream Chia Ice Popsicles

Preparation Time: 10 minutes

Cooking Time: 0 minutes

Servings: 4

Ingredients:

- 1 cup strawberries, sliced
- 2 tsp. chia seeds
- ¼ cup water
- ¼ cup cream
- Sweetener to taste

Directions:

1. Place the water, cream, chia seeds, and strawberries in a blender and pulse until the strawberries are completely broken up and well blended.

2. Add approximately 2 tablespoons of sweetener, according to taste.

3. Leave the mixture to thicken slightly before pouring into 4 molds.

4. Place the popsicles into the freezer until completely frozen, this will take 2- 4 hours depending on your molds and freezer.

5. Allow the popsicles to rest at room temperature for 5 minutes before eating.

Nutrition: Calories 63 Carbs 10g Carbs 8g Fat 2g Protein 2g Sodium 7mg

Low Carb Cookies 'n' Cream Ice Cream Cake

Preparation Time: 5 minutes

Cooking Time: 15 minutes

Servings: 9

Ingredients:

- 1 6oz packet sugar-free chocolate sandwich biscuits
- 3 tbsp. reduced-fat margarine, melted
- 1/3 cup pecans, chopped
- 1 quart diabetic vanilla ice cream, such as Frank's

Directions:

1. First, crush the biscuits in a plastic bag with a rolling pin. (If you can't find sugar-free biscuits in your supermarket, you can buy them online at Amazon or other retailers).

2. Now mix the biscuit crumbs, pecans and melted margarine together.

3. Press the mixture into the base of a 6-inch square tin, reserving one third for the topping.

4.   Spoon the ice cream into the tin and sprinkle over the remaining crumb mixture.

5.   Freeze until firm which will take 2-3 hours.

6.   Remove from the freezer and leave the cake to soften for 5 minutes.

7.   Cut into 9 squares and serve.

Nutrition: Calories 232 Carbs 34g Carbs 33g Fat 8g Protein 11g Sodium 96mg

Watermelon Sorbet

Preparation Time: 5 minutes
Cooking Time: 15 minutes
Servings: 12
Ingredients:

- 7 cup seedless watermelon, cubed
- 1 14oz can sweetened condensed milk
- 5 tbsp. lime juice
- Sweetener to taste
- Pinch of salt

Directions:

1.   Arrange the watermelon cubes in a single layer on a baking tray and freeze until frozen or overnight.

2.   Place the watermelon, condensed milk, lime juice, and a pinch of salt into a blender and blitz until smooth.

3.   Transfer the mixture into a container and freeze for around 4 hours or overnight.

4.   Soften the sorbet for 5 minutes at room temperature before scooping and serving.

Nutrition Calories 132 Carbs 23g Carbs 23g Fat 3g Protein 2g Sodium 66mg

Pineapple Peach Sorbet

Preparation Time: 5 minutes
Cooking Time: 0 minutes
Servings: 4
Ingredients:

- 1 cup frozen peaches
- 1 cup frozen pineapple chunks
- ½ cup sugar-free lemonade

Directions:

1.   Put all the ingredients in a blender and blitz until the fruit is broken up and the mixture is smooth.

2.   Place the sorbet in a container and freeze until solid.

Nutrition Calories 40 Carbs 10g Carbs 9g Fat 0g Protein 1g Sodium 0mg

Raspberry Frozen Yogurt

Preparation Time: 10 minutes
Cooking Time: 0 minutes
Servings: 11
Ingredients:

- 1½ cup fresh raspberries
- 2 cup Greek yogurt
- ½ cup sweetener

Directions:

1.   Purée half of the raspberries in a food processor.

2.   Mix in the yogurt and sweetener and pour into a container.

3.   After 1 hour gently fold in the remaining raspberries.

4.   Freeze again for 30 minutes, mix with a fork and freeze for a final 30 minutes or until solid.

5.   Remove from freezer 5 to 10 minutes before serving.

Nutrition Calories 79 Carbs 7g, Net Carbs 6g, Fat 4g, Protein 3g, Sodium 40mg

Sugar-Free Chocolate Chip Cookies

Preparation Time: 15 minutes
Cooking Time: 15 minutes
Servings: 8 cookies
Ingredients:

- ¼ cup butter
- ½ cup sweetener
- 3 tbsp. ground flax meal
- 3 tbsp. water
- ½ cup sugar-free chocolate chips
- 1½ cup almond flour
- 1 tsp. baking powder

Directions:

1.   Preheat the oven to 325°F.

2.   Line a baking tray with grease-proof paper.

3.   Pulse the sweetener in a food processor until it is powdered.

4. Cream the butter into the sweetener until fluffy.

5. Now mix in the flax seeds, almond flour, baking powder, and water.

6. Finally, stir the chocolate chips evenly throughout the cookie dough.

7. Form the dough into 8 cookies and place onto the baking tray.

8. Bake for 15-20 minutes or until golden brown.

9. Cool on a wire rack.

10. Store the cookies for up to a week in an airtight tin.

Nutrition: Calories 165, Total Carbs 9g, Fat 14g, Protein 3g, Sodium 1mg

Grandma Sue's Sugar-Free Simple Mocha Chocolate Cake

Preparation Time: 10 minutes
Cooking Time: 35 minutes
Servings: 12
Ingredients:
- 1¼ cup low-fat yogurt
- 1 cup strong brewed coffee
- ¾ cup cocoa powder
- 1 egg
- 1 cup sweetener
- 2 cup all-purpose flour
- 2 tsp. baking powder
- 4 tbsp. vegetable oil
- 2 tsp. vanilla extract

Directions:
1. Preheat the oven to 350°F.

2. Use cooking spray to coat a Bundt tin.

3. Mix the wet ingredients in a small bowl until well blended.

4. Now mix the dry ingredients in a large bowl.

5. Add the wet ingredients to the dry ingredients and mix with an electric whisk for 2-3 minutes.

6. Pour the batter into the tin.

7. Bake in the oven for around 35 minutes. Test the cake with a skewer to make sure it's cooked all the way through.

8. Leave the cake to cool on a wire rack.

9. Dust with powdered sweetener if desired.
Nutrition: Calories 144, Total Carbs 21g Fat 5g, Protein 4g, Sodium 34mg

Chocolate Orange Soufflé

Preparation Time: 10 minutes
Cooking Time: 6 minutes
Servings: 6
Ingredients:
- A little vegetable oil, for greasing
- Grated rind and juice of 2 large oranges
- ¾ cup sweetener
- 4 large egg whites, beaten until stiff
- ¼ cup cocoa powder
- 4 tbsp. light sour cream

Directions:
1. Preheat oven to 400°F.

2. Lightly grease 6 ovenproof teacups or ramekins.

3. Heat the orange rind, juice, and sweetener for 3–4 minutes until syrupy.

4. Pour the syrup over the stiff egg whites and beat for 2 minutes.

5. Fold in the cocoa until it is fully incorporated.

6. Pour into the ramekins and bake for around 5 minutes or until well risen.

7. Serve hot topped with crème fraiche.
Nutrition: Calories 100 Total Carbs 15g Net Carbs 14g Fat 4g Protein 4g Sodium 40mg

Chocolate Mousse with Raspberries

Preparation Time: 15 minutes
Cooking Time: 30 minutes
Servings: 6
Ingredients:
- 2/3 cup sugar-free chocolate (85% cocoa solids)
- 2 tbsp. sweetener
- 1 cup half-fat sour cream
- 2 egg whites, beaten until stiff
- 2½ cup raspberries

Directions:
1. Melt the chocolate and sweetener in a double boiler.

2. Add the sour cream and mix gently through the chocolate mixture.

3. Fold the egg whites into the chocolate.

4. Spoon the mixture into 6 serving dishes and refrigerate for at least 30 minutes.

5. Serve the raspberries alongside the mousse.

Nutrition: Calories 143 Net Carbs 12g Fat 10g Protein 3g Sodium 40mg

Double Chocolate Cake

Preparation Time: 10 minutes

Cooking Time: 20 minutes

Servings: 20

Ingredients:

- 1½ cup all-purpose flour
- ½ cup unsweetened cocoa powder
- 1 tsp. baking soda
- Pinch of salt
- ¼ cup canola oil
- ¼ cup unsweetened applesauce
- 2 eggs
- ½ cup sweetener
- ¼ cup brown blend sweetener
- 1 cup low-fat buttermilk
- 2 tsp. vanilla
- 1/3 cup mini chocolate chips
- ¼ cup sugar-free chocolate syrup

Directions:

1. Preheat the oven to 350°F.

2. Spray a 9 by 13-inch pan with cooking spray.

3. Combine the flour, cocoa powder, baking soda, and pinch of salt in a large bowl. Set aside.

4. Beat the oil, vanilla, applesauce, and eggs with an electric mixer.

5. Beat in the sweetener, buttermilk, and flour.

6. Fold in the chocolate chips by hand.

7. Pour the batter into the pan and bake for about 20 minutes. Test the cake for doneness.

8. Let the cake cool for 10 minutes, then cut into squares.

9. Drizzle with chocolate syrup before serving.

Nutrition: Calories 135 Total Carbs 21g Fat 5g Protein 3g Sodium 85mg

SPECIAL RECIPES

Kiwi-apple Smoothies

Preparation Time: 10 minutes

Cooking Time: 0 minutes

Servings: 4

Ingredients:

- 2 medium ripe kiwis, peeled and chopped
- 1 small Granny Smith apple, cored and chopped
- 1 cup ice cubes
- 1/3 cup unsweetened apple juice
- 2 teaspoons honey

Directions:

1. Combine all the ingredients in a blender and process until smooth, about 2 minutes.

Nutrition: 14 g carb 56 calories0 g fat0 mg cholesterol1 g fiber

1 g protein2 mg sodium

Creamy Avocado Sauce

Preparation Time: 10 minutes

Cooking Time: 0 minutes

Servings: 2

Ingredients:

- 1/2 ripe avocado, peeled, pitted, and chopped
- 1/2 cup plain low-fat yogurt
- 1/4 cup loosely packed fresh cilantro leaves
- 2 teaspoons lime juice
- 1/4 teaspoon kosher salt

Directions:

1. Place all the ingredients in a food processor or blender and process until smooth. Serve at once.

Nutrition: 5 g carb60 cal4 g fat1 g sat fat2 g fib2 g pro94 mg sod

Basic Boiled Beets

Preparation Time: 10 minutes

Cooking Time: 70 minutes

Ingredients:

- 1 pound beets, well-scrubbed (about 3 medium)

Directions:

1. Place the beets in a large saucepan and add water to cover. Bring to a boil over high heat. Reduce the heat to low, cover, and simmer until the beets are tender when pierced with a knife, about 1 hour.

2. Drain the beets in a colander. Cool slightly and use your hands to slip the skins off under cold running water.

Nutrition: 7 g carb 33 cal 0 g fat 0 mg chol 2 g fib 1 g pro59 mg sod

Yogurt-berry Parfaits

Preparation Time: 10 minutes

Cooking Time: 0 minutes

Servings: 4

Ingredients:

- 1 cup fresh raspberries
- 1 cup plain fat-free yogurt
- 2 cups fresh strawberries, halved if large
- 1 cup fresh blueberries

Directions:

1. Place the raspberries in a medium bowl and mash with a fork or a potato masher until lightly crushed. Add the yogurt and stir until blended.

2. To make the parfaits, layer 1/2 cup of the yogurt mixture, 1/2 cup of the strawberries, and 1/4 cup of the blueberries into each of four parfait glasses or glass bowls. Serve at once.

Nutrition: 19 g carb94 cal, 1 g fat1 g sat fat1 mg chol4 g fib

5 g pro 49 mg sod

Basic Polenta

Preparation Time: 10 minutes

Cooking Time: 0 minutes

Servings: 4

Ingredients:

- 2 cups Vegetable Stock or low-sodium vegetable broth
- 3/4 teaspoon kosher salt
- Pinch of freshly ground pepper
- 1/2 cup fine-grind yellow cornmeal

Directions:

1.   Combine the stock, salt, and pepper in a medium saucepan and bring to a boil over medium-high heat.

2.   Slowly sprinkle the cornmeal into the stock, whisking constantly. Reduce the heat to low and cook, stirring constantly, until the polenta is thickened, about 3 minutes. Spoon the polenta into a serving dish and serve at once.

Nutrition: 16 g carb 70 cal 0 g fat 0 mg chol 1 g fib 1 g pro 280 mg sod

Sautéed Fennel with Ginger

Preparation Time: 10 minutes

Cooking Time: 20 minutes

Servings: 4

Ingredients:

- 2 large bulbs fennel
- 1 tablespoon extra-virgin olive oil
- 1 tablespoon minced fresh ginger
- 1/2 teaspoon kosher salt
- 1 teaspoon lemon juice

Directions:

1.   Trim the tough outer stalks from the fennel bulbs. Cut each one in half vertically and discard the cores. Cut each half lengthwise into 1/2-inch slices.

2.   Heat a large nonstick skillet over medium heat. Add the oil and tilt the pan to coat the bottom evenly. Add the ginger and cook, stirring constantly, until fragrant, 30 seconds. Add the fennel and salt and cook, stirring frequently, until tender and lightly browned, 8 to 10 minutes. Stir in the lemon juice. Spoon the fennel into a serving dish and serve at once.

Nutrition: 9 g carb 69cal 4 g fat 0 mg chol 4 g fib 2 g pro 201 mg sod

Rich Chocolate Sauce

Preparation Time: 10 minutes

Cooking Time: 10 minutes

Servings: 11

Ingredients:

- 1 cup 1% low-fat milk
- 1/2 cup sugar

- 1/2 cup unsweetened cocoa
- 2 ounces unsweetened chocolate, chopped
- 1 teaspoon vanilla extract

Directions:

1.   Combine the milk, sugar, and cocoa in a medium saucepan and whisk until smooth. Cook over medium heat, stirring often, until the mixture comes to a simmer.

2.   Remove from the heat and stir in the unsweetened chocolate and vanilla, stirring until the chocolate melts. Serve warm or at room temperature. The sauce can be refrigerated, covered, for up to a week. Gently reheat in a saucepan over low heat or microwave for 1 to 11/2 minutes before serving.

Nutrition: 8 g carb 44 cal 2 g fat 1 g sat fat 1 mg chol 1 g fib1 g pro 7 mg sod

Miso-ginger Dressing

Preparation Time: 10 minutes

Cooking Time: 0 minutes

Servings: 4

Ingredients:

- 1 tablespoon unseasoned rice vinegar
- 1 tablespoon red or white miso
- 1 teaspoon grated fresh ginger
- 1 garlic clove, minced
- 3 tablespoons extra-virgin olive oil

Directions:

1.   In a small bowl, combine the vinegar and miso into a paste. Add the ginger and garlic, and mix well. While whisking, drizzle in the olive oil.

2.   Store in the refrigerator in an airtight container for up to 1 week.

Nutrition: Calories: 99 Fat: 10g Protein: 1g Carbohydrates: 1g Sugars: 0g Fiber: 0g Sodium: 169mg

Baked Wonton Chips

Preparation Time: 10 minutes

Cooking Time: 15 minutes

Servings: 4

Ingredients:

- 12 wonton wrappers
- 2 teaspoons extra virgin olive oil

- 1/8 teaspoon fennel seeds
- 1/8 teaspoon kosher salt
- Pinch of freshly ground pepper

Directions:

1. Preheat the oven to 375°F.
2. Brush both sides of each wonton wrapper with the oil. Cut each wrapper in half to form 2 triangles. Arrange the triangles in a single layer on a large baking sheet.
3. Sprinkle the fennel seeds, salt, and pepper evenly over the wonton wrappers. Bake until golden brown, 7 to 9 minutes. Transfer the chips to a wire rack to cool.

Nutrition: 14 g carb 91 cal 3 g fat 2 mg chol 0 g fib 2 g pro
172 mg sod

Orange and Pink Grapefruit Salad with Honey-rosemary Syrup

Preparation Time: 10 minutes

Cooking Time: 10 minutes

Servings: 4

Ingredients:

- 2 tablespoons honey
- 2 tablespoons orange juice
- 2 teaspoons fresh rosemary leaves
- 2 large navel oranges
- 1 large pink grapefruit

Directions:

1. Combine the honey, orange juice, and rosemary in a small saucepan. Bring to a boil over medium heat. Let stand 30 minutes to cool. Pour through a fine wire mesh strainer into a small bowl. Discard the rosemary.
2. Meanwhile, cut a thin slice from the top and bottom of the oranges and the grapefruit, exposing the flesh. Stand each fruit upright, and using a sharp knife, thickly cut off the peel, following the contour of the fruit and removing all the white pith and membrane. Thinly slice the fruit into rounds.
3. To serve, layer the grapefruit and orange slices alternately on a serving platter and drizzle with the syrup.

Nutrition: 25 g carb 96 cal 0 g fat 0 mg chol 2 g fib 1 g pro1 mg sod

Asparagus and Asiago Pizza with Red Pepper Sauce

Preparation Time: 10 minutes

Cooking Time: 15 minutes

Servings: 4

Ingredients:

- 8 asparagus spears, tough ends trimmed, spears halved lengthwise, and cut into 2-inch pieces
- 1 prepared Whole Wheat Pizza Crust or 1 (12-inch) purchased prebaked whole wheat thin pizza crust
- 1 recipe Roasted Red Pepper Pizza Sauce
- 3 ounces shredded Asiago cheese (about 3/4 cup)

Directions:

1. Position an oven rack on the lowest rung of the oven. Preheat the oven to 450°F.
2. Bring a small pot of water to a boil over high heat. Add the asparagus and cook until crisp-tender, 2 minutes. Drain and pat dry with paper towels.
3. Place the crust on the bottom rack of the oven and bake 5 minutes.
4. Remove the crust from the oven and spread the sauce evenly over the crust, leaving a 1/2-inch border. Arrange the asparagus evenly over the sauce. Sprinkle with the Asiago. Bake on the bottom rack until the crust is browned and the cheese melts, about 8 minutes. Cut into 8 wedges and serve at once.

Nutrition: 35 g carb 268 cal11 g fat19 mg chol6 g fib11 g pro425 mg sod

Grilled Peach and Coconut Yogurt Bowls

Preparation Time: 10 minutes

Cooking Time: 5 minutes

Servings: 4

Ingredients:

- 2 peaches, halved and pitted
- ½ cup plain nonfat Greek yogurt
- 1 teaspoon pure vanilla extract
- ¼ cup unsweetened dried coconut flakes

- 2 tablespoons unsalted pistachios, shelled and broken into pieces

Directions:

1. Preheat the broiler to high. Arrange the rack in the closest position to the broiler.

2. In a shallow pan, arrange the peach halves, cut-side up. Broil for 6 to 8 minutes until browned, tender, and hot.

3. In a small bowl, mix the yogurt and vanilla.

4. Spoon the yogurt into the cavity of each peach half.

5. Sprinkle 1 tablespoon of coconut flakes and 1½ teaspoons of pistachios over each peach half. Serve warm.

Nutrition: Calories: 102 Fat: 5g Protein: 5g Carbohydrates: 11g Sugars: 8g Fiber: 2g Sodium: 12mg

Homemade Noodles

Preparation Time: 10 minutes
Cooking Time: 240 minutes
Servings: 2

Ingredients:

- 1 cup mozzarella cheese, grated
- 1 egg yolk

Directions:

1. Add the mozzarella to a bowl and microwave for 1-2 minutes, until melted. Let cool for 30 seconds.

2. With a rubber spatula, gently fold the egg yolk into the cheese.

3. Turn the mixture out onto a parchment paper-lined baking sheet. Place another piece of parchment paper on top of the dough and press down with your hand until thin.

4. Remove the top piece of parchment and cut the dough into thin strips. Place the "pasta" on a rack and refrigerate for four hours or overnight.

5. To cook, place in boiling water for 1 minute. Drain and run cool water over to prevent sticking. Serve with your favorite sauce.

Nutrition: Calories 67 Carbs 1g Protein 5g Fat 5g Sugar 0g Fiber 0g

Cantaloupe Sorbet

Preparation Time: 10 minutes
Cooking Time: 5 minutes

Servings: 4

Ingredients:

- 11/4 cups water
- 1/3 cup sugar
- 2 cups chopped cantaloupe
- 2 teaspoons lime juice

Directions:

1. Stir together the water and sugar in a small saucepan. Cook over medium heat, stirring often, until the sugar dissolves, about 3 minutes. Let stand to cool to room temperature.

2. Combine the sugar syrup, cantaloupe, and lime juice in a food processor and process until smooth. Refrigerate until chilled, 2 hours.

3. Transfer to an ice cream maker and freeze according to manufacturer's instructions. Transfer to an airtight container and freeze overnight. Let stand at room temperature 10 minutes before serving. The sorbet can be frozen for 1 week.

Nutrition: 23 g carb 92 cal 0 g fat0 mg chol1 g fib 1 g pro13 mg sod

Mashed Butternut Squash

Preparation Time: 10 minutes
Cooking Time: 25 minutes
Servings: 6

Ingredients:

- 3 pounds whole butternut squash (about 2 medium)
- 2 tablespoons olive oil
- Salt and pepper

Directions:

1. Preheat the oven to 400°F and line a baking sheet with parchment.

2. Cut the squash in half and remove the seeds.

3. Cut the squash into cubes and toss with oil then spread on the baking sheet.

4. Roast for 25 minutes until tender then place in a food processor.

5. Blend smooth then season with salt and pepper to taste.

Nutrition: Calories 90 Fat 4.8g Carbs 8.5g Protein 2.1g Sugar 1.7g Fiber 3.9g Sodium 4mg

Fruit and Nut Muesli

Preparation Time: 10 minutes

Cooking Time: 0 minutes

Servings: 4

Ingredients:
- 1 cup skim milk
- 1 tablespoon honey
- 1 cup old-fashioned rolled oats
- 1 cup fresh blueberries
- 1/4 cup almonds, toasted and chopped

Directions:

1. Combine the milk and honey in a medium bowl and stir until well blended. Stir in the oats and blueberries.

2. Spoon into 4 bowls and sprinkle each serving with 1 tablespoon of the almonds. You can cover and refrigerate the muesli without the almonds for up to 4 days. Sprinkle with the remaining almonds just before serving.

Nutrition: 28 g carb 183 cal 6 g fat 1 mg chol 4 g fib 7 g pro 27 mg sod

Peaches and Cream Oatmeal Smoothie

Preparation Time: 10 minutes

Cooking Time: 5 minutes

Servings: 1

Ingredients:
- Frozen peach slices – 1 cup
- Greek yogurt – 1 cup
- Oatmeal – ¼ cup
- Vanilla extract – ¼ tsp.
- Almond milk – 1 cup

Directions:

1. Combine everything in a blender and blend until smooth.

Nutrition: Calories 331 Fat: 4gCarb: 46gProtein: 29g

Two-minute Microwave Broccoli with Lemon Butter

Preparation Time: 10 minutes

Cooking Time: 0 minutes

Servings: 2

Ingredients:

- 2 cups broccoli florets, cut into bite-size pieces
- 2 teaspoons lemon juice
- 1 teaspoon unsalted butter
- 1/4 teaspoon kosher salt

Directions:

1. Place the broccoli in a microwave-safe bowl and cover with plastic wrap. Microwave on high for 2 minutes.

2. Meanwhile, place the lemon juice, butter, and salt in a medium bowl.

3. Carefully uncover the broccoli and drain in a colander. Return to the bowl; add the lemon juice, butter, and salt; and toss gently to coat. Serve at once.

Nutrition: 3 g carb24 cal1 g fat3 mg chol2 g fib2 g pro85 mg sod

Chocolate Layer Cake with Fluffy White Frosting

Preparation Time: 10 minutes

Cooking Time: 30 minutes

Servings: 12

Ingredients:
- 1 recipe Chocolate Cake
- 1 recipe Fluffy White Frosting

Directions:

1. Prepare the cake recipe, baking the cake in round cake pans. To do so, line two 8- or 9-inch round cake pans with parchment paper. Brush the sides of the pans with the 2 teaspoons butter. Spoon the batter evenly into the pans. Bake 8-inch cakes for 25 minutes and 9-inch cakes for 23 minutes.

2. Cool the cakes in the pans on a wire rack for 10 minutes. Remove from the pans and cool completely on a wire rack. Spread the frosting between the layers and on the sides and top of the cake.

Nutrition: 38 g carb 222 cal 8 g fat 5 g sat fat 43 mg chol2 g fib

4 g pro 151 mg sod

Raspberry & Basil Jam

Preparation Time: 10 minutes
Cooking Time: 20 Minutes
Servings: 24
Ingredients:
- 2 lbs. fresh raspberries
- 1/3 cup fresh basil, diced fine
- 2 tbsp. lemon juice
- What you'll need from store cupboard
- ½ cup Splenda

Directions:
1. Add berries and lemon juice to a large saucepan and place over medium heat. Use a wooden spoon to break up the berries. Bring to a low boil and simmer 5-6 minutes, or until mixture starts to bubble.
2. Stir in Splenda and cook, stirring frequently, until Splenda is dissolved and mixture resembles syrup, about 15 minutes.
3. Remove from heat and stir in the basil. Spoon into glass jars with air tight lids. Let cool completely then add lids and refrigerate. Serving size is 1 tablespoon.
Nutrition: Calories 40 Carbs 8g Protein 0g Fat 0g Sugar 6g Fiber 2g

Orange Marmalade

Preparation Time: 10 minutes
Cooking Time: 30 minutes
Ingredients:
- 4 navel oranges
- 1 lemon
- What you'll need from store cupboard:
- 2 ½ cup water
- ¼ cup warm water
- 4 tbsp. Splenda
- 1 oz. gelatin

Directions:
1. Quarter the oranges and remove all the pulp. Scrap the white part off the rind and cut it into thin 2-inch strips. Remove as much of the membrane between orange segments as you can and place the seeds in a small piece of cheesecloth, pull up the sides to make a "bag" and tie closed.
2. Repeat with the lemon but discard the seeds. Cut the lemon rind into smaller strips than the orange rind.
3. Chop the orange and lemon pulp and add it to a medium saucepan along with 2 ½ cups water. Bring to a rapid boil over med-high heat.
4. Reduce heat to med-low and add the bag of seeds. Boil gently for 30 minutes, or until the citrus fruit is soft. Remove and discard the seed bag.
5. Dissolve the gelatin in the warm water. Add it to the orange mixture with ½ the Splenda. Being careful not to burn yourself, taste the marmalade and adjust sweetener as desired.
6. Spoon the marmalade into 3 ½-pint jars with air-tight lids. Seal and chill.
Nutrition: Calories 15 Carbs 3g Protein 1g Fat 0g Sugar 3g Fiber 0g

Homemade Pasta

Preparation Time: 10 minutes
Cooking Time: 5 minutes
Servings: 8
Ingredients:
- 1 egg + 2 egg yolks
- What you'll need from store cupboard:
- 1 ¾ cup soy flour
- ¼ cup ground wheat germ
- 3-4 tbsp. cold water
- 1 tsp. light olive oil
- ½ tsp. salt

Directions:
1. In a large bowl, whisk egg, egg yolks, oil and 3 tablespoons water until smooth.
2. In a separate bowl, combine flour, wheat germ, and salt. Stir into egg mixture until smooth. Use the last tablespoon of water if needed to make smooth dough.
3. Turn out onto a lightly floured surface and knead 5-8 minutes or until smooth. Cover and let rest 10 minutes.
4. Divide dough into 4 equal pieces and roll out, one at a time, as thin as possible, or run it through a pasta machine until it reaches the thinnest setting.

5.   Let dough dry out for 30 minutes. Cut into desired size with pasta machine or pizza cutter. It not using right away, let it dry overnight on a pasta or cooling rack. Fresh pasta should be used within 3 days.

6.   It will store in the freezer, after drying for just an hour, in an airtight bag, 6-8 months. Pasta dried overnight can be stored in an airtight container for up to 1 week.

7.   To cook it when fresh, add to a pot of boiling water for 4-5 minutes or until tender. Dried pasta will take a couple minutes longer.

Nutrition: Calories 152 Carbs 12g Carbs 9g Protein 16g Fat 5g Sugar 6g Fiber 3g

Pizza Sauce

Preparation Time: 10 minutes
Cooking Time: 5 minutes
Servings: 8
Ingredients:
- ½ cup yellow onion, diced
- What you'll need from store cupboard:
- 15 oz. tomatoes, crushed, no sugar added
- 1/3 cup + 1 tbsp. olive oil
- 3 cloves garlic, diced
- 2 tsp. parsley
- 1 tsp. rosemary
- 1 tsp. thyme
- 1 tsp. smoked paprika
- Salt, to taste

Directions:
1.   Heat 1 tablespoon oil in a small skillet over medium heat. Add onion and garlic and cook until onions are translucent.

2.   In a medium saucepan, over medium heat, stir all Ingredients together, along with onions. Bring to a simmer and cook 2-3 minutes, stirring constantly.

3.   Remove from heat and let cool completely. Store in a jar with an air tight lid in the refrigerator up to 2 weeks. Or in the freezer up to 6 months.

Nutrition: Calories 179 Carbs 8g Carbs 6g Protein 2g Fat 17g Sugar 5g Fiber 2g

Beef Burgundy & Mushroom Stew

Preparation Time: 10 minutes
Cooking Time: 8 Hours
Servings: 4
Ingredients:
- 1 lb. sirloin steak, cut into bite size pieces
- 2 carrots, peeled and cut into 1-inch pieces
- 1 cup mushrooms, sliced
- ¾ cup pearl onions, thawed if frozen
- What you'll need from store cupboard:
- 1 cup Burgundy wine
- ½ cup low sodium beef broth
- 3 cloves garlic, diced
- 2 tbsp. olive oil
- 1 bay leaf
- 1 tsp. marjoram
- ½ tsp. salt
- ½ tsp. thyme
- ¼ tsp. pepper

Directions:
1.   Heat the oil in a large skillet over med-high heat. Add steak and brown on all sides. Transfer to a crock pot.

2.   Add remaining Ingredients and stir to combine. Cover and cook on low 7-8 hours or until steak is tender and vegetables are cooked through. Discard the bay leaf before serving.

Nutrition: Calories 353 Carbs 8g Carbs 7g Protein 36g Fat 14g Sugar 3g Fiber 1g

Almond Vanilla Fruit Dip

Preparation Time: 10 minutes
Cooking Time: 10 minutes
Servings: 10
Ingredients:
- 2 ½ cup fat free half-n-half
- What you'll need from store cupboard:
- 4-Servings:fat-free sugar-free vanilla instant pudding mix
- 1 tbsp. Splenda
- 1 tsp. vanilla
- 1 tsp. almond extract

Directions:

1. Place all Ingredients in a medium bowl, and beat on medium speed 2 minutes.

2. Cover and chill until ready to serve. Serve with fruit for dipping. Serving is ¼ cup.

Nutrition: Calories 87 Carbs 4g Protein 2g Fat 7g Sugar 1g Fiber 0g

Pear & Poppy Jam

Preparation Time: 10 minutes
Cooking Time: 30 minutes
Servings: 3

Ingredients:

- 3 pears, peeled, seeded and chopped
- ½ lemon
- What you'll need from store cupboard:
- ¾ cup Splenda
- 1 tbsp. poppy seeds

Directions:

1. Place pears in a large bowl. Sprinkle with Splenda and toss to coat. Squeeze the lemon over the pears and toss again. Let sit for 2 hours so the fruit will release its juice.

2. Place poppy seeds in a medium saucepan over medium heat. Cook, stirring, 1-2 minutes to lightly toast the. Transfer them to a bowl.

3. Add the pears, with the juice, to the saucepan and bring to a boil, stirring frequently. Reduce the heat and let boil 10 minutes or until thickened.

4. Spoon ½ the pears into a blender and process until smooth. Add the puree back to the saucepan along with the poppy seeds. Continue cooking 5-10 minutes or the jam is thick.

5. Spoon into 2 pint sized jars with air tight lids. Let cool completely, screw on the lids and store in the refrigerator. Serving is 1 tablespoon.

Nutrition: Calories 36 Carbs 8g Carbs 7g Protein 0g Fat 0g Sugar 6g Fiber 1g

White Bean & Chicken Soup

Preparation Time: 10 minutes
Cooking Time: 2 Hours
Servings: 12

Ingredients:

- 2 lbs. chicken breasts, boneless, skinless, cut in cubes
- 3 carrots, sliced
- 2 stalks celery, slice thin
- 1 onion, diced
- ¼ cup fresh parsley, diced

What you'll need from store cupboard:

- ½ lb. baby lima beans, dried
- ½ lb. great northern beans, dried
- 4 cup low sodium chicken broth
- 2 cup water
- 1 clove garlic, diced
- 2 tbsp. sunflower oil, divided
- 1 tsp. salt, divided
- ½ tsp. pepper

Directions:

1. Sort the beans and discard any discolored ones. Rinse under cold water and add to a large pot. Add enough water to cover beans by 2 inches. Place over med-high heat and bring to a boil, cook 2 minutes. Remove from heat, cover, and let stand 2-4 hours or until beans have softened.

2. Drain and rinse beans, transfer to a large bowl.

3. Sprinkle chicken with ½ teaspoon salt. Heat 1 tablespoon oil in the large pot over med-high heat and add chicken. Cook until no longer pink. Transfer to a bowl and drain fat.

4. Heat remaining tablespoon of oil in the pot and add onion. Cook until tender. Add carrots and celery, and garlic and cook 1-2 minutes.

5. Stir in broth, water, pepper, beans and chicken and bring to a boil. Reduce heat, cover and simmer 2 hours, or until beans are tender. Stir in parsley and remaining salt and serve.

Nutrition: Calories 237 Carbs 18g Carbs 13g Protein 29g Fat 5g Sugar 2g Fiber 5g

Almond Banana Smoothie

Preparation Time: 10 minutes

Cooking Time: 5 minutes

Servings: 2

Ingredients:

- Baby spinach – 1 ½ oz.
- Rolled oats – 3 Tbsps.
- Cinnamon – 1 tsp.
- Ice – 1 cup
- Bananas – 2, peeled
- Walnuts – 3 Tbsps.
- Almond milk – 1 cup

Directions:

1. Except for the cinnamon and walnuts, blend everything in the blender.
2. Top with cinnamon and walnuts and serve.

Nutrition: Calories 266 Fat: 10g Carb: 47g Protein: 5g

Lamb Chops with Cherry Glaze

Preparation Time: 10 minutes

Cooking Time: 10 minutes

Servings: 4

Ingredients:

- 4 (4-ounce) lamb chops
- 1½ teaspoons chopped fresh rosemary
- ¼ teaspoon salt
- ¼ teaspoon freshly ground black pepper
- 1 cup frozen cherries, thawed
- ¼ cup dry red wine
- 2 tablespoons orange juice
- 1 teaspoon extra-virgin olive oil

Directions:

1. Season the lamb chops with the rosemary, salt, and pepper.
2. In a small saucepan over medium-low heat, combine the cherries, red wine, and orange juice, and simmer, stirring regularly, until the sauce thickens, 8 to 10 minutes.
3. Heat a large skillet over medium-high heat. When the pan is hot, add the olive oil to lightly coat the bottom.

4. Cook the lamb chops for 3 to 4 minutes on each side until well-browned yet medium rare.
5. Serve, topped with the cherry glaze.

Nutrition: Calories: 356 Fat: 27g Protein: 20g Carbohydrates: 6g Sugars: 4g Fiber: 1g

Cauliflower Pizza Crust

Preparation Time: 10 minutes

Cooking Time: 30 minutes

Servings: 8

Ingredients:

- 1 ½ lb. cauliflower, separated in florets
- 1 egg
- What you'll need from store cupboard:
- 1 ½ cup reduced fat parmesan cheese
- ½ tbsp. Italian seasoning
- ½ tsp. garlic powder

Directions:

1. Heat oven to 400 degrees. Line a pizza pan, or stone, with parchment paper.
2. Place the cauliflower in a food processor and pulse until it resembles rice.
3. Cook the cauliflower in a skillet over medium heat, stirring frequently, until soft, about 10 minutes.
4. In a large bowl, whisk the egg, cheese and seasonings.
5. Place the cauliflower in a clean kitchen towel and squeeze out any excess moisture. Stir into cheese mixture to form soft dough, press with a spatula if needed.
6. Spread the dough on the prepared pan about ¼-inch thick. Bake 20 minutes, or until top is dry and firm and edges are golden brown.
7. Let cool 5-10 minutes, the crust will firm up as it cools. Add desired toppings and bake 5-10 minutes more. Slice and serve.

Nutrition: Calories 158 Carbs 10g net Carbs 6g Protein 12g

Fat 9g Sugar 4g Fiber 4g

Crispy Cowboy Black Bean Fritters

Preparation Time: 10 minutes

Cooking Time: 20 minutes

Ingredients:

- 1¾ cups all-purpose flour
- ½ teaspoon cumin
- 2 teaspoons baking powder
- 2 teaspoons salt
- ½ teaspoon black pepper
- 4 egg whites, lightly beaten
- 1 cup salsa
- 2 (16-ounce / 454-g) cans no-salt-added black beans, rinsed and drained
- 1 tablespoon canola oil, plus extra if needed

Directions:

1. Combine the flour, cumin, baking powder, salt, and pepper in a large bowl, then mix in the egg whites and salsa. Add the black beans and stir to mix well.
2. Heat the canola oil in a nonstick skillet over medium-high heat.
3. Spoon 1 teaspoon of the mixture into the skillet to make a fritter. Make more fritters to coat the bottom of the skillet. Keep a little space between each two fritters. You may need to work in batches to avoid overcrowding.
4. Cook for 3 minutes or until the fritters are golden brown on both sides. Flip the fritters and flatten with a spatula halfway through the cooking time. Repeat with the remaining mixture. Add more oil as needed.
5. Serve immediately.

Nutrition: Calories: 115 Fat: 1.0g Protein: 6.0g Carbs: 20.0g

Fiber: 5.0g Sugar: 2.0g Sodium: 350mg

Seafood, Mango, and Avocado Salad

Preparation Time: 10 minutes

Cooking Time: 20 minutes

Servings: 4

Ingredients:

- 1 cup quinoa, rinsed
- ½ pound (227 g) medium shrimps, peeled and deveined
- ½ pound (227 g) scallops
- 1 tablespoon olive oil
- ½ red bell pepper, chopped
- 1 roam plum tomatoes, deseeded and chopped
- 1 jalapeño pepper, stemmed and finely chopped
- ½ cup cooked black beans
- 1 mango, chopped
- 1 avocado, chopped
- 2 small scallions, chopped
- 2 tablespoons cilantro leaves, chopped
- Citrus Dressing:
- 2 tablespoons lime juice
- 2 tablespoons orange juice
- 1 teaspoon honey
- ¼ teaspoon cayenne pepper
- 1 tablespoon extra-virgin olive oil
- Sea salt, to taste

Directions:

1. Pour the quinoa in a pot, then pour in enough water to cover. Bring to a boil, then reduce the heat to low and simmer to 10 to 15 minutes or until the liquid has been absorbed. Fluffy with a fork and let stand until ready to use.
2. Meanwhile, combine the ingredients for the citrus dressing in a small bowl. Stir to mix well. Set aside until ready to use.
3. Put the shrimps and scallops in a separate bowl, then drizzle with the olive oil. Toss to coat well.
4. Add the oiled shrimps and scallops in a nonstick skillet and grill over medium-high heat for 4 minutes or until opaque. Flip them halfway through. Remove them from the skillet and allow to cool.
5. Combine the cooked quinoa, shrimp and scallops with bell pepper, tomato, jalapeño, beans, mango, avocado, and scallions in a large salad bowl, then drizzle with the citrus dressing. Toss to combine well.
6. Garnish with cilantro leaves and serve immediately.

Nutrition: Calories: 470 Fat: 16.0g Protein: 30.0g Carbs: 56.0g

Fiber: 10.0g Sugar: 16.0g Sodium: 320mg

Winter Chicken and Citrus Salad

Preparation Time: 10 minutes

Cooking Time: 10 minutes

Servings: 4

Ingredients:

- 4 cups baby spinach
- 2 tablespoons extra-virgin olive oil
- 1 tablespoon freshly squeezed lemon juice
- 1/8 teaspoon salt
- Freshly ground black pepper
- 2 cups chopped cooked chicken
- 2 mandarin oranges, peeled and sectioned
- ½ peeled grapefruit, sectioned
- ¼ cup sliced almonds

Directions:

1. In a large mixing bowl, toss the spinach with the olive oil, lemon juice, salt, and pepper.
2. Add the chicken, oranges, grapefruit, and almonds to the bowl. Toss gently.
3. Arrange on 4 plates and serve.

Nutrition: Calories: 249 Fat: 12g Protein: 24g Carbohydrates: 11g Sugars: 7g Fiber: 3g Sodium: 135mg

Blueberry Orange Dessert Sauce

Preparation Time: 10 minutes

Cooking Time: 10 minutes

Servings: 16

Ingredients:

- 1 ½ cup orange segments
- 1 cup blueberries
- ¼ cup orange juice

What you'll need from store cupboard:

- ¼ cup water
- 1/3 cup almonds, sliced
- 3 tbsp. Splenda
- 1 tbsp. cornstarch
- 1/8 tsp. salt

Directions:

1. In a small saucepan, combine Splenda, cornstarch, and salt. Whisk in orange juice and water until smooth.

2. Bring to a boil over med-high heat, cook, stirring frequently, 1-2 minutes or until thickened.
3. Reduce heat and stir in fruit. Cook 5 minutes. Remove from heat and let cool completely.
4. Store in an airtight jar in the refrigerator until ready to use. Serving is 1 tablespoon.

Nutrition: Calories 46 Carbs 8g Protein 1g Fat 1g Sugar 6g

Fiber 0g Sodium: 199mg

Asian Swordfish

Preparation Time: 10 Minutes

Cooking Time: 6 to 11 Minutes

Servings: 4

Ingredients:

- 4 (4-ounces) of swordfish steaks
- ½ teaspoon of toasted sesame oil (see Tip)
- 1 jalapeño pepper, finely minced
- 2 garlic cloves, grated
- 1 tablespoon of grated fresh ginger
- ½ teaspoon of Chinese five-spice powder
- 1/8 teaspoon of freshly ground black pepper
- 2 tablespoons of freshly squeezed lemon juice

Directions:

1. Place the swordfish steaks on a work surface and drizzle with the sesame oil.
2. In a small bowl, mix the jalapeño, garlic, ginger, five-spice powder, pepper, and lemon juice. Rub this mixture into the fish and let it stand for 10 minutes.
3. Roast the swordfish in the Air Fryer for 6 to 11 minutes, or until the swordfish reaches an internal temperature of at least 140°F on a meat thermometer. Serve immediately.

Nutrition: Calories: 187 Fat: 6g (29% of calories from fat) Saturated Fat: 1g Protein: 29g Carbohydrates: 2g Sodium: 132mg Fiber: 0g

Full English breakfast

Preparation Time: 30 minutes

Cooking Time: 30 minutes

Servings: 4

Ingredients:

- 8 Bacon Rashers

- 8 Sausages
- 10 oz. of Canned Baked Beans, drained
- 8 Medium Eggs
- 16 Cherry Tomatoes, halved
- 16 Button Mushrooms, halved
- Salt to taste
- Ground Black Pepper to taste
- 8 Toast Slices

Directions:

1. Put sausages and bacon in the Air Fryer, use the grill pan accessory if available, and cook them for 10 minutes at 360°F.
2. When done, transfer them to serving plates.
3. While sausages and bacon are cooking, take four 4 ounces ramekins and crack two eggs in each of them. Add salt and pepper to taste.
4. Pour beans in a 10 ounces ramekin, add salt and pepper.
5. Place both ramekins with eggs and beans in the Air Fryer and cook for 10 minutes at 400 °F.
6. Remove ramekins from the Air Fryer and place in it mushroom halves, and cook them for 6 minutes at 400°F.
7. Transfer eggs to the plates with bacon and sausages.
8. Stir beans and then spoon a quarter next to eggs on each plate.
9. Add the cherry tomatoes to the Air Fryer, sprinkle both mushrooms and tomatoes with salt and pepper to taste, and cook for another 4 minutes at 400°F.
10. Divide tomatoes and mushrooms onto each plate.
11. Enjoy!

Nutrition: Calories: 297Fat: 21.7gCarbs: 11.7gProtein: 15.3gSugars: 2.6g

Country Breakie Chicken Tenders

Preparation Time: 10 minutes
Cooking Time: 15 minutes
Servings: 4

Ingredients:

- ¾ lb. of chicken tenders

For breading:

- 2 tablespoons of olive oil
- 1 teaspoon of black pepper
- ½ teaspoon of salt
- ½ cup of seasoned breadcrumbs
- ½ cup of all-purpose flour
- 2 eggs, beaten

Directions:

1. Preheat your Air Fryer to 330 °F.
2. In three separate bowls, set aside breadcrumbs, eggs, and flour. Season the breadcrumbs with salt and pepper. Add olive oil to the breadcrumbs and mix well.
3. Place chicken tenders into flour, then dip into eggs, and finally dip into breadcrumbs. Press to ensure that the breadcrumbs are evenly coating the chicken. Shake off excess breading in the cooking basket. Cook the chicken tenders for 10-minutes in the Air Fryer. Serve warm.

Nutrition: Calories: 276Total Fat: 8.6gCarbs: 7gProtein: 13.2g

Greek Lamb Pita Pockets

Preparation Time: 15 minutes
Cooking Time: 5-7 minutes
Servings: 4

Ingredients:

Dressing:

- 1 cup of plain Greek yogurt
- 1 tablespoon of lemon juice
- 1 teaspoon of dried dill weed, crushed
- 1 teaspoon of ground oregano
- ½ teaspoon of salt

Meatballs:

- ½ pound (227 g) of ground lamb
- 1 tablespoon of diced onion
- 1 teaspoon of dried parsley
- 1 teaspoon of dried dill weed, crushed
- ¼ teaspoon of oregano
- ¼ teaspoon of coriander
- ¼ teaspoon of ground cumin
- ¼ teaspoon of salt
- 4 pita halves

Suggested Toppings:

- Red onion, slivered

- Seedless cucumber, thinly sliced
- Crumbled feta cheese
- Sliced black olives
- Chopped fresh peppers

Directions:

1. Stir all the dressing ingredients together and refrigerate while preparing lamb.

2. Mix all the meatball ingredients in a large bowl and stir to distribute seasonings.

3. Shape meat mixture into 12 small meatballs, rounded or slightly flattened if you prefer.

4. Air fry at 390ºF (199ºC) for 5 to 7 minutes, until well done. Remove and drain on paper towels.

5. To serve, pile meatballs and your choice of toppings in pita pockets and drizzle with dressing.

Nutrition: Calories: 270Fat: 14gProtein: 18gCarbs: 18gFiber: 2gSugar: 2gSodium: 618mg

Asian Sesame Cod

Preparation Time: 5 minutes
Cooking Time: 7-9 minutes
Servings: 1

Ingredients:

- 1 tablespoon of reduced-sodium soy sauce
- 2 teaspoons of honey
- 1 teaspoon of sesame seeds
- 6 ounces (170 g) of cod fillet

Directions:

1. In a small bowl, mix the soy sauce and honey.

2. Spray the Air Fryer basket with nonstick cooking spray, then place the cod in the basket, brush with the soy mixture, and sprinkle sesame seeds on top. Roast at 360 ºF (182 ºC) for 7 to 9 minutes or until opaque.

3. Remove the fish from the fryer and let it cool on a wire rack for 5 minutes before serving.

Nutrition: Calories: 141Fat: 1gProtein: 26gCarbs: 7gFiber: 1gSugar: 6gSodium: 466mg

Dijon Pork Tenderloin

Preparation Time: 10 minutes
Cooking Time: 12 to 14 minutes
Servings: 4

Ingredients:

- 1 pound (454 g) of pork tenderloin, cut into 1-inch slices
- Pinch salt
- Freshly ground black pepper, to taste
- 2 tablespoons of Dijon mustard
- 1 clove garlic, minced
- ½ teaspoon of dried basil
- 1 cup of soft bread crumbs
- 2 tablespoons of olive oil

Directions:

1. Slightly pound the pork slices until they are about ¾ inch thick. Sprinkle with salt and pepper on both sides.

2. Coat the pork with the Dijon mustard and sprinkle with the garlic and basil.

3. On a plate, mix the bread crumbs and olive oil and mix well. Coat the pork slices with the bread crumb mixture, patting so the crumbs adhere.

4. Place the pork in the Air Fryer basket, leaving a little space between each piece. Air fry at 390ºF (199ºC) for 12 to 14 minutes or until the pork reaches at least 145ºF (63ºC) on a meat thermometer and the coating is crisp and brown. Serve immediately.

Nutrition: Calories: 336Fat: 13gProtein: 34gCarbs: 20gFiber: 2gSugar: 2gSodium: 390mg

Greek Chicken Kebabs

Preparation Time: 15 minutes
Cooking Time: 15 minutes
Servings: 4

Ingredients:

- 3 tablespoons of freshly squeezed lemon juice
- 2 teaspoons of olive oil
- 2 tablespoons of chopped fresh flat-leaf parsley
- ½ teaspoon of dried oregano
- ½ teaspoon of dried mint
- 1 pound (454 g) of low-sodium boneless, skinless chicken breasts, cut into 1-inch pieces
- 1 cup of cherry tomatoes
- 1 small yellow summer squash, cut into 1-inch cubes

Directions:

1.   In a large bowl, whisk the lemon juice, olive oil, parsley, oregano, and mint.

2.   Add the chicken and stir to coat. Let it stand for 10 minutes at room temperature.

3.   Alternating the items, thread the chicken, tomatoes, and squash onto 8 bamboo or metal skewers that fit in an Air Fryer. Brush with marinade.

4.   Air fry the kebabs at 380ºF (193ºC) for about 15 minutes, brushing once with any remaining marinade until the chicken reaches an internal temperature of 165ºF (74ºC) on a meat thermometer. Discard any remaining marinade. Serve immediately.

Nutrition: Calories: 164Fat: 4gProtein: 27gCarbs: 4gFiber: 1gSugar: 1gSodium: 70mg

Scotch Eggs

Preparation Time: 10 minutes
Cooking Time: 15 minutes
Servings: 4

Ingredients:

- 1-pound of pork sausage, pastured
- 2 tablespoons of chopped parsley
- 1/8 teaspoon of salt
- 1/8 teaspoon of grated nutmeg
- 1 tablespoon of chopped chives
- 1/8 teaspoon of ground black pepper
- 2 teaspoons of ground mustard, and more as needed
- 4 eggs, hard-boiled, shell peeled
- 1 cup of shredded Parmesan cheese, low-fat

Directions:

1.   Switch on the Air Fryer, insert fryer basket, grease it with olive oil, then shut with its lid, set the fryer at 400°F and preheat for 10 minutes.

2.   Meanwhile, place sausage in a bowl, add salt, black pepper, parsley, chives, nutmeg, and mustard, then stir until well mixed and shape the mixture into four patties.

3.   Peel each boiled egg, then place an egg on a patty and shape the meat around it until the egg has evenly covered.

4.   Place cheese in a shallow dish, and then roll the egg in the cheese until covered completely with cheese; prepare remaining eggs the same way.

5.   Then open the fryer, add eggs in it close with its lid and cook for 15 minutes at the 400°F until nicely golden and crispy, turning the eggs and spraying with oil halfway through the frying.

6.   When Air Fryer beeps, open its lid, transfer eggs onto a serving plate and serve with mustard.

Nutrition: Calories: 533 CalCarbs: 2 gFat: 43 gProtein: 33 gFiber: 1 g

SOUP AND STEW

Delicious Chicken Soup

Preparation Time: 10 minutes
Cooking Time: 4 hours 30 minutes
Servings: 4

Ingredients:

- 1 lb. chicken breasts, boneless and skinless
- 2 Tbsp. fresh basil, chopped
- 1 1/2 cups mozzarella cheese, shredded
- 2 garlic cloves, minced
- 1 Tbsp. Parmesan cheese, grated
- 2 Tbsp. dried basil
- 2 cups chicken stock
- 28 oz. tomatoes, diced
- 1/4 tsp. pepper
- 1/2 tsp. salt

Directions:

1.   Add chicken, Parmesan cheese, dried basil, tomatoes, garlic, pepper, and salt to a crock pot and stir well to combine.
2.   Cover and cook on low for 4 hours.
3.   Add fresh basil and mozzarella cheese and stir well.
4.   Cover again and cook for 30 more minutes or until cheese is melted.
5.   Remove chicken from the crock pot and shred using forks.
6.   Return shredded chicken to the crock pot and stir to mix.
7.   Serve and enjoy.

Nutrition: Calories 299 Fat 11.6 g Carbohydrates 9.3 g Sugar 5.6 g Protein 38.8 g Cholesterol 108 mg

Flavorful Broccoli Soup

Preparation Time: 10 minutes
Cooking Time: 4 hours 15 minutes
Servings: 6

Ingredients:

- 20 oz. broccoli florets
- 4 oz. cream cheese
- 8 oz. cheddar cheese, shredded
- 1/2 tsp. paprika
- 1/2 tsp. ground mustard
- 3 cups chicken stock
- 2 garlic cloves, chopped
- 1 onion, diced
- 1 cup carrots, shredded
- 1/4 tsp. baking soda
- 1/4 tsp. salt

Directions:

1.   Add all ingredients except cream cheese and cheddar cheese to a crock pot and stir well.
2.   Cover and cook on low for 4 hours.
3.   Purée the soup using an immersion blender until smooth.
4.   Stir in the cream cheese and cheddar cheese.
5.   Cover and cook on low for 15 minutes longer.
6.   Season with pepper and salt.
7.   Serve and enjoy.

Nutrition: Calories 275 Fat 19.9 g Carbohydrates 11.9 g Sugar 4 g Protein 14.4 g Cholesterol 60 mg

Healthy Chicken Kale Soup

Preparation Time: 10 minutes
Cooking Time: 6 hours 15 minutes
Servings: 6

Ingredients:

- 2 lb. chicken breasts, skinless and boneless
- 1/4 cup fresh lemon juice
- 5 oz. baby kale
- 32 oz. chicken stock
- 1/2 cup olive oil
- 1 large onion, sliced
- 14 oz. chicken broth
- 1 Tbsp. extra-virgin olive oil
- Salt

Directions:

1.   Heat the extra-virgin olive oil in a pan over medium heat.
2.   Season chicken with salt and place in the hot pan.
3.   Cover pan and cook chicken for 15 minutes.

4. Remove chicken from the pan and shred it using forks.

5. Add shredded chicken to a crock pot.

6. Add sliced onion, olive oil, and broth to a blender and blend until combined.

7. Pour blended mixture into the crock pot.

8. Add remaining ingredients to the crock pot and stir well.

9. Cover and cook on low for 6 hours.

10. Stir well and serve.

Nutrition: Calories 493 Fat 31.3 g Carbohydrates 5.8 g Sugar 1.9 g Protein 46.7 g Cholesterol 135 mg

Spicy Chicken Pepper Stew

Preparation Time: 10 minutes
Cooking Time: 6 hours
Servings: 6
Ingredients:
- 3 chicken breasts, skinless and boneless, cut into small pieces
- 1 tsp. garlic, minced
- 1 tsp. ground ginger
- 2 tsp. olive oil
- 2 tsp. soy sauce
- 1 Tbsp. fresh lemon juice
- 1/2 cup green onions, sliced
- 1 Tbsp. crushed red pepper
- 8 oz. chicken stock
- 1 bell pepper, chopped
- 1 green chili pepper, sliced
- 2 jalapeño peppers, sliced
- 1/2 tsp. black pepper
- 1/4 tsp. sea salt

Directions:
1. Add all ingredients to a large mixing bowl and mix well. Place in the refrigerator overnight.

2. Pour marinated chicken mixture into a crock pot.

3. Cover and cook on low for 6 hours.

4. Stir well and serve.

Nutrition: Calories 171 Fat 7.4 g Carbohydrates 3.7 g Sugar 1.7 g Protein 22 g Cholesterol 65 mg

Tasty Basil Tomato Soup

Preparation Time: 10 minutes
Cooking Time: 6 hours

Servings: 6
Ingredients:
- 28 oz. can whole peeled tomatoes
- 1/2 cup fresh basil leaves
- 4 cups chicken stock
- 1 tsp. red pepper flakes
- 3 garlic cloves, peeled
- 2 onions, diced
- 3 carrots, peeled and diced
- 3 Tbsp. olive oil
- 1 tsp. salt

Directions:
1. Add all ingredients to a crock pot and stir well.

2. Cover and cook on low for 6 hours.

3. Purée the soup until smooth using an immersion blender.

4. Season soup with pepper and salt.

5. Serve and enjoy.

Nutrition: Calories 126 Fat 7.5 g Carbohydrates 13.3 g Sugar 7 g Protein 2.5 g Cholesterol 0 mg

Healthy Spinach Soup

Preparation Time: 10 minutes
Cooking Time: 3 hours
Servings: 8
Ingredients:
- 3 cups frozen spinach, chopped, thawed and drained
- 8 oz. cheddar cheese, shredded
- 1 egg, lightly beaten
- 10 oz. can cream of chicken soup
- 8 oz. cream cheese, softened

Directions:
1. Add spinach to a large bowl. Purée the spinach.

2. Add egg, chicken soup, cream cheese, and pepper to the spinach purée and mix well.

3. Transfer spinach mixture to a crock pot.

4. Cover and cook on low for 3 hours.

5. Stir in cheddar cheese and serve.

Nutrition: Calories 256 Fat 21.9 g Carbohydrates 4.1 g Sugar 0.5 g Protein 11.1 g Cholesterol 84 mg

Mexican Chicken Soup

Preparation Time: 10 minutes
Cooking Time: 4 hours
Servings:: 6

Ingredients:

- 1 1/2 lb. chicken thighs, skinless and boneless
- 14 oz. chicken stock
- 14 oz. salsa
- 8 oz. Monterey Jack cheese, shredded

Directions:

- Place chicken into a crock pot.
- Pour remaining ingredients over the chicken.
- Cover and cook on high for 4 hours.
- Remove chicken from crock pot and shred using forks.
- Return shredded chicken to the crock pot and stir well.
- Serve and enjoy.

Nutrition: Calories 371 Fat 19.5 g Carbohydrates 5.7 g Sugar 2.2 g Protein 42.1 g Cholesterol 135 mg

Beef Stew

Preparation Time: 10 minutes
Cooking Time: 5 hours 5 minutes
Servings: 8

Ingredients:

- 3 lb. beef stew meat, trimmed
- 1/2 cup red curry paste
- 1/3 cup tomato paste
- 13 oz. can coconut milk
- 2 tsp. ginger, minced
- 2 garlic cloves, minced
- 1 medium onion, sliced
- 2 Tbsp. olive oil
- 2 cups carrots, julienned
- 2 cups broccoli florets
- 2 tsp. fresh lime juice
- 2 Tbsp. fish sauce
- 2 tsp. sea salt

Directions:

1. Heat 1 tablespoon of oil in a pan over medium heat.
2. Brown the meat on all sides in the pan.
3. Add brown meat to a crock pot.
4. Add remaining oil to the same pan and sauté the ginger, garlic, and onion over medium-high heat for 5 minutes.
5. Add coconut milk and stir well.
6. Transfer pan mixture to the crock pot.
7. Add remaining ingredients except for carrots and broccoli.
8. Cover and cook on high for 5 hours.
9. Add carrots and broccoli during the last 30 minutes of cooking.
10. Serve and enjoy.

Nutrition: Calories 537 Fat 28.6 g Carbohydrates 13 g Sugar 12.6 g Protein 54.4 g Cholesterol 152 mg

Creamy Broccoli Cauliflower Soup

Preparation Time: 10 minutes
Cooking Time: 6 hours
Servings: 6

Ingredients:

- 2 cups cauliflower florets, chopped
- 3 cups broccoli florets, chopped
- 3 1/2 cups chicken stock
- 1 large carrot, diced
- 1/2 cup shallots, diced
- 2 garlic cloves, minced
- 1 cup plain yogurt
- 6 oz. cheddar cheese, shredded
- 1 cup coconut milk
- Pepper
- Salt

Directions:

1. Add all ingredients except milk, cheese, and yogurt to a crock pot and stir well.
2. Cover and cook on low for 6 hours.
3. Purée the soup using an immersion blender until smooth.
4. Add cheese, milk, and yogurt and blend until smooth and creamy.
5. Season with pepper and salt.
6. Serve and enjoy.

Nutrition: Calories 281 Fat 20 g Carbohydrates 14.4 g Sugar 6.9 g Protein 13.1 g Cholesterol 32 mg

Squash Soup

Preparation Time: 10 minutes
Cooking Time: 8 hours
Servings: 6

Ingredients:

- 2 lb. butternut squash, peeled, chopped into chunks
- 1 tsp. ginger, minced
- 1/4 tsp. cinnamon
- 1 Tbsp. curry powder
- 2 bay leaves
- 1 tsp. black pepper
- 1/2 cup heavy cream
- 2 cups chicken stock
- 1 Tbsp. garlic, minced
- 2 carrots, cut into chunks
- 2 apples, peeled, cored and diced
- 1 large onion, diced
- 1 tsp. salt

Directions:

1. Spray a crock pot inside with cooking spray.
2. Add all ingredients except cream to the crock pot and stir well.
3. Cover and cook on low for 8 hours.
4. Purée the soup using an immersion blender until smooth and creamy.
5. Stir in heavy cream and season soup with pepper and salt.
6. Serve and enjoy.

Nutrition: Calories 170 Fat 4.4 g Carbohydrates 34.4 g Sugar 13.4g Protein 2.9 g Cholesterol 14 mg

Herb Tomato Soup

Preparation Time: 10 minutes
Cooking Time: 6 hours
Servings: 8

Ingredients:

- 55 oz. can tomatoes, diced
- 1/2 onion, minced
- 2 cups chicken stock
- 1 cup half and half
- 4 Tbsp. butter
- 1 bay leaf
- 1/2 tsp. black pepper
- 1/2 tsp. garlic powder
- 1 tsp. oregano
- 1 tsp. dried thyme
- 1 cup carrots, diced
- 1/4 tsp. black pepper
- 1/2 tsp. salt

Directions:

1. Add all ingredients to a crock pot and stir well.
2. Cover and cook on low for 6 hours.
3. Discard bay leaf and purée the soup using an immersion blender until smooth.
4. Serve and enjoy.

Nutrition: Calories 145 Fat 9.4 g Carbohydrates 13.9 g Sugar 7.9 g Protein 3.2 g Cholesterol 26 mg

Easy Beef Mushroom Stew

Preparation Time: 10 minutes
Cooking Time: 8 hours
Servings: 8

Ingredients:

- 2 lb. stewing beef, cubed
- 1 packet dry onion soup mix
- 4 oz. can mushrooms, sliced
- 14 oz. can cream of mushroom soup
- 1/2 cup water
- 1/4 tsp. black pepper
- 1/2 tsp. salt

Directions:

1. Spray a crock pot inside with cooking spray.
2. Add all ingredients into the crock pot and stir well.
3. Cover and cook on low for 8 hours.
4. Stir well and serve.

Nutrition: Calories 237 Fat 8.5 g Carbohydrates 2.7 g Sugar 0.4 g Protein 35.1 g Cholesterol 101 mg

Lamb Stew

Preparation Time: 10 minutes

Cooking Time: 8 hours

Servings: 2

Ingredients:

- 1/2 lb. lean lamb, boneless and cubed
- 2 Tbsp. lemon juice
- 1/2 onion, chopped
- 2 garlic cloves, minced
- 2 fresh thyme sprigs
- 1/4 tsp. turmeric
- 1/4 cup green olives, sliced
- 1/2 tsp. black pepper
- 1/4 tsp. salt

Directions:

1. Add all ingredients to a crock pot and stir well.
2. Cover and cook on low for 8 hours.
3. Stir well and serve.

Nutrition: Calories 297 Fat 20.3 g Carbohydrates 5.4 g Sugar 1.5 g Protein 21 g Cholesterol 80 mg

Vegetable Chicken Soup

Preparation Time: 10 minutes

Cooking Time: 6 hours

Servings: 6

Ingredients:

- 4 cups chicken, boneless, skinless, cooked and diced
- 4 tsp. garlic, minced
- 2/3 cups onion, diced
- 1 1/2 cups carrot, diced
- 6 cups chicken stock
- 2 Tbsp. lime juice
- 1/4 cup jalapeño pepper, diced
- 1/2 cup tomatoes, diced
- 1/2 cup fresh cilantro, chopped
- 1 tsp. chili powder
- 1 Tbsp. cumin
- 1 3/4 cups tomato juice
- 2 tsp. sea salt

Directions:

1. Add all ingredients to a crock pot and stir well.

2. Cover and cook on low for 6 hours.
3. Stir well and serve.

Nutrition: Calories 192 Fat 3.8 g Carbohydrates 9.8 g Sugar 5.7 g Protein 29.2 g Cholesterol 72 mg

Slow Cooker Lentil & Ham Soup

Preparation Time: 20 minutes

Cooking Time: 11 hours

Servings: 6

Ingredients:

- Chopped celery - 1 cup
- Dried lentils - 1 cup
- Chopped onion - 1 cup
- Chopped carrots - 1 cup
- Cooked ham, chopped - 1½ cups
- Minced garlic - 2 cloves
- Dried thyme - ¼ teaspoon
- Dried basil - ½ teaspoon
- Bay leaf - 1
- Dried oregano - 1/2 teaspoon
- Chicken broth - 32 ounces
- Black pepper - ¼ teaspoon
- Tomato sauce - 8 teaspoons
- Water - 1 cup

Directions:

1. Put celery, lentils, onion, carrots, ham, and garlic in a 4-quart slow cooker and combine thoroughly.
2. Season the ingredients with thyme, basil, bay leaf, oregano, and pepper.
3. Pour chicken broth and stir well.
4. Now add the tomato sauce and water into the slow cooker.
5. Close the lid and slow cook for 11 hours.
6. Remove bay leaf before serving.
7. Serve hot.

Nutrition: Calories: 222 | Carbohydrate: 26.3g | Protein: 15.1g | Fat: 6.1g | Sugars: 4g | Dietary Fiber: 11.4g | Cholesterol: 20mg | Sodium: 1170mg |Potassium: 594mg

Beef Barley Vegetable Soup

Preparation Time: 20 minutes

Cooking Time: 5 hours 30 minute

Servings: 10

Ingredients:

- Barley - ½ cup
- Beef chuck roast - 3 pounds
- Oil - 2 tablespoons
- Bay leaf - 1
- Chopped celery - 3 stalks
- Chopped carrots - 3
- Mixed vegetables - 16 ounces
- Chopped onion - 1
- Beef bouillon - 4 cubes
- Water - 4 cups
- Ground black pepper - ¼ teaspoon
- White sugar - 1 tablespoon
- Salt - ¼ teaspoon
- Stewed tomatoes, diced - 28 ounces

Directions:

1. Take a slow cooker and
2. Cook chuck roast in the slow cooker at high heat for 5 until it becomes soft.
3. Add a bay leaf and barley into the slow cooker one hour before the end of cooking.
4. Remove the meat and chop it into small pieces.
5. Discard the bay leaf as well.
6. Set the broth, beef and the barley aside.
7. Pour oil in a large cooking pot and bring it on medium heat.
8. Sauté celery, onion, frozen mixed vegetables, and carrots until they become soft.
9. Add beef bouillon cubes, water, pepper, sugar, beef or barley mixture, tomatoes.
10. Boil the mix and reduce the heat and let it simmer for about ten to twenty minutes.
11. Season it with salt and pepper before serving.

Nutrition: Calories: 321 | Carbohydrate: 22.4g | Protein: 20g | Fat: 17.3g | Sugars: 6g | Dietary Fiber: 5.1g | Cholesterol: 62mg | Sodium: 605mg |Potassium: 552mg

Slow Cooker Corn Chowder

Preparation Time: 15 minutes

Cooking Time: 4 hours

Servings: 8

Ingredients:

- Cream style corn - 14¾ ounces
- Milk - 3 cups
- Chopped green chilies - 4 ounces
- Condensed mushroom cream soup - 10¾ ounces
- Hash brown potatoes, frozen & shredded - 2 cups
- Frozen corn - 2 cups
- Chopped onion - 1 large
- Cooked ham, cubed - 2 cups
- Hot sauce - 2 tablespoons
- Butter - 2 tablespoons
- Chili powder - 1 teaspoon
- Dried parsley - 2 teaspoons
- Salt - ¼ teaspoon
- Ground black pepper - ½ teaspoon

Directions:

1. Stir in cream-style corn, milk, chopped green chilies, cream of mushroom soup, hash brown potatoes, frozen corn, ham, butter, onion, parsley, chili powder and hot sauce in a slow cooker.
2. Season the soup with black pepper and salt as per your taste.
3. Cover the cooker and slow cook for 6 hours.
4. Serve hot.

Nutrition: Calories: 376 | Carbohydrate: 47.1g | Protein: 14.9g | Fat: 18.7g | Sugars: 12g | Dietary Fiber: 3.6g | Cholesterol: 34mg | Sodium: 1716mg |Potassium: 787mg

Slow Cooker Chicken Posole

Preparation Time: 10 minutes

Cooking Time: 6 hours 40 minutes

Servings: 6

Ingredients:

- Skinless, boneless chicken breasts - 3
- Chicken broth, low sodium - 4 cups
- Chopped white onion - 1
- Chopped poblano peppers - 2

- Cumin - 1 tablespoon
- Minced garlic - 2 cloves
- Chili powder - 2 teaspoons
- Oregano - 1 tablespoon
- Kosher salt - 2 teaspoons
- Ground black pepper, fresh - ½ teaspoon
- Drained hominy - 15 ounces

For Garnish:
- Sliced green cabbage - ¾ cup
- Thinly sliced radish - ½ cup
- Fresh cilantro, chopped - ¼ cup

Directions:

1. In a slow cooker combine all items, except the ingredients for garnish and hominy.
2. Cover and slow cook for 8 hours.
3. After cooking, take the chicken out of the slow cooker and shred it using a fork
4. Return it to the slow cooker along with hominy.
5. Cook it further 30 minutes.
6. Garnish it with cabbage, radish, and cilantro before serving.

Nutrition: Calories: 105 | Carbohydrate: 16.6g | Protein: 5.5g | Fat: 2.1g | Sugars: 3.9g | Dietary Fiber: 3.6g | Cholesterol: 0mg | Sodium: 1451mg |Potassium: 317mg

Potlikker Soup

Preparation Time: 15 minutes
Cooking Time: 20 minutes
Servings: 6

Ingredients:

- 3 cups Chicken Broth (here) or store-bought low-sodium chicken broth, divided
- 1 medium onion, chopped
- 3 garlic cloves, minced
- 1 bunch collard greens or mustard greens including stems, roughly chopped
- 1 fresh ham bone
- 5 carrots, peeled and cut into 1-inch rounds
- 2 fresh thyme sprigs
- 3 bay leaves
- Freshly ground black pepper

Directions:

1. Select the Sauté setting on an electric pressure cooker, and combine ½ cup of chicken broth, the onion, and garlic and cook for 3 to 5 minutes, or until the onion and garlic are translucent.
2. Add the collard greens, ham bone, carrots, and remaining 2½ cups of broth, the thyme, and bay leaves.
3. Close and lock the lid and set the pressure valve to sealing.
4. Change to the Manual/Pressure Cook setting, and cook for 15 minutes.
5. Once cooking is complete, quick-release the pressure. Carefully remove the lid. Discard the bay leaves.
6. Serve with Skillet Bivalves.

Substitution tip:

To make this soup vegan, replace the ham bone with dried mushrooms and swap out the chicken broth for low-sodium vegetable broth.

Nutrition: Calories: 99 Fat: 4g Cholesterol: 13mg Carbohydrates: 10g Sugar: 4g Fiber: 3g Protein: 6g

Burgoo

Preparation Time: 15 minutes
Cooking Time: 60 minutes
Servings: 16

Ingredients:

- 2 pounds pork butt, chopped into 1-inch pieces
- 2 pounds beef stew meat, chopped into 1-inch pieces
- 1 pound boneless, skinless chicken thighs, chopped into 1-inch pieces
- 1 teaspoon cayenne pepper
- 1 teaspoon Not Old Bay Seasoning
- 3 cups Chicken Broth (here) or store-bought low-sodium chicken broth
- 2 pounds potatoes, cut into 1-inch cubes
- 3 onions, chopped
- 2 green bell peppers, chopped
- 4 carrots, peeled and chopped
- 2 cups frozen corn
- 1 pound okra, cut into 1-inch rounds
- 2 celery stalks, roughly chopped
- 1 cup frozen lima beans
- 2 large tomatoes, chopped

- 2 tablespoons tomato paste
- ¼ large cabbage, roughly chopped

Directions:

1. In an electric pressure cooker, combine the pork, beef, chicken, cayenne, and seasoning.

2. Cover with the broth, close and lock the lid, and set the pressure valve to sealing.

3. Select the Manual/Pressure Cook setting, and cook for 20 minutes.

4. Once cooking is complete, allow the pressure to release naturally. Carefully remove the lid.

5. Remove the meat, and shred with two forks.

6. To the pressure cooker, add the potatoes, onions, peppers, carrots, corn, okra, celery, lima beans, tomatoes, tomato paste, and cabbage. Close and lock the lid and set the pressure valve to sealing.

7. Select the Manual/Pressure Cook setting, and cook for 10 minutes.

8. Once cooking is complete, allow the pressure to release naturally. Carefully remove the lid.

9. Return the meat to the pressure cooker, change to the Sauté setting, and cook for 5 minutes, uncovered, or until the flavors meld.

10. Storage Tip: This dish can be stored in the refrigerator in an airtight container for up to 3 days.

Nutrition: Calories: 354 Fat: 12g Cholesterol: 109mg Sodium: 140mg Carbohydrates: 24g Sugar: 6g Fiber: 5g Protein: 36g

She-Crab Soup

Preparation Time: 15 minutes

Cooking Time: 25 minutes

Servings: 6

Ingredients:

- 2 cups Seafood Broth (here)
- 1 shallot, chopped
- 2 celery stalks, chopped
- 1 garlic clove, minced
- 1 teaspoon Not Old Bay Seasoning
- 1 cup fat-free milk
- ½ cup half-and-half
- 1 teaspoon hot sauce
- 1 teaspoon Worcestershire sauce

- 11/8 pounds backfin lump crab meat
- 1 bunch chives, chopped
- Freshly ground black pepper
- Lemon wedges

Directions:

1. In a heavy-bottomed stockpot, bring the broth to a simmer.

2. Add the shallot, celery, garlic, and seasoning and cook for 3 to 5 minutes, or until softened.

3. Reduce the heat to low, and whisk in the milk, half-and-half, hot sauce, and Worcestershire sauce. Simmer for 10 minutes.

4. Add the crab and cook for 5 to 7 minutes, or until the flavors come together.

5. Serve with the chives, pepper, and lemon wedges.

Substitution Tip: If you don't have access to shallots, use half of a white onion.

Nutrition: Calories: 116 Fat: 4g Cholesterol: 60mg Sodium: 421mg Carbohydrates: 4g Sugar: 3g Fiber: 1g Protein: 16g

Sweet Potato and Pumpkin Soup with Peanuts

Preparation Time: 10 minutes

Cooking Time: 45 minutes

Servings: 8-10

Ingredients:

- 3 cups Vegetable Broth (here) or store-bought low-sodium vegetable broth, divided
- 1 celery stalk, roughly chopped
- 1 cup roughly chopped tomato
- 1 red bell pepper, chopped
- 1 large sweet potato, peeled and cut into 2-inch cubes
- 1 small pumpkin, peeled and cut into 2-inch cubes
- 1 bay leaf
- 1 teaspoon paprika
- 2 cups roasted unsalted peanuts
- Baby sage leaves (optional)

Directions:

1. In a large Dutch oven, bring 1 cup of broth to a simmer over medium heat.

2. Add the celery, tomato, and bell pepper and cook for 5 to 7 minutes, or until softened.

3. Add the sweet potato, pumpkin, bay leaf, paprika, and the remaining 2 cups of broth. Cover and cook for 30 minutes, or until the sweet potato and pumpkin are soft.

4. Add the peanuts and cook for 5 minutes, or until the peanuts become less crunchy. Discard the bay leaf.

5. Transfer to a heat-safe blender, and pulse until the soup has a batter-like consistency.

6. Serve with Grilled Hearts of Romaine with Buttermilk Dressing and protein of your choice. If using, garnish with baby sage leaves.

Prep Tip: If you prefer a less nutty flavor, reduce the quantity of peanuts, or simply use ½ cup as garnish and divide it between each serving.

Nutrition: Calories: 266 Fat: 18g Cholesterol: 0mg Sodium: 50mg Carbohydrates: 19g Sugar: 6g Fiber: 5g Protein: 12g

Spicy Chicken Stew

Preparation Time: 15 minutes
Cooking Time: 20 minutes
Servings: 8

Ingredients:

- 3 cups Chicken Broth (here) or store-bought low-sodium chicken broth
- 6 boneless, skinless chicken breasts
- 1 tablespoon Blackened Rub
- 2 carrots, peeled and cut into 1-inch rounds
- 1 onion, roughly chopped
- 2 celery stalks, roughly chopped
- 1 medium sweet potato, cut into 1-inch chunks
- 2 cups fresh peas
- 2 cups roughly chopped green beans
- 2 garlic cloves, minced
- 1 cup chopped tomatoes
- 1 tablespoon tomato paste

Directions:

1. Select the Sauté setting on an electric pressure cooker, and combine the broth, chicken, and rub. Cook for 5 minutes, or until the exterior of the chicken is lightly browned.

2. Add the carrots, onion, celery, sweet potato, peas, green beans, garlic, tomatoes, and tomato paste.

3. Close and lock the lid and set the pressure valve to sealing.

4. Change to the Manual/Pressure Cook setting, and cook for 15 minutes at high pressure.

5. Once cooking is complete, quick-release the pressure. Carefully remove the lid, and serve.

Storage Tip: This soup can be stored in the refrigerator in an airtight container for up to 3 days.

Prep Tip: To make on the stovetop, in a large Dutch oven, combine ½ cup of broth, the chicken, and seasoning and cook over medium heat, stirring often, for 3 to 5 minutes. Add the remaining ingredients, reduce the heat to low, cover, and cook for 35 minutes.

Nutrition: Calories: 145 Fat: 1g Cholesterol: 49mg Sodium: 109mg Carbohydrates: 12g Sugar: 4g Fiber: 4g Protein: 22g

Brunswick stew

Preparation Time: 15 minutes
Cooking Time: 60 minutes
Servings: 6-8

Ingredients:

- 5 cups Chicken Broth (here) or store-bought low-sodium chicken broth, divided
- 1 medium onion, roughly chopped
- 2 garlic cloves, minced
- 4 boneless, skinless chicken thighs, roughly cut into chunks
- 3 sun-dried tomatoes, drained and roughly chopped
- 2 cups fresh lima beans
- 1 cup fresh corn kernels
- 1 zucchini, cut into 1-inch chunks
- 1 cup Barbecue Sauce
- 1 tablespoon Worcestershire sauce
- ½ teaspoon Not Old Bay Seasoning

Directions:

1. Select the Sauté setting on an electric pressure cooker, and combine 1 cup of broth, the onion, and garlic and cook for 1 to 2 minutes, or until the onion and garlic are translucent.

2. Add the chicken, sun-dried tomatoes, lima beans, corn, zucchini, and barbecue sauce, remaining 4 cups broth, the Worcestershire sauce, and seasoning.

3. Close and lock the lid and set the pressure valve to sealing.

4. Change to the Manual/Pressure Cook setting, and cook for 1 hour at high pressure.

5. Once cooking is complete, quick-release the pressure. Carefully remove the lid, and serve.

Cooking Tip: If you don't have an electric pressure cooker, use a Dutch oven and cook for the same amount of time.

Nutrition: Calories: 262 Fat: 4g Cholesterol: 63mg Sodium: 251mg Carbohydrates: 36g Sugar: 8g Fiber: 5g Protein: 22g

Down South Corn Soup

Preparation Time: 10 minutes

Cooking Time: 35 minutes

Servings: 8-10

Ingredients:

- 1 tablespoon extra-virgin olive oil
- ½ Vidalia onion, minced
- 2 garlic cloves, minced
- 3 cups chopped cabbage
- 1 small cauliflower, broken into florets or 1 (10-ounce) bag frozen cauliflower
- 1 (10-ounce) bag frozen corn
- 1 cup Vegetable Broth (here) or store-bought low-sodium vegetable broth
- 1 teaspoon smoked paprika
- 1 teaspoon ground cumin
- 1 teaspoon dried dill
- ½ teaspoon freshly ground black pepper
- 1 cup plain unsweetened cashew milk

Directions:

1. In a large stockpot, heat the oil over medium heat.

2. Add the onion and garlic, and sauté, stirring to prevent the garlic from scorching, for 3 to 5 minutes, or until translucent.

3. Add the cabbage and a splash of water, cover, and cook for 5 minutes, or until tender.

4. Add the cauliflower, corn, broth, paprika, cumin, dill, and pepper. Cover and cook for 20 minutes, or until tender.

5. Add the cashew milk and stir well. Cover and cook for 5 minutes, letting the flavors come together.

6. Serve with a heaping plate of greens and seafood of your choice.

Substitution Tip: Use any unsweetened non-dairy milk alternative you like instead of cashew milk.

Nutrition: Calories: 120 Fat: 4g Cholesterol: 0mg Sodium: 53mg Carbohydrates: 18g Sugar: 4g Fiber: 3g Protein: 3g

Carrot Soup

Preparation Time: 15 minutes

Cooking Time: 25 minutes

Servings: 6

Ingredients:

- 4 cups Vegetable Broth (here) or store-bought low-sodium vegetable broth, divided
- 2 celery stalks, halved
- 1 small yellow onion, roughly chopped
- ½ fennel bulb, cored and roughly chopped
- 1 (1-inch) piece fresh ginger, peeled and chopped
- 1 pound carrots, peeled and halved
- 2 teaspoons ground cumin
- 1 garlic clove, peeled
- 1 tablespoon almond butter

Directions:

1. Select the Sauté setting on an electric pressure cooker, and combine ½ cup of broth, the celery, onion, fennel, and ginger. Cook for 5 minutes, or until the vegetables are tender.

2. Add the carrots, cumin, garlic, remaining 3½ cups of broth, and the almond butter.

3. Close and lock the lid, and set the pressure valve to sealing.

4.   Change to the Manual/Pressure Cook setting, and cook for 15 minutes.

5.   Once cooking is complete, quick-release the pressure. Carefully remove the lid, and let cool for 5 minutes.

6.   Using a stand mixer or an immersion blender, carefully purée the soup. Serve with a heaping plate of greens.

Storage Tip: This soup can be stored for 3 to 5 days in an airtight container in the refrigerator.

Nutrition: Calories: 82 Fat: 2g Cholesterol: 0mg Sodium: 121mg Carbohydrates: 13g Sugar: 5g Fiber: 3g Protein: 3g

Four-Bean Field Stew

Preparation Time: 10 minutes
Cooking Time: 40 minutes
Servings: 8-10
Ingredients:
•   6 cups Vegetable Broth (here) or store-bought low-sodium vegetable broth
•   1 cup dried lima beans
•   1 cup dried black beans
•   1 cup dried pinto beans
•   1 cup dried kidney beans
•   1 cup roughly chopped tomato
•   2 carrots, peeled and roughly chopped
•   1 zucchini, chopped
•   ½ cup chopped white onion
•   1 celery stalk, roughly chopped
•   2 garlic cloves, minced
•   1 teaspoon dried oregano
•   1 teaspoon dried thyme
•   ¼ teaspoon freshly ground black pepper
Directions:
1.   In an electric pressure cooker, combine the broth, lima beans, black beans, pinto beans, kidney beans, tomato, carrots, zucchini, onion, celery, garlic, oregano, thyme, and pepper.

2.   Close and lock the lid, and set the pressure valve to sealing.

3.   Select the Manual/Pressure Cook setting, and cook for 40 minutes.

4.   Once cooking is complete, quick-release the pressure. Carefully remove the lid.

5.   Serve with Barbecue Chicken.

Substitution Tip: To reduce the cooking time by 20 minutes, use well-rinsed low-sodium beans instead of dried beans.

Nutrition: Calories: 298 Fat: 1g Cholesterol: 0mg Sodium: 82mg Carbohydrates: 54g Sugar: 4g Fiber: 13g Protein: 19g

Pumpkin Soup

Preparation Time: 15 minutes
Cooking Time: 30 minutes
Servings: 6
Ingredients:
•   2 cups Seafood Broth (here), divided
•   1 bunch collard greens, stemmed and cut into ribbons
•   1 tomato, chopped
•   1 garlic clove, minced
•   1 butternut squash or other winter squash, peeled and cut into 1-inch cubes
•   1 teaspoon paprika
•   1 teaspoon dried dill
•   2 (5-ounce) cans boneless, skinless salmon in water, rinsed
Directions:
1.   In a heavy-bottomed large stockpot, bring ½ cup of broth to a simmer over medium heat.

2.   Add the collard greens, tomato, and garlic and cook for 5 minutes or until the greens are wilted and the garlic is softened.

3.   Add the squash, paprika, dill, and remaining 1½ cups of broth. Cover and cook for 20 minutes, or until the squash is tender.

4.   Add the salmon and cook for 3 minutes, or just enough for the flavors to come together.

Substitution Tip: Swap in solid white albacore canned tuna if you don't have access to canned salmon.

Nutrition: Calories: 152 Fat: 2g Cholesterol: 14mg Sodium: 213mg Carbohydrates: 19g Sugar: 4g Fiber: 4g Protein: 14g

SIDE DISHES

Air Fryer Chicken Fried Rice

Preparation Time: 10 minutes

Cooking Time: minutes

Servings: 3

Ingredients

- 3 cups cooked white rice cold
- 1 tablespoon vegetable oil
- 6 tablespoons soy sauce
- 1 cup diced cooked chicken
- 1/2 cup frozen peas
- 1/2 cup frozen carrots
- 1/2 cup diced onion

Directions

1. Combine in a large mixing bowl the cold cooked white rice, soy sauce, and vegetable oil.

2. Add the diced onion, diced chicken, and frozen vegetables to the rice mixture, tossing to combine well.

3. Transfer the rice mixture into a nonstick pan and place into the air fryer. Cook the rice-chicken mixture at 360 degrees for twenty minutes.

4. Quickly remove the pan from the fryer when the timer countdown is finished.

5. Ladle into serving bowl and serve.

6. Enjoy!

Nutrition: 405 calories 6.4 g fat (1.4 g saturated fat) 36 mg cholesterol 63 g carbohydrates 3.2 g dietary fiber3.5 g total sugars 21.7 g protein

Air Fryer Copycat Chick-fil-a Chicken Nuggets

Preparation Time: 10 minutes

Cooking Time: minutes

Servings: 6 nuggets

Ingredients

- 1 pound raw chicken breast meat
- 3/4 cup pickle juice
- 1 egg
- 3/4 cups milk
- 2 tablespoons powdered sugar
- 1 1/4 cup flour
- 1/2 teaspoon paprika
- 1/2 teaspoon salt
- 1/2 teaspoon pepper

Directions

1. Cut chicken breast meat into one-inch pieces.

2. Pour the pickle juice into a bowl and add the chicken pieces; marinate for half an hour. Set aside.

3. In a separate bowl, whisk the egg and milk together, set aside.

4. In another bowl, combine the powdered sugar, flour, paprika, pepper, and salt. Drain the pickle juice.

5. Remove the chicken from juice and dip in the egg mixture, and then dredge in the flour mixture.

6. Mist the air fryer basket with cooking spray. Arrange the breaded chicken in a single layer of the air fryer and mist with olive oil spray.

7. Cook the chicken for nine minutes at 370° F. Remove nuggets from fryer.

8. Serve with dipping sauce.

9. Enjoy!

Nutrition: 275 calories;5.2 g fat (1.6 g saturated fat)99 mg cholesterol513 mg sodium20.1 g carbohydrates;1.1 g dietary fiber4.3 g total sugars30 g protein.

Garlic Parmesan Air Fryer Asparagus

Preparation Time: 10 minutes

Cooking Time: minutes

Servings: 4

Ingredients

- 1 pound asparagus
- 1 teaspoon garlic powder
- 1 tablespoons olive oil
- 1 tablespoon grated parmesan
- Pinch of kosher salt
- Dash of pepper

Directions

1. Prepare the asparagus by cutting the bottom at least 1 or two inches.

2. Transfer the asparagus slices on a tray or plate and then drizzle all over with olive oil.

3. Sprinkle all over with garlic powder, grated cheese, and season with pepper and salt.

4. Using your clean hands, toss the asparagus to coat thoroughly.

5. Transfer the asparagus to the air fryer basket and cook for ten minutes at 400 degrees F. Serve hot!

6. Enjoy!

Nutrition: 56 calories;3.7 g fat (0.6 g saturated fat) 0 mg cholesterol 42 mg sodium 4.9 g carbohydrates 2.5 g dietary fiber 2.3 g total sugars 2.7 g protein.

Air Fryer Baked Potato

Preparation Time: 10 minutes

Cooking Time: minutes

Servings: 3

Ingredients

- 3 Idaho or Russet Baking Potatoes
- 1 to 2 tablespoons olive oil
- 1 teaspoon parsley
- 1 tablespoon garlic
- 1 tablespoon salt

Directions

1. Wash the potatoes very well.

2. Poke several holes in the potatoes with a fork.

3. Sprinkle the potatoes with olive oil. Evenly rub the potatoes with parsley, garlic, and salt.

4. Arrange the potatoes in the air fryer basket and cook for 35 to 40 minutes at 392 degrees F until fork tender.

5. Serve with your favorite dipping, sour cream or fresh parsley.

6. Enjoy!

Nutrition: 213 calories; 4 g fat; 39 g carbohydrates; 2336 mg sodium; 2 g dietary fiber; 1 g total sugars; 4 g protein.

Air Fryer Mexican Street Corn

Preparation Time: 10 minutes

Cooking Time: minutes

Servings: 4

Ingredients

- 4 pieces fresh corn on the cob
- 1/4 cup crumbled Feta cheese or cotija cheese
- 1/4 cup chopped fresh cilantro

- 1/2 teaspoon Stone House Seasoning or Mrs. Dash Southwest Chipotle Seasoning
- 1/4 teaspoon chili powder
- 1 medium lime cut into wedges

Directions

1. Arrange the corn in the basket of air fryer. Cook at 390 degrees for ten minutes.

2. While cooking, sprinkle the cheese all over the corn, and cook for another five minutes at 390 degrees F.

3. Quickly remove corn from the air fryer.

4. Sprinkle on top with Stone House or Mrs. Dash seasoning, cilantro, and chili powder.

5. Serve corn with lime wedges alongside.

6. Enjoy!

Nutrition: 102 calories 3 g fat (1 g saturated fat) 8 mg cholesterol 120 mg sodium 17 g carbohydrates 1 g dietary fiber 6 g total sugars 4 g protein.

Air Fryer Corn on the Cob

Preparation Time: 10 minutes

Cooking Time: minutes

Servings: 2

Ingredients

- 2 ears of fresh sweet corn husk
- 1 tablespoon oil
- Pinch salt
- Dash pepper

Directions

1. Remove silk of corn and cut in half to yield four pieces.

2. Slowly pour 1 tablespoon of oil all over the corn and spread by rubbing with your hands.

3. Arrange the corn halves in the air fryer basket. Cook for eight minutes at 380 degrees Fahrenheit.

4. When the fryer strikes at exactly four minute mark, quickly remove the basket and shake, and then return to the fryer to continue cooking for the remaining 4 minutes.

5. Remove the corn from the basket when the timer is up. Sprinkle with additional pepper and salt if desired.

6. Serve hot.

7. Enjoy!

Nutrition: 140 calories 7.8 g fat (0.9 g saturated fat) 0 mg cholesterol 78 mg sodium 18 g carbohydrates 3 g dietary fiber 5 g total sugars 3 g protein.

Air Fryer Taco Bell Crunch Wrap

Preparation Time: 10 minutes
Cooking Time: minutes
Servings: 6

Ingredients

- 2 pounds ground beef
- 1 1/3 cups water
- 2 servings Homemade Taco Seasoning, see accompanying recipe below
- 6 large12-inch flour tortillas
- 12 ounces nacho cheese
- 3 roma tomatoes
- 2 cup shredded lettuce
- 2 cups sour cream
- 2 cups Mexican blend cheese
- 6 tostada shell
- Cooking Spray

For Homemade Taco Seasoning:

- 1 1/2 tablespoons ground cumin
- 1 tablespoon chili powder
- 1 teaspoon garlic powder
- 1 teaspoon paprika
- 1 teaspoon salt
- 1 teaspoon onion powder
- 1/2 teaspoon dried oregano
- 1 teaspoon black pepper

Directions

1. Preheat the air fryer at 400 degrees F.
2. Cook the ground beef in a skillet on medium heat until pink color has disappeared.
3. Stir in two servings of the homemade taco seasoning and 1 ½ cups water; bring to a boil. Reduce heat and cook the beef in a simmer until thickens. Set aside.
4. Spread each flour tortilla on a large plate and fill with 2/3 cups of cooked beef, 4 tablespoons nacho cheese, 1/3 cup sour cream, 1 tostada, 1/3 cup lettuce, 1/6th roma tomatoes and 1/3 cup cheese.

5. Seal the taco bell by folding the edges up and over the center to resemble a pinwheel. Repeat the steps with the remaining wraps.
6. Spray the fry basket with oil.
7. Arrange the taco bell, seam side down in the fryer and spray with oil. Cook for two minutes until golden brown.
8. Gently flip the taco bell with a spatula and spray with oil. Cook for two minutes longer and repeat with the rest of the wraps. Let cool for a minute.
9. Ready to serve!

For Homemade Taco Seasoning:

1. Combine all taco seasoning ingredients in a bowl. Transfer to an airtight container and store in a dry, dark place.
2. Enjoy!

Nutrition: 954 calories 30 g saturated fat 187 mg cholesterol 1235 mg sodium 19 g carbohydrates 2 g dietary fiber 7 g total sugars 42 g protein.

Crispy Veggie Fries

Preparation Time: 10 minutes
Cooking Time: minutes
Servings: 6

Ingredients

- 1 cup rice flour
- 2 tablespoons Follow Your Heart Vegan Egg powder*
- 2 tablespoons nutritional yeast flakes, divided
- 1 cup panko bread crumbs (gluten-free or regular)
- 2/3 cup cold water
- Pinch of salt
- Dash of pepper
- Assorted vegetables (green beans, cauliflower, zucchini, or cauliflower)

Directions

1. Cut assorted veggies into French fry shapes or bite size chunks.
2. Pour the rice flour in a shallow dish.
3. Whisk together in another shallow dish the Vegan Egg powder, 2/3 cup of water and 1 tablespoon nutritional yeast flakes until smooth.

4. Combine in separate shallow dish the panko breadcrumbs, 1 tablespoon nutritional yeast, salt, and pepper.

5. Dip each vegetable in the rice flour, and then dip in the Vegan Egg mixture, and lastly in the breadcrumb mixture.

6. Press the vegetable to coat well. Repeat the steps until all the vegetables are coated.

7. Lightly mist your air fryer basket or line your baking sheet with parchment and then spray more oil.

8. Gently load the veggie fries into the basket and spray a little amount of oil.

9. Cook the veggie fries for eight minutes at 380 degrees F until crisp-golden.

10. Serve!

Nutrition: 229 calories 1.6 g fat (0.4 g saturated fat 0 mg cholesterol 189 mg sodium 45.5 g carbohydrates 5.6 g dietary fiber 3.5 g total sugars 7.8 g protein.

Air Fryer Soft Pretzels

Preparation Time: 10 minutes
Cooking Time: minutes
Servings: 12 pretzels

Ingredients
- 1 1/2 cups warm (110 to 115 degrees F) water
- 2 teaspoons kosher salt
- 1 tablespoon sugar
- 1 package active dry yeast
- 2 ounces melted butter
- 4 1/2 cups all-purpose flour
- 2/3 cup baking soda
- 10 cups water
- 1 egg yolk
- Pretzel salt

Directions
1. In a bowl of your stand mixer fitted with a dough hook, mix the water, salt, and sugar together. Sprinkle on top with yeast and let sit for five minutes.

2. Pour the flour into the bowl and add the butter; combine mixture together on low speed.

3. Increase the speed to medium and knead the dough for 5 minutes until smooth and does not stick to the side of the bowl.

4. Transfer the dough to a greased bowl; cover with plastic wrap. Let dough sit for 50 to 60 minutes in a warm temperature until the size has doubled.

5. Prepare two baking sheets and line them with parchment paper and then mist with nonstick spray.

6. Heat up your air fryer at 400 degrees Fahrenheit.

7. Meanwhile, combine in a large roasting pan or stock pot the baking soda and 10 cups of water; bring to a boil.

8. Lay the pretzel dough on a greased work surface and equally divide into 12 pieces. Roll each dough piece into an 18" rope and then twist to form into pretzel shape.

9. Working on each piece of pretzel, place in the boiling water for thirty seconds and quickly remove from water. Transfer the pretzels to the prepared baking sheet.

10. Beat the egg yolk in 1 tablespoon of water and brush over the pretzels.

11. Sprinkle the pretzels with pretzel salt and load about 3 to 4 pieces into the air fryer basket. Cook for 6 minutes at 400 degrees Fahrenheit; turn over and cook for additional 6 minutes or until dark golden brown.

12. Serve!

Nutrition: 214 calories 4.7 g fat (2.6 g saturated fat) 28 mg cholesterol 3774 mg sodium 17 g carbohydrates 1.4 g dietary fiber 1.1 g total sugars 5.3 g protein.

Rosemary Potatoes

Preparation Time: 5 minutes
Cooking Time: 25 minutes
Servings: 2

Ingredients:
- 1lb red potatoes
- 1 cup vegetable stock
- 2tbsp olive oil
- 2tbsp rosemary sprigs

Directions:
1. Situate potatoes in the steamer basket and add the stock into the Instant Pot.

2. Steam the potatoes in your Instant Pot for 15 minutes.

3. Depressurize and pour away the remaining stock.

4.	Set to sauté and add the oil, rosemary, and potatoes.
5.	Cook until brown.

Nutrition: 195 Calories 31g Carbohydrates 1g Fat

Corn on the Cob

Preparation Time: 10 minutes
Cooking Time: 5 minutes
Servings: 12

Ingredients:
*	6 ears corn

Directions:
1.	Take off husks and silk from the corn. Cut or break each ear in half.
2.	Pour 1 cup of water into the bottom of the electric pressure cooker. Insert a wire rack or trivet.
3.	Place the corn upright on the rack, cut-side down. Seal lid of the pressure cooker.
4.	Cook on high pressure for 5 minutes.
5.	When it's complete, select Cancel and quick release the pressure.
6.	When pin drops, unlock and take off lid.
7.	Pull out the corn from the pot. Season as desired and serve immediately.

Nutrition 62 Calories 14g Carbohydrates 1g Fiber

Chili Lime Salmon

Preparation Time: 6 minutes
Cooking Time: 10 minutes
Servings: 2

Ingredients:
For Sauce:
*	1 jalapeno pepper
*	1 tablespoon chopped parsley
*	1 teaspoon minced garlic
*	1/2 teaspoon cumin
*	1/2 teaspoon paprika
*	1/2 teaspoon lime zest
*	1 tablespoon honey
*	1 tablespoon lime juice
*	1 tablespoon olive oil
*	1 tablespoon water
For Fish:

*	2 salmon fillets, each about 5 ounces
*	1 cup water
*	1/2 teaspoon salt
*	1/8 teaspoon ground black pepper

Directions:
1.	Prepare salmon and for this, season salmon with salt and black pepper until evenly coated.
2.	Plugin instant pot, inserts the inner pot, pour in water, then place steamer basket and place seasoned salmon on it.
3.	Seal instant pot with its lid, press the 'steam' button, then press the 'timer' to set the cooking time to 5 minutes and cook on high pressure, for 5 minutes.
4.	Transfer all the ingredients for the sauce in a bowl, whisk until combined and set aside until required.
5.	When the timer beeps, press 'cancel' button and do quick pressure release until pressure nob drops down.
6.	Open the instant pot, then transfer salmon to a serving plate and drizzle generously with prepared sauce.
7.	Serve straight away.

Nutrition: 305 Calories 29g Carbohydrates 6g Fiber

Mashed Pumpkin

Preparation Time: 9 minutes
Cooking Time: 15 minutes
Servings: 2

Ingredients:
*	2 cups chopped pumpkin
*	0.5 cup water
*	2tbsp powdered sugar-free sweetener of choice
*	1tbsp cinnamon

Directions:
1.	Place the pumpkin and water in your Instant Pot.
2.	Seal and cook on Stew 15 minutes.
3.	Remove and mash with the sweetener and cinnamon.

Nutrition: 12 Calories 3g Carbohydrates 1g Sugar

Parmesan-Topped Acorn Squash

Preparation Time: 8 minutes

Cooking Time: 20 minutes

Servings: 4

Ingredients:

- 1 acorn squash (about 1 pound)
- 1 tablespoon extra-virgin olive oil
- 1 teaspoon dried sage leaves, crumbled
- ¼ teaspoon freshly grated nutmeg
- 1/8 teaspoon kosher salt
- 1/8 teaspoon freshly ground black pepper
- 2 tablespoons freshly grated Parmesan cheese

Directions:

1. Chop acorn squash in half lengthwise and remove the seeds. Cut each half in half for a total of 4 wedges. Snap off the stem if it's easy to do.

2. In a small bowl, combine the olive oil, sage, nutmeg, salt, and pepper. Brush the cut sides of the squash with the olive oil mixture.

3. Fill 1 cup of water into the electric pressure cooker and insert a wire rack or trivet.

4. Place the squash on the trivet in a single layer, skin-side down.

5. Set the lid of the pressure cooker on sealing.

6. Cook on high pressure for 20 minutes.

7. Once done, press Cancel and quick release the pressure.

8. Once the pin drops, open it.

9. Carefully remove the squash from the pot, sprinkle with the Parmesan, and serve.

Nutrition: 85 Calories 12g Carbohydrates 2g Fiber

Quinoa Tabbouleh

Preparation Time: 8 minutes

Cooking Time: 16 minutes

Servings: 6

Ingredients:

- 1 cup quinoa, rinsed
- 1 large English cucumber
- 2 scallions, sliced
- 2 cups cherry tomatoes, halved
- 2/3 cup chopped parsley
- 1/2 cup chopped mint
- ½ teaspoon minced garlic
- 1/2 teaspoon salt
- ½ teaspoon ground black pepper
- 2 tablespoon lemon juice
- 1/2 cup olive oil

Directions:

1. Plugin instant pot, insert the inner pot, add quinoa, then pour in water and stir until mixed.

2. Close instant pot with its lid and turn the pressure knob to seal the pot.

3. Select 'manual' button, then set the 'timer' to 1 minute and cook in high pressure, it may take 7 minutes.

4. Once the timer stops, select 'cancel' button and do natural pressure release for 10 minutes and then do quick pressure release until pressure nob drops down.

5. Open the instant pot, fluff quinoa with a fork, then spoon it on a rimmed baking sheet, spread quinoa evenly and let cool.

6. Meanwhile, place lime juice in a small bowl, add garlic and stir until just mixed.

7. Then add salt, black pepper, and olive oil and whisk until combined.

8. Transfer cooled quinoa to a large bowl, add remaining ingredients, then drizzle generously with the prepared lime juice mixture and toss until evenly coated.

9. Taste quinoa to adjust seasoning and then serve.

Nutrition: 283 Calories 30.6g Carbohydrates 3.4g Fiber

Wild Rice Salad with Cranberries and Almonds

Preparation Time: 6 minutes

Cooking Time: 25 minutes

Servings: 18

Ingredients:

For the rice

- 2 cups wild rice blend, rinsed
- 1 teaspoon kosher salt
- 2½ cups Vegetable Broth

For the dressing

- ¼ cup extra-virgin olive oil
- ¼ cup white wine vinegar

- 1½ teaspoons grated orange zest
- Juice of 1 medium orange (about ¼ cup)
- 1 teaspoon honey or pure maple syrup

For the salad
- ¾ cup unsweetened dried cranberries
- ½ cup sliced almonds, toasted
- Freshly ground black pepper

Directions:
1. To make the rice
2. In the electric pressure cooker, combine the rice, salt, and broth.
3. Close and lock the lid. Set the valve to sealing.
4. Cook on high pressure for 25 minutes.
5. When the cooking is complete, hit Cancel and allow the pressure to release naturally for 1minutes, then quick release any remaining pressure.
6. Once the pin drops, unlock and remove the lid.
7. Let the rice cool briefly, and then fluff it with a fork.
8. To make the dressing
9. While the rice cooks, make the dressing: In a small jar with a screw-top lid, combine the olive oil, vinegar, zest, juice, and honey. (If you don't have a jar, whisk the ingredients together in a small bowl.) Shake to combine.
10. To make the salad
11. Mix rice, cranberries, and almonds.
12. Add the dressing and season with pepper.
13. Serve warm or refrigerate.

Nutrition 126 Calories 18g Carbohydrates 2g Fiber

Low Fat Roasties

Preparation Time: 8 minutes
Cooking Time: 25 minutes
Servings: 2

Ingredients:
- 1lb roasting potatoes
- 1 garlic clove
- 1 cup vegetable stock
- 2tbsp olive oil

Directions:
1. Position potatoes in the steamer basket and add the stock into the Instant Pot.
2. Steam the potatoes in your Instant Pot for 15 minutes.
3. Depressurize and pour away the remaining stock.
4. Set to sauté and add the oil, garlic, and potatoes. Cook until brown.

Nutrition: 201 Calories 3g Carbohydrates 6g Fat

Roasted Parsnips

Preparation Time: 9 minutes
Cooking Time: 25 minutes
Servings: 2

Ingredients:
- 1lb parsnips
- 1 cup vegetable stock
- 2tbsp herbs
- 2tbsp olive oil

Directions:
1. Put the parsnips in the steamer basket and add the stock into the Instant Pot.
2. Steam the parsnips in your Instant Pot for 15 minutes.
3. Depressurize and pour away the remaining stock.
4. Set to sauté and add the oil, herbs and parsnips.
5. Cook until golden and crisp.

Nutrition: 130 Calories 14g Carbohydrates 4g Protein

Sweet and Sour Red Cabbage

Preparation Time: 7 minutes
Cooking Time: 10 minutes
Servings: 8

Ingredients:
- 2 cups Spiced Pear Applesauce
- 1 small onion, chopped
- ½ cup apple cider vinegar
- ½ teaspoon kosher salt
- 1 head red cabbage

Directions:
1. In the electric pressure cooker, combine the applesauce, onion, vinegar, salt, and cup of water. Stir in the cabbage.
2. Seal lid of the pressure cooker.
3. Cook on high pressure for 10 minutes.

4.   When the cooking is complete, hit Cancel and quick release the pressure.

5.   Once the pin drops, unlock and remove the lid.

6.   Spoon into a bowl or platter and serve.

Nutrition: 91 Calories18g Carbohydrates4g Fiber

Pinto Beans

Preparation Time: 6 minutes

Cooking Time: 55 minutes

Servings: 10

Ingredients:

- 2 cups pinto beans, dried
- 1 medium white onion
- 1 ½ teaspoon minced garlic
- ¾ teaspoon salt
- 1/4 teaspoon ground black pepper
- 1 teaspoon red chili powder
- 1/4 teaspoon cumin
- 1 tablespoon olive oil
- 1 teaspoon chopped cilantro
- 5 ½ cup vegetable stock

Directions:

1.   Plugin instant pot, insert the inner pot, press sauté/simmer button, add oil and when hot, add onion and garlic and cook for 3 minutes or until onions begin to soften.

2.   Add remaining ingredients, stir well, then press the cancel button, shut the instant pot with its lid and seal the pot.

3.   Click 'manual' button, then press the 'timer' to set the cooking time to 45 minutes and cook at high pressure.

4.   Once done, click 'cancel' button and do natural pressure release for 10 minutes until pressure nob drops down.

5.   Open the instant pot, spoon beans into plates and serve.

Nutrition: 107 Calories11.7g Carbohydrates4g Fiber

Parmesan Cauliflower Mash

Preparation Time: 19 minutes

Cooking Time: 5 minutes

Servings: 4

Ingredients:

- 1 head cauliflower
- ½ teaspoon kosher salt
- ½ teaspoon garlic pepper
- 2 tablespoons plain Greek yogurt
- ¾ cup freshly grated Parmesan cheese
- 1 tablespoon unsalted butter or ghee (optional)
- Chopped fresh chives

Directions:

1.   Pour cup of water into the electric pressure cooker and insert a steamer basket or wire rack.

2.   Place the cauliflower in the basket.

3.   Cover lid of the pressure cooker to seal.

4.   Cook on high pressure for 5 minutes.

5.   Once complete, hit Cancel and quick release the pressure.

6.   When the pin drops, remove the lid.

7.   Remove the cauliflower from the pot and pour out the water. Return the cauliflower to the pot and add the salt, garlic pepper, yogurt, and cheese. Use an immersion blender to purée or mash the cauliflower in the pot.

8.   Spoon into a serving bowl, and garnish with butter (if using) and chives.

Nutrition: 141 Calories12g Carbohydrates4g Fiber

Squash Medley

Preparation Time: 10 minutes

Cooking Time: 20 minutes

Servings: 2

Ingredients:

- 2 lbs. mixed squash
- ½ cup mixed veg
- 1 cup vegetable stock
- 2 tbsps. olive oil
- 2 tbsps. mixed herbs

Direction:

1.   Put the squash in the steamer basket and add the stock into the Instant Pot.

2.   Steam the squash in your Instant Pot for 10 minutes.

3.   Depressurize and pour away the remaining stock.

4. Set to sauté and add the oil and remaining ingredients.
5. Cook until a light crust form.
Nutrition: 100 Calories10g Carbohydrates6g Fat

Eggplant Curry

Preparation Time: 15 minutes
Cooking Time: 20 minutes
Servings: 2
Ingredients:
- 3 cups chopped eggplant
- 1 thinly sliced onion
- 1 cup coconut milk
- 3 tbsps. curry paste
- 1 tbsp. oil or ghee

Direction:
1. Select Instant Pot to sauté and put the onion, oil, and curry paste.
2. Once the onion is soft, stir in remaining ingredients and seal.
3. Cook on Stew for 20 minutes. Release the pressure naturally.
Nutrition: 350 Calories15g Carbohydrates25g Fat

Lentil and Eggplant Stew

Preparation Time: 15 minutes
Cooking Time: 35 minutes
Servings: 2
Ingredients:
- 1 lb. eggplant
- 1 lb. dry lentils
- 1 cup chopped vegetables
- 1 cup low sodium vegetable broth

Direction:
1. Incorporate all the ingredients in your Instant Pot, cook on Stew for 35 minutes.
2. Release the pressure naturally and serve.
Nutrition: 310 Calories22g Carbohydrates10g Fat

Tofu Curry

Preparation Time: 15 minutes
Cooking Time: 20 minutes
Servings: 2
Ingredients:
- 2 cups cubed extra firm tofu
- 2 cups mixed stir fry vegetables
- ½ cup soy yogurt
- 3 tbsps. curry paste
- 1 tbsp. oil or ghee

Direction:
1. Set the Instant Pot to sauté and add the oil and curry paste.
2. Once soft, place the remaining ingredients except for the yogurt and seal.
3. Cook on Stew for 20 minutes.
4. Release the pressure naturally and serve with a scoop of soy yogurt.
Nutrition: 300 Calories 9g Carbohydrates 14g Fat

Lentil and Chickpea Curry

Preparation Time: 15 minutes
Cooking Time: 20 minutes
Servings: 2
Ingredients:
- 2 cups dry lentils and chickpeas
- 1 thinly sliced onion
- 1 cup chopped tomato
- 3 tbsps. curry paste
- 1 tbsp. oil or ghee

Direction:
1. Press Instant Pot to sauté and mix onion, oil, and curry paste.
2. Once the onion is cooked, stir the remaining ingredients and seal.
3. Cook on Stew for 20 minutes.
4. Release the pressure naturally and serve.
Nutrition: 360 Calories 26g Carbohydrates 19g Fat

Kidney Bean Stew

Preparation Time: 15 minutes
Cooking Time: 15 minutes
Servings: 2
Ingredients:
- 1 lb. cooked kidney beans
- 1 cup tomato pasta
- 1 cup low sodium beef broth

- 3 tbsps. Italian herbs

Direction:

1. Incorporate all the ingredients in your Instant Pot, cook on Stew for 15 minutes.

2. Release the pressure naturally and serve.

Nutrition: 270 Calories 16g Carbohydrates 10g Fat

Fried Tofu Hotpot

Preparation Time: 15 minutes

Cooking Time: 15 minutes

Servings: 2

Ingredients:

- ½ lb. fried tofu
- 1 lb. chopped Chinese vegetable mix
- 1 cup low sodium vegetable broth
- 2 tbsps. 5 spice seasoning
- 1 tbsp. smoked paprika

Direction:

1. Combine all the ingredients in your Instant Pot, set on Stew for 15 minutes.

2. Release the pressure naturally and serve.

Nutrition: 320 Calories 11g Carbohydrates 23g Fat

Chili Sin Carne

Preparation Time: 15 minutes

Cooking Time: 35 minutes

Servings: 2

Ingredients:

- 3 cups mixed cooked beans
- 2 cups chopped tomatoes
- 1 tbsp. yeast extract
- 2 squares very dark chocolate
- 1 tbsp. red chili flakes

Direction:

1. Combine all the ingredients in your Instant Pot, cook for 35 minutes.

2. Release the pressure naturally and serve.

Nutrition: 240 Calories 20g Carbohydrates 3g Fat

SAVORY

Ravioli

Preparation time: 5 minutes

Cooking time: 16 minutes

Servings: 4

Ingredients:

- 8 ounces frozen vegan ravioli, thawed
- 1 teaspoon dried basil
- 1 teaspoon garlic powder
- 1/8 teaspoon ground black pepper
- ¼ teaspoon salt
- 1 teaspoon dried oregano
- 2 teaspoons nutritional yeast flakes
- 1/2 cup marinara sauce, unsweetened
- 1/2 cup panko bread crumbs
- 1/4 cup liquid from chickpeas can

Directions:

1. Place breadcrumbs in a bowl, sprinkle with salt, basil, oregano, and black pepper, add garlic powder and yeast and stir until mixed.

2. Take a bowl and then pour in chickpeas liquid in it.

3. Working on one ravioli at a time, first dip a ravioli in chickpeas liquid and then coat with breadcrumbs mixture.

4. Prepare remaining ravioli in the same manner, then take a fryer basket, grease it well with oil and place ravioli in it in a single layer.

5. Switch on the air fryer, insert fryer basket, sprinkle oil on ravioli, shut with its lid, set the fryer at 390 degrees F, then cook for 6 minutes, turn the ravioli and continue cooking 2 minutes until nicely golden and heated thoroughly.

6. Cook the remaining ravioli in the same manner and serve with marinara sauce.

Nutrition: Calories: 150 Cal Carbs: 27 g Fat: 3 g Protein: 5 g Fiber: 2 g

Onion Rings

Preparation time: 10 minutes

Cooking time: 32 minutes

Servings: 4

Ingredients:

- 1 large white onion, peeled
- 2/3 cup pork rinds
- 3 tablespoons almond flour
- 1/2 teaspoon garlic powder
- 1/2 teaspoon paprika
- 1/4 teaspoon sea salt
- 3 tablespoons coconut flour
- 2 eggs, pastured

Directions:

1. Switch on the air fryer, insert fryer basket, grease it with olive oil, then shut with its lid, set the fryer at 400 degrees F and preheat for 10 minutes.

2. Meanwhile, slice the peeled onion into ½ inch thick rings.

3. Take a shallow dish, add almond flour and stir in garlic powder, paprika, and pork rinds; take another shallow dish, add coconut flour and salt and stir until mixed.

4. Crack eggs in a bowl and then whisk until combined.

5. Working on one onion ring at a time, first coat onion ring in coconut flour mixture, then it in egg, and coat with pork rind mixture by scooping over the onion until evenly coated.

6. Open the fryer, place coated onion rings in it in a single layer, spray oil over onion rings, close with its lid and cook for 16 minutes until nicely golden and thoroughly cooked, flipping the onion rings halfway through the frying.

7. When air fryer beeps, open its lid, transfer onion rings onto a serving plate and cook the remaining onion rings in the same manner.

8. Serve straight away.

Nutrition: Calories: 135 Cal Carbs: 8 g Fat: 7 g Protein: 8 g Fiber: 3 g

Cauliflower Fritters

Preparation time: 10 minutes
Cooking time: 14 minutes
Servings: 2
Ingredients:
- 5 cups chopped cauliflower florets
- 1/2 cup almond flour
- 1/2 teaspoon baking powder
- ½ teaspoon ground black pepper
- ½ teaspoon salt
- 2 eggs, pastured

Directions:
1. Add chopped cauliflower in a blender or food processor, pulse until minced and then tip the mixture in a bowl.
2. Add remaining ingredients, stir well and then shape the mixture into 1/3-inch patties, an ice cream scoop of mixture per patty.
3. Switch on the air fryer, insert fryer basket, grease it with olive oil, then shut with its lid, set the fryer at 390 degrees F and preheat for 5 minutes.
4. Then open the fryer, add cauliflower patties in it in a single layer, spray oil over patties, close with its lid and cook for 14 minutes at the 375 degrees F until nicely golden and cooked, flipping the patties halfway through the frying.
5. Serve straight away with the dip.
Nutrition: Calories: 272 Cal Carbs: 57 g Fat: 0.3 g Protein: 11 g Fiber: 8 g

Zucchini Fritters

Preparation time: 20 minutes
Cooking time: 12 minutes
Servings: 4
Ingredients:
- 2 medium zucchinis, ends trimmed
- 3 tablespoons almond flour
- 1 tablespoon salt
- 1 teaspoon garlic powder
- ¼ teaspoon paprika
- ¼ teaspoon ground black pepper
- ¼ teaspoon onion powder

- 1 egg, pastured
Directions:
1. Wash and pat dry the zucchini, then cut its ends and grate the zucchini.
2. Place grated zucchini in a colander, sprinkle with salt and let it rest for 10 minutes.
3. Then wrap zucchini in a kitchen cloth and squeeze moisture from it as much as possible and place dried zucchini in another bowl.
4. Add remaining ingredients into the zucchini and then stir until mixed.
5. Take fryer basket, line it with parchment paper, grease it with oil and drop zucchini mixture on it by a spoonful, about 1-inch apart and then spray well with oil.
6. Switch on the air fryer, insert fryer basket, then shut with its lid, set the fryer at 360 degrees F and cook the fritter for 12 minutes until nicely golden and cooked, flipping the fritters halfway through the frying.
7. Serve straight away.
Nutrition: Calories: 57 Cal Carbs: 8 g Fat: 1 g Protein: 3 g Fiber: 1 g

Kale Chips

Preparation time: 5 minutes
Cooking time: 7 minutes
Servings: 2
Ingredients:
- 1 large bunch of kale
- ¾ teaspoon red chili powder
- 1 teaspoon salt
- ¾ teaspoon ground black pepper

Directions:
1. Remove the hard spines form the kale leaves, then cut kale into small pieces and place them in a fryer basket.
2. Spray oil over kale, then sprinkle with salt, chili powder and black pepper and toss until well mixed.
3. Switch on the air fryer, insert fryer basket, then shut with its lid, set the fryer at 375 degrees F and cook for 7 minutes until kale is crispy, shaking halfway through the frying.
4. When air fryer beeps, open its lid, transfer kale chips onto a serving plate and serve.

Nutrition: Calories: 66.2 Cal Carbs: 7.3 g Fat: 4 g Protein: 2.5 g Fiber: 2.6 g

Radish Chips

Preparation time: 5 minutes
Cooking time: 20 minutes
Servings: 2

Ingredients:

- 8 ounces radish slices
- ½ teaspoon garlic powder
- 1 teaspoon salt
- ½ teaspoon onion powder
- ½ teaspoon ground black pepper

Directions:

1. Wash the radish slices, pat them dry, place them in a fryer basket, and then spray oil on them until well coated.

2. Sprinkle salt, garlic powder, onion powder, and black pepper over radish slices and then toss until well coated.

3. Switch on the air fryer, insert fryer basket, then shut with its lid, set the fryer at 370 degrees F and cook for 10 minutes, stirring the slices halfway through.

4. Then spray oil on radish slices, shake the basket and continue frying for 10 minutes, stirring the chips halfway through.

5. Serve straight away.

Nutrition: Calories: 21 Cal Carbs: 1 g Fat: 1.8 g Protein: 0.2 g Fiber: 0.4 g

Zucchini Fries

Preparation time: 10 minutes
Cooking time: 20 minutes
Servings: 4

Ingredients:

- 2 medium zucchinis
- ½ cup almond flour
- 1/8 teaspoon ground black pepper
- ½ teaspoon garlic powder
- 1/8 teaspoon salt
- 1 teaspoon Italian seasoning
- ½ cup grated parmesan cheese, reduced-fat
- 1 egg, pastured, beaten

Directions:

1. Switch on the air fryer, insert fryer basket, grease it with olive oil, then shut with its lid, set the fryer at 400 degrees F and preheat for 10 minutes.

2. Meanwhile, cut each zucchini in half and then cut each zucchini half into 4-inch-long pieces, each about ½-inch thick.

3. Place flour in a shallow dish, add remaining ingredients except for the egg and stir until mixed.

4. Crack the egg in a bowl and then whisk until blended.

5. Working on one zucchini piece at a time, first dip it in the egg, then coat it in the almond flour mixture and place it on a wire rack.

6. Open the fryer, add zucchini pieces in it in a single layer, spray oil over zucchini, close with its lid and cook for 10 minutes until nicely golden and crispy, shaking halfway through the frying.

7. Cook remaining zucchini pieces in the same manner and serve.

Nutrition: Calories: 147 Cal Carbs: 6 g Fat: 10 g Protein: 9 g Fiber: 2 g

Avocado fries

Preparation time: 10 minutes
Cooking time: 20 minutes
Servings: 2

Ingredients:

- 1 medium avocado, pitted
- 1 egg
- 1/2 cup almond flour
- ¼ teaspoon salt
- ¼ teaspoon ground black pepper
- 1/2 teaspoon salt

Directions:

1. Switch on the air fryer, insert fryer basket, grease it with olive oil, then shut with its lid, set the fryer at 400 degrees F and preheat for 10 minutes.

2. Meanwhile, cut the avocado in half and then cut each half into wedges, each about ½-inch thick.

3. Place flour in a shallow dish, add salt and black pepper and stir until mixed.

4.   Crack the egg in a bowl and then whisk until blended.

5.   Working on one avocado piece at a time, first dip it in the egg, then coat it in the almond flour mixture and place it on a wire rack.

6.   Open the fryer, add avocado pieces in it in a single layer, spray oil over avocado, close with its lid and cook for 10 minutes until nicely golden and crispy, shaking halfway through the frying.

7.   When air fryer beeps, open its lid, transfer avocado fries onto a serving plate and serve.

Nutrition: Calories: 251 Cal Carbs: 19 g Fat: 17 g Protein: 6 g Fiber: 7 g

Roasted Peanut Butter Squash

Preparation time: 5 minutes
Cooking time: 22 minutes
Servings: 4
Ingredients:
- 1 butternut squash, peeled
- 1 teaspoon cinnamon
- 1 tablespoon olive oil

Directions:
1.   Switch on the air fryer, insert fryer basket, grease it with olive oil, then shut with its lid, set the fryer at 220 degrees F and preheat for 5 minutes.

2.   Meanwhile, peel the squash400 cut it into 1-inch pieces, and then place them in a bowl.

3.   Drizzle oil over squash pieces, sprinkle with cinnamon and then toss until well coated.

4.   Open the fryer, add squash pieces in it, close with its lid and cook for 17 minutes until nicely golden and crispy, shaking every 5 minutes.

5.   When air fryer beeps, open its lid, transfer squash onto a serving plate and serve.

Nutrition: Calories: 116 Cal Carbs: 22 g Fat: 3 g Protein: 1 g Fiber: 4 g

Roasted Chickpeas

Preparation time: 35 minutes
Cooking time: 25 minutes
Servings: 6
Ingredients:
- 15-ounce cooked chickpeas
- 1 teaspoon garlic powder
- 1 tablespoon nutritional yeast
- 1/8 teaspoon cumin
- 1 teaspoon smoked paprika
- 1/2 teaspoon salt
- 1 tablespoon olive oil

Directions:
1.   Take a large baking sheet, line it with paper towels, then spread chickpeas on it, cover the peas with paper towels, and let rest for 30 minutes or until chickpeas are dried.

2.   Then switch on the air fryer, insert fryer basket, grease it with olive oil, then shut with its lid, set the fryer at 355 degrees F and preheat for 5 minutes.

3.   Place dried chickpeas in a bowl, add remaining ingredients and toss until well coated.

4.   Open the fryer, add chickpeas in it, close with its lid and cook for 20 minutes until nicely golden and crispy, shaking the chickpeas every 5 minutes.

5.   When air fryer beeps, open its lid, transfer chickpeas onto a serving bowl and serve.

Nutrition: Calories: 124 Cal Carbs: 17.4 g Fat: 4.4 g Protein: 4.7 g Fiber: 4 g

KETO DIABETIC EXTRA RECIPES

Coleslaw

Preparation Time: 10 minutes
Cooking Time: minutes
Servings: 4
Ingredients:
- 1 Onion, Chopped
- ½ Cup Avocado Based Mayonnaise
- 1 Carrot, Peeled & Shredded
- ½ Cabbage, Shredded
- ¼ Cup Coconut Milk, Full Fat
- 2 Tablespoons Red Wine Vinegar
- 1 Lemon, Juiced

Directions:
1. Put your carrot, cabbage and onion in a bowl, and mix well.
2. In a different bowl whisk your mayonnaise, red wine vinegar, coconut milk and lemon juice.
3. Pour this mixture over your vegetable mixture, and mix well before serving immediately or chilling first.
Nutrition: Calories: 267 Protein: 3 Grams Fat: 24 Grams Net Carbs: 8 Grams

Pureed Peas

Preparation Time: 10 minutes
Cooking Time: 15 minutes
Servings: 4
Ingredients:
- ¼ Cup Heavy Cream
- 1 Cup Peas, Frozen
- 1 Tablespoon Butter
- Sea Salt & Black Pepper to Taste

Directions:
1. Add your peas into a pot of boiling water. Boil for five minutes before draining the water away.
2. Transfer them to a food processor processing until smooth.
Nutrition: Calories: 106 Protein: 2 Grams Fat: 9 Grams Net Carbs: 4 Grams

Collard Greens

Preparation Time: 10 minutes
Cooking Time: 10 minutes
Servings: 4
Ingredients:
- 4 Cups Collard Greens
- 2 Tablespoons Butter
- 2 Teaspoons Cayenne Pepper
- 1 Clove Garlic, Minced
- 1 Teaspoon Sea Salt, Fine

Directions:
1. Start by rinsing your collard greens, and pat them dry using a paper towel. Stem them, and then cut it into small strips.
2. Melt your butter in a skillet, adding all ingredients. Sauté until wilted, which will take up to ten minutes.
Nutrition: Calories: 64 Protein: 1 Gram Fat: 6 Grams Net Carbs: 1 Gram

Keto "hummus"

Preparation Time: 10 minutes
Cooking Time: 15 minutes
Servings: 4
Ingredients:
- 3 Tablespoons Olive Oil
- 1 Teaspoon Smoked Paprika
- 2 Cloves Garlic
- 3 Tablespoons Lemon Juice, Fresh
- 3 Cups Cauliflower, Chopped into Florets
- 4 Tablespoons tahini
- 1 Zucchini, Seeded & Chopped
- ¼ Cup Heavy Cream
- 1 Tablespoon Butter
- Sea Salt & Black Pepper to Taste

Directions:
1. Start by heating your butter up, and then add in your cauliflower florets. Sauté until they turn tender.
2. Place the cooked cauliflower in a blender, and add in the remaining ingredients. Blend for two minutes

or until creamy and smooth. If your mixture becomes out too thick, add a little water until you reach your desired consistency.

3. Refrigerate for a half hour before serving chilled.

Nutrition: Calories: 265 Protein: 5 Grams Fat: 25 Grams
Net Carbs: 6 Grams

Cauliflower & Onion Salad

Preparation Time: 10 minutes
Cooking Time: 30 minutes
Servings: 3
Ingredients:
- 2 Cups Cauliflower Florets, Chopped Fine
- 3 Hard Boiled Eggs, Chopped
- 4 Tablespoons Heavy Cream
- 5 Tablespoons Sour Cream
- 2 Tablespoons Red Onion, Minced
- ½ Red Bell Pepper, Seeded & Chopped
- 2 Tablespoons Oregano, Fresh & Chopped
- 2 Tablespoons Chives, Fresh & Chopped
- Sea Salt & Black Pepper to Taste

Directions:

1. Get out a large pot of water and bring the water to a boil. Cook your cauliflower florets for five minutes. They should be tender, and then drain the water away. Run your florets over cold water to stop the cooking process, but drain well.

2. Get out a large bowl and whisk your heavy cream and sour cream, adding in your cauliflower next. Mix in your eggs, red onion, oregano, chive sand bell pepper. Season with salt and pepper before tossing until well combined.

3. Refrigerate for at least a half hour before serving.

Nutrition: Calories: 215 Protein: 9 Grams Fat: 16 Grams Net Carbs: 6 Grams

Sweet Potato Fritters

Preparation Time: 10 minutes
Cooking Time: 20 minutes
Servings: 4
Ingredients:
- ¼ Cup Flaxseed Meal

- 1 Egg
- ½ Teaspoon Garlic Powder
- ¼ Teaspoon Cumin
- ¼ Cup Almonds, Chopped Fine
- 1 Sweet Potato, Small & Peeled
- ¼ Teaspoon Turmeric
- 2 Tablespoons Butter
- Sea Salt & Black Pepper to Taste

Directions:

1. Shred your sweet potato using a food processor or a grater.

2. Get out a bowl and whisk your turmeric, salt, a tablespoon of butter and egg together.

3. Mix in the shredded sweet potato, flaxseed meal and almonds. Season with salt and pepper, and mix again.

4. Place a frying pan over medium-heat, melting your remaining butter.

5. When your butter is hot, drop in the sweet potato mixture using a large spoon. Fry for five minutes, flip and then fry for three more minutes. Continue until you're out of batter. Serve warm.

Nutrition: Calories: 196 Protein: 6 Grams Fat: 15 Grams Net Carbs: 6 Grams

Avocado Deviled Eggs

Preparation Time: 10 minutes
Cooking Time: 25 minutes
Servings: 3
Ingredients:
- 2 Tablespoons Lemon Juice, Fresh
- 1 Clove Garlic, Minced
- 1 Red Chili Pepper, Seeded & Minced
- 4 Slices Bacon, Cooked & Crumbled
- 1 Avocado
- 4 Hard Boiled Eggs, Large
- Sea Salt & Black Pepper to Taste

Directions:

1. Peel your eggs before slicing them lengthwise. Take the yolks and place them in a bowl with your chili pepper, avocado, garlic and lemon juice.

2. Mash your yolks, and combine the ingredients. Season with salt and pepper, and pipe the mixture back into your egg whites. Top with bacon, and serve chilled.

Nutrition: Calories: 146 Protein: 5 Grams Fat: 12 Grams Net Carbs: 11 Grams

Lime & Chipotle Kale Chips

Preparation Time: 10 minutes
Cooking Time: 30 minutes
Servings: 3

Ingredients:

- 1 Large Bunch Kale, Torn
- 1 Teaspoon Lime Zest
- 2 Teaspoons Lime Juice, Fresh
- 1 Teaspoon Chipotle Powder
- 3 Tablespoons Olive Oil
- Sea Salt & Black Pepper to Taste

Directions:

1. Start by heating the oven to 325, and then take two baking sheets out. Line them with parchment paper, and get out a bowl. Combine your lime juice, kale leaves, lime zest and olive oil. Toss until they're well coated, and spread them in a thin, even layer on the baking sheet.

2. Sprinkle your salt, pepper and chipotle powder over each one, baking for a half hour. They should be crisp.

Nutrition: Calories: 160 Protein: 2 Grams Fat: 14 Grams Net Carbs: 6 Grams

Garlic Egg Noodles

Preparation Time: 10 minutes
Cooking Time: 10 minutes
Servings: 2

Ingredients:

- 2 Eggs, Room Temperature
- ½ Teaspoon Onion Powder
- 2 Tablespoons Cream Cheese
- ½ Teaspoon Garlic Powder
- Sea Salt & Black Pepper to Taste

Directions:

1. Preheat your oven to 300 before getting out a baking sheet. Line your baking sheet with parchment paper, and then get out your food processor. While your oven heats up, add your ingredients to a food processor, and blend.

2. Pour this on top of your baking sheet, making sure it's smooth.

3. Bake for three to five minutes, and allow them to cool for two to three minutes before slicing into noodle shapes.

Nutrition: Calories: 102 Protein: 7 Grams Fat: 8 Grams Net Carbs: 2 Grams

Ketogenic Lava Cake

Preparation time: 10 minutes
Cooking time: 10 minutes
Servings: 2

Ingredients:

- 2 Oz of dark chocolate; you should at least use chocolate of 85% cocoa solids
- 1 Tablespoon of super-fine almond flour
- 2 Oz of unsalted almond butter
- 2 Large eggs

Directions:

1. Heat your oven to a temperature of about 350 Fahrenheit.

2. Grease 2 heat proof ramekins with almond butter.

3. Now, melt the chocolate and the almond butter and stir very well.

4. Beat the eggs very well with a mixer.

5. Add the eggs to the chocolate and the butter mixture and mix very well with almond flour and the swerve; then stir.

6. Pour the dough into 2 ramekins.

7. Bake for about 9 to 10 minutes.

8. Turn the cakes over plates and serve with pomegranate seeds!

Nutrition: Calories: 459 Fat: 39gCarbohydrates: 3.5g Fiber: 0.8g Protein: 11.7g

Ketogenic Cheese Cake

Preparation time: 15 minutes
Cooking time: 50 minutes
Servings: 6

Ingredients:

For the Almond Flour Cheesecake Crust:

- 2 Cups of Blanched almond flour
- 1/3 Cup of almond Butter
- 3 Tablespoons of Erythritol (powdered or granular)
- 1 Teaspoon of Vanilla extract

For the Keto Cheesecake Filling:

- 32 Oz of softened Cream cheese
- 1 and ¼ cups of powdered erythritol
- 3 Large Eggs
- 1 Tablespoon of Lemon juice
- 1 Teaspoon of Vanilla extract

Directions:

1. Preheat your oven to a temperature of about 350 degrees F.
2. Grease a spring form pan of 9¨ with cooking spray or just line its bottom with a parchment paper.
3. In order to make the cheesecake rust, stir in the melted butter, the almond flour, the vanilla extract and the erythritol in a large bowl.
4. The dough will get will be a bit crumbly; so press it into the bottom of your prepared tray.
5. Bake for about 12 minutes; then let cool for about 10 minutes.
6. In the meantime, beat the softened cream cheese and the powdered sweetener at a low speed until it becomes smooth.
7. Crack in the eggs and beat them in at a low to medium speed until it becomes fluffy. Make sure to add one a time.
8. Add in the lemon juice and the vanilla extract and mix at a low to medium speed with a mixer.
9. Pour your filling into your pan right on top of the crust. You can use a spatula to smooth the top of the cake.
10. Bake for about 45 to 50 minutes.
11. Remove the baked cheesecake from your oven and run a knife around its edge.
12. Let the cake cool for about 4 hours in the refrigerator.
13. Serve and enjoy your delicious cheese cake!

Nutrition: Calories: 325 Fat: 29gCarbohydrates: 6gFiber: 1g Protein: 7g

Ginger Cake

Preparation time: 15 minutes
Cooking time: 20 minutes
Servings: 9

Ingredients:

- 1/2 Tablespoon of unsalted almond butter to grease the pan
- 4 Large eggs
- ¼ Cup coconut milk
- 2 Tablespoons of unsalted almond butter
- 1 and 1/2 teaspoons of stevia
- 1 Tablespoon of ground cinnamon
- 1 Tablespoon of natural unweeded cocoa powder
- 1 Tablespoon of fresh ground ginger
- 1/2 Teaspoon of kosher salt
- 1 and 1/2 cups of blanched almond flour
- 1/2 Teaspoon of baking soda

Directions:

1. Preheat your oven to a temperature of 325 F.
2. Grease a glass baking tray of about 8X8 inches generously with almond butter.
3. In a large bowl, whisk all together the coconut milk, the eggs, the melted almond butter, the stevia, the cinnamon, the cocoa powder, the ginger and the kosher salt.
4. Whisk in the almond flour, then the baking soda and mix very well.
5. Pour the batter into the prepared pan and bake for about 20 to 25 minutes.
6. Let the cake cool for about 5 minutes; then slice; serve and enjoy your delicious cake.

Nutrition: Calories: 175 Fat: 15gCarbohydrates: 5gFiber: 1.9gProtein: 5g

Cinnamon Cake

Preparation time: 15 minutes

Cooking time: 35 minutes

Servings: 8

Ingredients

For the Cinnamon Filling:

* 3 Tablespoons of Swerve Sweetener
* 2 Teaspoons of ground cinnamon

For the Cake:

* 3 Cups of almond flour
* ¾ Cup of Swerve Sweetener
* ¼ Cup of unflavored whey protein powder
* 2 Teaspoon of baking powder
* 1/2 Teaspoon of salt
* 3 large pastured eggs
* 1/2 Cup of melted coconut oil
* 1/2 Teaspoon of vanilla extract
* 1/2 Cup of almond milk
* 1 Tablespoon of melted coconut oil

For the cream cheese Frosting:

* 3 Tablespoons of softened cream cheese
* 2 Tablespoons of powdered Swerve Sweetener
* 1 Tablespoon of coconut heavy whipping cream
* 1/2 Teaspoon of vanilla extract

Directions:

1. Preheat your oven to a temperature of about 325 F and grease a baking tray of 8x8 inch.

2. For the filling, mix the Swerve and the cinnamon in a mixing bowl and mix very well; then set it aside.

3. For the preparation of the cake; whisk all together the almond flour, the sweetener, the protein powder, the baking powder, and the salt in a mixing bowl.

4. Add in the eggs, the melted coconut oil and the vanilla extract and mix very well.

5. Add in the almond milk and keep stirring until your ingredients are very well combined.

6. Spread about half of the batter in the prepared pan; then sprinkle with about two thirds of the filling mixture.

7. Spread the remaining mixture of the batter over the filling and smooth it with a spatula.

8. Bake for about 35 minutes in the oven.

9. Brush with the melted coconut oil and sprinkle with the remaining cinnamon filling.

10. Prepare the frosting by beating the cream cheese, the powdered erythritol, the cream and the vanilla extract in a mixing bowl until it becomes smooth.

11. Drizzle frost over the cooled cake.

12. Slice the cake; then serve and enjoy your cake!

Nutrition: Calories: 222Fat: 19.2g Carbohydrates: 5.4g Fiber: 1.5gProtein: 7.3g

Ketogenic Orange Cake

Preparation time: 10 minutes

Cooking time: 50 minutes

Servings: 8

Ingredients:

* 2 and 1/2 cups of almond flour
* 2 Unwaxed washed oranges
* 5 Large separated eggs
* 1 Teaspoon of baking powder
* 2 Teaspoons of orange extract
* 1 Teaspoon of vanilla bean powder
* 6 Seeds of cardamom pods crushed
* 16 drops of liquid stevia; about 3 teaspoons
* 1 Handful of flaked almonds to decorate

Directions:

1. Preheat your oven to a temperature of about 350 Fahrenheit.

2. Line a rectangular bread baking tray with a parchment paper.

3. Place the oranges into a pan filled with cold water and cover it with a lid.

4. Bring the saucepan to a boil, then let simmer for about 1 hour and make sure the oranges are totally submerged.

5. Make sure the oranges are always submerged to remove any taste of bitterness.

6. Cut the oranges into halves; then remove any seeds; and drain the water and set the oranges aside to cool down.

7. Cut the oranges in half and remove any seeds, then puree it with a blender or a food processor.

8. Separate the eggs; then whisk the egg whites until you see stiff peaks forming.

9. Add all your ingredients except for the egg whites to the orange mixture and add in the egg whites; then mix.

10. Pour the batter into the cake tin and sprinkle with the flaked almonds right on top.

11. Bake your cake for about 50 minutes.

12. Remove the cake from the oven and set aside to cool for 5 minutes.

13. Slice your cake; then serve and enjoy its incredible taste!

Nutrition: Calories: 164 Fat: 12g Carbohydrates: 7.1 Fiber: 2.7g
Protein: 10.9g

Lemon Cake

Preparation time: 20 minutes

Cooking time: 20 minutes

Servings: 9

Ingredients:
- 2 Medium lemons
- 4 Large eggs
- 2 Tablespoons of almond butter
- 2 Tablespoons of avocado oil
- 1/3 cup of coconut flour
- 4-5 tablespoons of honey (or another sweetener of your choice)
- 1/2 tablespoon of baking soda

Directions:
1. Preheat your oven to a temperature of about 350 F.

2. Crack the eggs in a large bowl and set two egg whites aside.

3. Whisk the 2 whites of eggs with the egg yolks, the honey, the oil, the almond butter, the lemon zest and the juice and whisk very well together.

4. Combine the baking soda with the coconut flour and gradually add this dry mixture to the wet ingredients and keep whisking for a couple of minutes.

5. Beat the two eggs with a hand mixer and beat the egg into foam.

6. Add the white egg foam gradually to the mixture with a silicone spatula.

7. Transfer your obtained batter to tray covered with a baking paper.

8. Bake your cake for about 20 to 22 minutes.

9. Let the cake cool for 5 minutes; then slice your cake.

10. Serve and enjoy your delicious cake!

Nutrition: Calories: 164Fat: 12g Carbohydrates: 7.1 Fiber: 2.7g Protein: 10.9g

VEGETABLE

Avocado Fries with Roasted Garlic Mayonnaise

Preparation Time: 50 minutes

Cooking Time: 3 minutes

Servings: 4

Ingredients

- 1/2 head garlic (6-7 cloves
- 3/4 cup all-purpose flour
- Sea salt and ground black pepper, to taste
- 2 eggs
- 1 cup tortilla chips, crushed
- 3 avocados, cut into wedges

Sauce:

- 1/2 cup mayonnaise
- 1 teaspoon lemon juice
- 1 teaspoon mustard

Directions

1. Place the garlic on a piece of aluminum foil and spritz with cooking spray. Wrap the garlic in the foil.

2. Cook in the preheated Air Fryer at 400 degrees for 12 minutes. Check the garlic, open the top of the foil and continue to cook for 10 minutes more.

3. Let it cool for 10 to 15 minutes; remove the cloves by squeezing them out of the skins; mash the garlic and reserve.

4. In a shallow bowl, combine the flour, salt, and black pepper. In another shallow dish, whisk the eggs until frothy.

5. Place the crushed tortilla chips in a third shallow dish. Dredge the avocado wedges in the flour mixture, shaking off the excess. Then, dip in the egg mixture; lastly, dredge in crushed tortilla chips.

6. Spritz the avocado wedges with cooking oil on all sides.

7. Cook in the preheated Air Fryer at 395 degrees F approximately 8 minutes, turning them over halfway through the cooking time.

8. Meanwhile, combine the sauce ingredients with the smashed roasted garlic. To serve, divide the avocado fries between plates and top with the sauce. Enjoy!

Nutrition: 351 Calories 27.7g Fat; 21.5g Carbs; 6.4g Protein

1.1g Sugars

Roasted Broccoli with Sesame Seeds

Preparation Time: 15 minutes

Cooking Time: 4 minutes

Servings: 2

Ingredients

- 1 pound broccoli florets
- 2 tablespoons sesame oil
- 1/2 teaspoon shallot powder
- 1/2 teaspoon porcini powder
- 1 teaspoon garlic powder
- Sea salt and ground black pepper, to taste
- 1/2 teaspoon cumin powder
- 1/4 teaspoon paprika
- 2 tablespoons sesame seeds

Directions

1. Start by preheating the Air Fryer to 400 degrees F.

2. Blanch the broccoli in salted boiling water until al dente, about 3 to 4 minutes. Drain well and transfer to the lightly greased Air Fryer basket.

3. Add the sesame oil, shallot powder, porcini powder, garlic powder, salt, black pepper, cumin powder, paprika, and sesame seeds.

4. Cook for 6 minutes, tossing halfway through the cooking time. Bon appétit!

Nutrition: 267 Calories19.5g Fat20.2g Carbs8.9g Protein5.2g Sugars

Corn on the Cob with Herb Butter

Preparation Time: 15 minutes

Cooking Time: 12 minutes

Servings: 2

Ingredients

- 2 ears fresh corn, shucked and cut into halves

- 2 tablespoons butter, room temperature
- 1 teaspoon granulated garlic
- 1/2 teaspoon fresh ginger, grated
- Sea salt and ground black pepper, to taste
- 1 tablespoon fresh rosemary, chopped
- 1 tablespoon fresh basil, chopped
- 2 tablespoons fresh chives, roughly chopped

Directions

1. Spritz the corn with cooking spray. Cook at 395 degrees F for 6 minutes, turning them over halfway through the cooking time.
2. In the meantime, mix the butter with the granulated garlic, ginger, salt, black pepper, rosemary, and basil.
3. Spread the butter mixture all over the corn on the cob. Cook in the preheated Air Fryer an additional 2 minutes. Bon appétit!

Nutrition: 239 Calories; 13.3g Fat; 30.2g Carbs; 5.4g Protein; 5.8g Sugars

Rainbow Vegetable Fritters

Preparation Time: 20 minutes
Cooking Time: 12 minutes
Servings: 2

Ingredients

- 1 zucchini, grated and squeezed
- 1 cup corn kernels
- 1/2 cup canned green peas
- 4 tablespoons all-purpose flour
- 2 tablespoons fresh shallots, minced
- 1 teaspoon fresh garlic, minced
- 1 tablespoon peanut oil
- Sea salt and ground black pepper, to taste
- 1 teaspoon cayenne pepper

Directions

1. In a mixing bowl, thoroughly combine all ingredients until everything is well incorporated.
2. Shape the mixture into patties. Spritz the Air Fryer basket with cooking spray.
3. Cook in the preheated Air Fryer at 365 degrees F for 6 minutes. Turn them over and cook for a further 6 minutes
4. Serve immediately and enjoy!

Nutrition: 215 Calories; 8.4g Fat; 31.6g Carbs; 6g Protein; 4.1g Sugars

Mediterranean Vegetable Skewers

Preparation Time: 30 minutes
Cooking Time: 13 minutes
Servings: 4

Ingredients

- 2 medium-sized zucchini, cut into 1-inch pieces
- 2 red bell peppers, cut into 1-inch pieces
- 1 green bell pepper, cut into 1-inch pieces
- 1 red onion, cut into 1-inch pieces
- 2 tablespoons olive oil
- Sea salt, to taste
- 1/2 teaspoon black pepper, preferably freshly cracked
- 1/2 teaspoon red pepper flakes

Directions

1. Soak the wooden skewers in water for 15 minutes.
2. Thread the vegetables on skewers; drizzle olive oil all over the vegetable skewers; sprinkle with spices.
3. Cook in the preheated Air Fryer at 400 degrees F for 13 minutes. Serve warm and enjoy!

Nutrition: 138 Calories; 10.2g Fat; 10.2g Carbs; 2.2g Protein; 6.6g Sugars

Roasted Veggies with Yogurt-Tahini Sauce

Preparation Time: 20 minutes
Cooking Time: 10 minutes
Servings: 4

Ingredients

- 1 pound Brussels sprouts
- 1 pound button mushrooms
- 2 tablespoons olive oil
- 1/2 teaspoon white pepper
- 1/2 teaspoon dried dill weed
- 1/2 teaspoon cayenne pepper
- 1/2 teaspoon celery seeds
- 1/2 teaspoon mustard seeds
- Salt, to taste

- Yogurt Tahini Sauce:
- 1 cup plain yogurt
- 2 heaping tablespoons tahini paste
- 1 tablespoon lemon juice
- 1 tablespoon extra-virgin olive oil
- 1/2 teaspoon Aleppo pepper, minced

Directions

1. Toss the Brussels sprouts and mushrooms with olive oil and spices. Preheat your Air Fryer to 380 degrees F.
2. Add the Brussels sprouts to the cooking basket and cook for 10 minutes.
3. Add the mushrooms, turn the temperature to 390 degrees and cook for 6 minutes more.
4. While the vegetables are cooking, make the sauce by whisking all ingredients. Serve the warm vegetables with the sauce on the side. Bon appétit!

Nutrition: 254 Calories; 17.2g Fat; 19.6g Carbs; 11.1g Protein; 8.1g Sugars

Swiss Cheese & Vegetable Casserole

Preparation Time: 10 minutes
Cooking Time: 48 minutes
Servings: 4

Ingredients

- 1 pound potatoes, peeled and sliced (1/4-inch thick
- 2 tablespoons olive oil
- 1/2 teaspoon red pepper flakes, crushed
- 1/2 teaspoon freshly ground black pepper
- Salt, to taste
- 3 bell peppers, thinly sliced
- 1 serrano pepper, thinly sliced
- 2 medium-sized tomatoes, sliced
- 1 leek, thinly sliced
- 2 garlic cloves, minced
- 1 cup Swiss cheese, shredded

Directions

1. Start by preheating your Air Fryer to 350 degrees F. Spritz a casserole dish with cooking oil.
2. Place the potatoes in the casserole dish in an even layer; drizzle 1 tablespoon of olive oil over the top. Then, add the red pepper, black pepper, and salt.

3. Add 2 bell peppers and 1/2 of the leeks. Add the tomatoes and the remaining 1 tablespoon of olive oil.
4. Add the remaining peppers, leeks, and minced garlic. Top with the cheese.
5. Cover the casserole with foil and bake for 32 minutes. Remove the foil and increase the temperature to 400 degrees F; bake an additional 16 minutes. Bon appétit!

Nutrition: 328 Calories; 16.5g Fat; 33.1g Carbs; 13.1g Protein; 7.6g Sugars

Easy Sweet Potato Hash Browns

Preparation Time: 10 minutes
Cooking Time: 45 minutes
Servings: 2

Ingredients

- 1 pound sweet potatoes, peeled and grated
- 2 eggs, whisked
- 1/4 cup scallions, chopped
- 1 teaspoon fresh garlic, minced
- Sea salt and ground black pepper, to taste
- 1/4 teaspoon ground allspice
- 1/2 teaspoon cinnamon
- 1 tablespoon peanut oil

Directions

1. Allow the sweet potatoes to soak for 25 minutes in cold water. Drain the water; dry the sweet potatoes with a kitchen towel.
2. Add the remaining ingredients and stir to combine well.
3. Cook in the preheated Air Fryer at 395 degrees F for 20 minutes. Shake the basket once or twice. Serve with ketchup.

Nutrition: 381 Calories; 16.7g Fat; 44.8g Carbs; 14.3g Protein;
3.9g Sugars

American-Style Brussel Sprout Salad

Preparation Time: 5 minutes
Cooking Time: 30 minutes
Servings: 4

Ingredients

- 1 pound Brussels sprouts

- 1 apple, cored and diced
- 1/2 cup mozzarella cheese, crumbled
- 1/2 cup pomegranate seeds
- 1 small-sized red onion, chopped
- 4 eggs, hardboiled and sliced

Dressing:

1. 1/4 cup olive oil
2. 2 tablespoons champagne vinegar
3. 1 teaspoon Dijon mustard
4. 1 teaspoon honey
5. Sea salt and ground black pepper, to taste
6. Directions
7. Start by preheating your Air Fryer to 380 degrees F.
8. Add the Brussels sprouts to the cooking basket. Spritz with cooking spray and cook for 15 minutes. Let it cool to room temperature about 15 minutes.
9. Toss the Brussels sprouts with the apple, cheese, pomegranate seeds, and red onion.
10. Mix all ingredients for the dressing and toss to combine well. Serve topped with the hard-boiled eggs. Bon appétit!

Nutrition: 319 Calories; 18.5g Fat; 27g Carbs; 14.7g Protein; 14.6g Sugars

The Best Cauliflower Tater Tots

Preparation Time: 5 minutes
Cooking Time: 20 minutes
Servings: 4

Ingredients

- 1 pound cauliflower florets
- 2 eggs
- 1 tablespoon olive oil
- 2 tablespoons scallions, chopped
- 1 garlic clove, minced
- 1 cup Colby cheese, shredded
- 1/2 cup breadcrumbs
- Sea salt and ground black pepper, to taste
- 1/4 teaspoon dried dill weed
- 1 teaspoon paprika

Directions

1. Blanch the cauliflower in salted boiling water about 3 to 4 minutes until al dente. Drain well and pulse in a food processor.
2. Add the remaining ingredients; mix to combine well. Shape the cauliflower mixture into bite-sized tots.
3. Spritz the Air Fryer basket with cooking spray.
4. Cook in the preheated Air Fryer at 375 degrees F for 16 minutes, shaking halfway through the cooking time. Serve with your favorite sauce for dipping. Bon appétit!

Nutrition: 267 Calories; 19.2g Fat; 9.6g Carbs; 14.9g Protein; 2.9g Sugars

Skinny Pumpkin Chips

Preparation Time: 10 minutes
Cooking Time: 13 minutes
Servings: 2

Ingredients

- 1 pound pumpkin, cut into sticks
- 1 tablespoon coconut oil
- 1/2 teaspoon rosemary
- 1/2 teaspoon basil
- Salt and ground black pepper, to taste

Directions

1. Start by preheating the Air Fryer to 395 degrees F. Brush the pumpkin sticks with coconut oil; add the spices and toss to combine.
2. Cook for 13 minutes, shaking the basket halfway through the cooking time.
3. Serve with mayonnaise. Bon appétit!

Nutrition: 118 Calories; 7g Fat; 14.7g Carbs; 2.2g Protein; 6.2g Sugars

Cheese Stuffed Roasted Peppers

Preparation Time: 10 minutes
Cooking Time: 15 minutes
Servings: 2

Ingredients

- 2 red bell peppers, tops and seeds removed
- 2 yellow bell peppers, tops and seeds removed
- Salt and pepper, to taste
- 1 cup cream cheese
- 4 tablespoons mayonnaise

- 2 pickles, chopped

Directions

1.　Arrange the peppers in the lightly greased cooking basket. Cook in the preheated Air Fryer at 400 degrees F for 15 minutes, turning them over halfway through the cooking time.

2.　Season with salt and pepper.

3.　Then, in a mixing bowl, combine the cream cheese with the mayonnaise and chopped pickles. Stuff the pepper with the cream cheese mixture and serve. Enjoy!

Nutrition:367 Calories; 21.8g Fat; 21.9g Carbs; 21.5g Protein; 14.1g Sugars

Three-Cheese Stuffed Mushrooms

Preparation Time: 10 minutes

Cooking Time: 7 minutes

Servings: 3

Ingredients

- 9 large button mushrooms, stems removed
- 1 tablespoon olive oil
- Salt and ground black pepper, to taste
- 1/2 teaspoon dried rosemary
- 6 tablespoons Swiss cheese shredded
- 6 tablespoons Romano cheese, shredded
- 6 tablespoons cream cheese
- 1 teaspoon soy sauce
- 1 teaspoon garlic, minced
- 3 tablespoons green onion, minced

Directions

1.　Brush the mushroom caps with olive oil; sprinkle with salt, pepper, and rosemary.

2.　In a mixing bowl, thoroughly combine the remaining ingredients; mix to combine well and divide the filling mixture among the mushroom caps.

3.　Cook in the preheated Air Fryer at 390 degrees F for 7 minutes.

4.　Let the mushrooms cool slightly before serving. Bon appétit!

Nutrition:345 Calories; 28g Fat; 11.2g Carbs; 14.4g Protein; 8.1g Sugars

Sweet Potato Chips with Greek Yogurt Dip

Preparation Time: 5 minutes

Cooking Time: 30 minutes

Servings: 2

Ingredients

- 4 sweet potatoes, sliced
- 2 tablespoons olive oil
- Coarse sea salt and freshly ground black pepper, to taste
- 1 teaspoon paprika

Dipping Sauce:

- 1/2 cup Greek-style yogurt
- 1 clove garlic, minced
- 1 tablespoon fresh chives, chopped

Directions

1.　Soak the sweet potato slices in icy cold water for 20 to 30 minutes. Drain the sweet potatoes and pat them dry with kitchen towels.

2.　Toss the sweet potato slices with olive oil, salt, black pepper, and paprika.

3.　Place in the lightly greased cooking basket. Cook in the preheated Air Fryer at 360 degrees F for 14 minutes.

4.　Meanwhile, make the sauce by whisking the remaining ingredients. Serve the sweet potato chips with the sauce for dipping and enjoy!

Nutrition:378 Calories; 13.9g Fat; 55.2g Carbs; 9.4g Protein; 12.6g Sugars

Classic Onion Rings

Preparation Time: 10 minutes

Cooking Time: 25 minutes

Servings: 2

Ingredients

- 1 medium-sized onion, slice into rings
- 1 cup all-purpose flour
- 1 teaspoon baking powder
- Coarse sea salt and ground black pepper, to your liking
- 1/2 cup yogurt
- 2 eggs, beaten
- 3/4 cup bread crumbs

- 1 teaspoon onion powder
- 1 teaspoon garlic powder
- 1/2 teaspoon celery seeds

Directions

1. Place the onion rings in the bowl with cold water; let them soak approximately 20 minutes; drain the onion rings and pat dry using a pepper towel.

2. In a shallow bowl, mix the flour, baking powder, salt, and black pepper. Add the yogurt and eggs and mix well to combine.

3. In another shallow bowl, mix the bread crumbs, onion powder, garlic powder, and celery seeds. Dip the onion rings in the flour/egg mixture; then, dredge in the breadcrumb mixture.

4. Spritz the Air Fryer basket with cooking spray; arrange the breaded onion rings in the basket.

5. Cook in the preheated Air Fryer at 400 degrees F for 4 to 5 minutes, turning them over halfway through the cooking time. Bon appétit!

Nutrition:440 Calories; 12.7g Fat; 60g Carbs; 19.2g Protein; 5.6g Sugars

Greek-Style Roasted Tomatoes with Feta

Preparation Time: 10 minutes
Cooking Time: 12 minutes
Servings: 2

Ingredients

- 3 medium-sized tomatoes, cut into four slices, pat dry
- 1 teaspoon dried basil
- 1 teaspoon dried oregano
- 1/4 teaspoon red pepper flakes, crushed
- 1/2 teaspoon sea salt
- 3 slices Feta cheese

Directions

1. Spritz the tomatoes with cooking oil and transfer them to the Air Fryer basket. Sprinkle with seasonings.

2. Cook at 350 degrees F approximately 8 minutes turning them over halfway through the cooking time.

3. Top with the cheese and cook an additional 4 minutes. Bon appétit!

Nutrition:148 Calories; 9.4g Fat; 9.4g Carbs; 7.8g Protein; 6.6g Sugars

Sweet Corn Fritters with Avocado

Preparation Time: 10 minutes
Cooking Time: 15 minutes
Servings: 3

Ingredients

- 2 cups sweet corn kernels
- 1 small-sized onion, chopped
- 1 garlic clove, minced
- 2 eggs, whisked
- 1 teaspoon baking powder
- 2 tablespoons fresh cilantro, chopped
- Sea salt and ground black pepper, to taste
- 1 avocado, peeled, pitted and diced
- 2 tablespoons sweet chili sauce

Directions

1. In a mixing bowl, thoroughly combine the corn, onion, garlic, eggs, baking powder, cilantro, salt, and black pepper.

2. Shape the corn mixture into 6 patties and transfer them to the lightly greased Air Fryer basket.

3. Cook in the preheated Air Fry at 370 degrees for 8 minutes; turn them over and cook for 7 minutes longer.

4. Serve the fritters with the avocado and chili sauce.

Nutrition:383 Calories; 21.3g Fat; 42.8g Carbs; 12.7g Protein; 9.2g Sugars

Cauliflower and Goat Cheese Croquettes

Preparation Time: 10 minutes
Cooking Time: 26 minutes
Servings: 2

Ingredients

- 1/2 pound cauliflower florets
- 2 garlic cloves, minced
- 1 cup goat cheese, shredded
- Sea salt and ground black pepper, to taste
- 1/2 teaspoon shallot powder
- 1/4 teaspoon cumin powder
- 1 cup sour cream
- 1 teaspoon Dijon mustard

Directions

1. Place the cauliflower florets in a saucepan of water; bring to the boil; reduce the heat and cook for 10 minutes or until tender.

2. Mash the cauliflower using your blender; add the garlic, cheese, and spices; mix to combine well.

3. Form the cauliflower mixture into croquettes shapes.

4. Cook in the preheated Air Fryer at 375 degrees F for 16 minutes, shaking halfway through the cooking time. Serve with the sour cream and mustard. Bon appétit!

Nutrition:297 Calories; 21.7g Fat; 11.7g Carbs; 15.3g Protein; 2.6g Sugars

Greek-Style Vegetable Bake

Preparation Time: 15 minutes

Cooking Time: 20 minutes

Servings: 4

Ingredients

- 1 eggplant, peeled and sliced
- 2 bell peppers, seeded and sliced
- 1 red onion, sliced
- 1 teaspoon fresh garlic, minced
- 4 tablespoons olive oil
- 1 teaspoon mustard
- 1 teaspoon dried oregano
- 1 teaspoon smoked paprika
- Salt and ground black pepper, to taste
- 1 tomato, sliced
- 6 ounces halloumi cheese, sliced lengthways

Directions

1. Start by preheating your Air Fryer to 370 degrees F. Spritz a baking pan with nonstick cooking spray.

2. Place the eggplant, peppers, onion, and garlic on the bottom of the baking pan. Add the olive oil, mustard, and spices. Transfer to the cooking basket and cook for 14 minutes.

3. Top with the tomatoes and cheese; increase the temperature to 390 degrees F and cook for 5 minutes

more until bubbling. Let it sit on a cooling rack for 10 minutes before serving.

4. Bon appétit!

Nutrition:296 Calories; 22.9g Fat; 16.1g Carbs; 9.3g Protein; 9.9g Sugars

Japanese Tempura Bowl

Preparation Time: 10 minutes

Cooking Time: 10 minutes

Servings: 3

Ingredients

- 1 cup all-purpose flour
- Kosher salt and ground black pepper, to taste
- 1/2 teaspoon paprika
- 2 eggs
- 3 tablespoons soda water
- 1 cup panko crumbs
- 2 tablespoons olive oil
- 1 cup green beans
- 1 onion, cut into rings
- 1 zucchini, cut into slices
- 2 tablespoons soy sauce
- 1 tablespoon mirin
- 1 teaspoon dashi granules

Directions

1. In a shallow bowl, mix the flour, salt, black pepper, and paprika. In a separate bowl, whisk the eggs and soda water. In a third shallow bowl, combine the panko crumbs with olive oil.

2. Dip the vegetables in flour mixture, then in the egg mixture; lastly, roll over the panko mixture to coat evenly.

3. Cook in the preheated Air Fryer at 400 degrees F for 10 minutes, shaking the basket halfway through the cooking time. Work in batches until the vegetables are crispy and golden brown.

4. Then, make the sauce by whisking the soy sauce, mirin, and dashi granules. Bon appétit!

Nutrition:446 Calories; 14.7g Fat; 63.5g Carbs; 14.6g Protein; 3.8g Sugars

FISH AND SEAFOOD

Salmon Milano

Preparation time: 10 minutes,
Cooking time: 20 minutes,
Servings: 6

Ingredients:
- 2 ½ lb. salmon filet
- 2 tomatoes, sliced
- ½ cup margarine
- What you'll need from store cupboard:
- ½ cup basil pesto

Directions:
1. Heat the oven to 400 degrees. Line a 9x15-inch baking sheet with foil, making sure it covers the sides. Place another large piece of foil onto the baking sheet and place the salmon filet on top of it.
2. Place the pesto and margarine in blender or food processor and pulse until smooth. Spread evenly over salmon. Place tomato slices on top.
3. Wrap the foil around the salmon, tenting around the top to prevent foil from touching the salmon as much as possible. Bake 15-25 minutes, or salmon flakes easily with a fork. Serve.

Nutrition: Calories 444 Total Carbs 2g Protein 55g Fat 24g Sugar 1g Fiber 0g

Shrimp & Artichoke Skillet

Preparation time: 5 minutes
Cooking time: 10 minutes
Servings: 4

Ingredients:
- 1 ½ cups shrimp, peel & devein
- 2 shallots, diced
- 1 tbsp. margarine
What you'll need from store cupboard
- 2 12 oz. jars artichoke hearts, drain & rinse
- 2 cups white wine
- 2 cloves garlic, diced fine

Directions:

1. Melt margarine in a large skillet over med-high heat. Add shallot and garlic and cook until they start to brown, stirring frequently.
2. Add artichokes and cook 5 minutes. Reduce heat and add wine. Cook 3 minutes, stirring occasionally.
3. Add the shrimp and cook just until they turn pink. Serve.

Nutrition: Calories 487 Total Carbs 26g Net Carbs 17g Protein 64g Fat 5g Sugar 3g Fiber 9g

Tuna Carbonara

Preparation time: 5 minutes
Cooking time: 25 minutes
Servings: 4

Ingredients:
- ½ lb. tuna fillet, cut in pieces
- 2 eggs
- 4 tbsp. fresh parsley, diced
- What you'll need from store cupboard:
- ½ Homemade Pasta, cook & drain,
- ½ cup reduced fat parmesan cheese
- 2 cloves garlic, peeled
- 2 tbsp. extra virgin olive oil
- Salt & pepper, to taste

Directions:
1. In a small bowl, beat the eggs, parmesan and a dash of pepper.
2. Heat the oil in a large skillet over med-high heat. Add garlic and cook until browned. Add the tuna and cook 2-3 minutes, or until tuna is almost cooked through. Discard the garlic.
3. Add the pasta and reduce heat. Stir in egg mixture and cook, stirring constantly, 2 minutes. If the sauce is too thick, thin with water, a little bit at a time, until it has a creamy texture.
4. Salt and pepper to taste and serve garnished with parsley.

Nutrition: Calories 409 Total Carbs 7g Net Carbs 6g Protein 25g Fat 30g Sugar 3g Fiber 1g

Mediterranean Fish Fillets

Preparation Time: 10 minutes

Cooking Time: 3 minutes

Servings: 4

Ingredients:

- 4 cod fillets
- 1 lb. grape tomatoes, halved
- 1 cup olives, pitted and sliced
- 2 tbsp. capers
- 1 tsp. dried thyme
- 2 tbsp. olive oil
- 1 tsp. garlic, minced
- Pepper
- Salt

Directions:

1. Pour 1 cup water into the instant pot then place steamer rack in the pot.
2. Spray heat-safe baking dish with cooking spray.
3. Add half grape tomatoes into the dish and season with pepper and salt.
4. Arrange fish fillets on top of cherry tomatoes. Drizzle with oil and season with garlic, thyme, capers, pepper, and salt.
5. Spread olives and remaining grape tomatoes on top of fish fillets.
6. Place dish on top of steamer rack in the pot.
7. Seal pot with a lid and select manual and cook on high for 3 minutes.
8. Once done, release pressure using quick release. Remove lid.
9. Serve and enjoy.

Nutrition: Calories 212 Fat 11.9 g Carbohydrates 7.1 g Sugar 3 g Protein 21.4 g Cholesterol 55 mg

Flavors Cioppino

Preparation Time: 10 minutes

Cooking Time: 5 minutes

Servings: 6

Ingredients:

- 1 lb. codfish, cut into chunks
- 1 1/2 lbs. shrimp
- 28 oz. can tomatoes, diced
- 1 cup dry white wine
- 1 bay leaf

- 1 tsp. cayenne
- 1 tsp. oregano
- 1 shallot, chopped
- 1 tsp. garlic, minced
- 1 tbsp. olive oil
- 1/2 tsp. salt

Directions:

1. Add oil into the inner pot of instant pot and set the pot on sauté mode.
2. Add shallot and garlic and sauté for 2 minutes.
3. Add wine, bay leaf, cayenne, oregano, and salt and cook for 3 minutes.
4. Add remaining ingredients and stir well.
5. Seal pot with a lid and select manual and cook on low for 0 minutes.
6. Once done, release pressure using quick release. Remove lid.
7. Serve and enjoy.

Nutrition: Calories 281 Fat 5 g Carbohydrates 10.5 g Sugar 4.9 g Protein 40.7 g Cholesterol 266 mg

Delicious Shrimp Alfredo

Preparation Time: 10 minutes

Cooking Time: 3 minutes

Servings: 4

Ingredients:

- 12 shrimp, remove shells
- 1 tbsp. garlic, minced
- 1/4 cup parmesan cheese
- 2 cups whole wheat rotini noodles
- 1 cup fish broth
- 15 oz. alfredo sauce
- 1 onion, chopped
- Salt

Directions:

1. Add all ingredients except parmesan cheese into the instant pot and stir well.
2. Seal pot with lid and cook on high for 3 minutes.
3. Once done, release pressure using quick release. Remove lid.
4. Stir in cheese and serve.

Nutrition: Calories 669 Fat 23.1 g Carbohydrates 76 g Sugar 2.4 g Protein 37.8 g Cholesterol 190 mg

Tomato Olive Fish Fillets

Preparation Time: 10 minutes
Cooking Time: 8 minutes
Servings: 4

Ingredients:
- 2 lbs. halibut fish fillets
- 2 oregano sprigs
- 2 rosemary sprigs
- 2 tbsp. fresh lime juice
- 1 cup olives, pitted
- 28 oz. can tomatoes, diced
- 1 tbsp. garlic, minced
- 1 onion, chopped
- 2 tbsp. olive oil

Directions:

1.	Add oil into the inner pot of instant pot and set the pot on sauté mode.
2.	Add onion and sauté for 3 minutes.
3.	Add garlic and sauté for a minute.
4.	Add lime juice, olives, herb sprigs, and tomatoes and stir well.
5.	Seal pot with lid and cook on high for 3 minutes.
6.	Once done, release pressure using quick release. Remove lid.
7.	Add fish fillets and seal pot again with lid and cook on high for 2 minutes.
8.	Once done, release pressure using quick release. Remove lid.
9.	Serve and enjoy.

Nutrition: Calories 333 Fat 19.1 g Carbohydrates 31.8 g Sugar 8.4 g Protein 13.4 g Cholesterol 5 mg

POULTRY

Cheesy Stuffed Chicken

Preparation Time: 15 minutes

Cooking Time: 20 minutes

Servings: 4

Ingredients:

- 1 lb. chicken breasts, boneless and butterflied
- 2 cups fresh spinach, chopped
- 4 oz. low fat cream cheese, soft
- ¼ cup mozzarella cheese, grated
- What you'll need from store cupboard:
- ¼ cup reduced fat Parmesan cheese
- 1 tbsp. garlic, diced fine
- 1 tbsp. olive oil
- 1 tsp. chili powder
- 1 tsp. Italian seasoning
- ¾ tsp. black pepper, divided
- ½ tsp. salt

Directions:

1. In a medium bowl, combine spinach, cream cheese, parmesan, mozzarella, garlic, ½ teaspoon salt and ½ teaspoon pepper, stir to combine.
2. In a small bowl, stir together the chili powder, Italian seasoning, salt, and pepper, use it to season both sides of the chicken. Spoon ¼ of the cheese mixture into the middle of the chicken and fold over to seal it inside.
3. Heat oil in a large skillet over med-high heat. Add the chicken, cover and cook 9-10 minutes per side, or until cooked through. Serve.

Nutrition: Calories 256 Total Carbs 2g Net Carbs 1g Protein 29g Fat 14g Sugar 0g Fiber 1g

Chicken Marsala

Preparation Time: 10 minutes

Cooking Time: 25 minutes

Servings: 4

Ingredients:

- 4 boneless chicken breasts
- ½ lb. mushrooms, sliced
- 1 tbsp. margarine
- What you'll need from store cupboard:
- 1 cup Marsala wine
- ¼ cup flour
- 1 tbsp. oil
- Pinch of white pepper
- Pinch of oregano
- Pinch of basil

Directions:

1. On a shallow plate, combine flour and seasonings.
2. Dredge the chicken in the flour mixture to coat both sides.
3. In a large skillet, over medium heat, heat oil until hot. Add chicken and cook until brown on both sides, about 15 minutes. Transfer chicken to a plate.
4. Reduce heat to low and add mushrooms and ¼ cup of the wine. Cook about 5 minutes. Scrape bottom of pan to loosen any flour. Stir in reserved flour mixture and the remaining wine.
5. Simmer until mixture starts to thicken, stirring constantly. Add the chicken back to the pan and cook an additional 5 minutes. Serve.

Nutrition: Calories 327 Total Carbs 9g Net Carbs 8g Protein 21g Fat 14g Sugar 1g Fiber 1g

Chicken Zucchini Patties with Salsa

Preparation Time: 10 minutes

Cooking Time: 10 minutes

Servings: 8

Ingredients:

- 2 cup chicken breast, cooked, divided
- 1 zucchini, cut in ¾-inch pieces
- ¼ cup cilantro, diced
- What you'll need from store cupboard:
- 1/3 cup bread crumbs
- 1/3 cup lite mayonnaise
- 2 tsp. olive oil
- ½ tsp. salt
- ¼ tsp. pepper
- Roasted Tomato Salsa

Directions:

1.   Place 1 ½ cups chicken and zucchini into a food processor. Cover and process until coarsely chopped. Add bread crumbs, mayonnaise, pepper, cilantro, remaining chicken, and salt. Cover and pulse until chunky.

2.   Heat oil in a large skillet over med-high heat. Shape chicken mixture into 8 patties and cook 4 minutes per side, or until golden brown. Serve topped with salsa.

Nutrition: Calories 146 Total Carbs 10g Net Carbs 8g Protein 12g Fat 7g Sugar 5g Fiber 2g

Creamy Chicken Tenders

Preparation Time; 5 minutes

Cooking Time: 15 minutes

Servings: 4

Ingredients:

*   1 lb. chicken breast tenders
*   1 cup half-n-half
*   4 tbsp. margarine

What you'll need from store cupboard:

*   2 tsp. garlic powder
*   2 tsp. chili powder

Directions:

1.   In a small bowl, stir together seasonings with a little salt if desired. Sprinkle over chicken to coat.

2.   Heat 2 tablespoons margarine in a large skillet over medium heat. Cook chicken until no longer pink, 3-4 minutes per side. Transfer to a plate.

3.   Add half-n-half and stir, scraping up the brown bits from the bottom of the skillet, and cook until it starts to boil. Reduce heat to med-low and simmer until sauce is reduced by half. Stir in remaining margarine and add chicken back to sauce to heat through. Serve.

Nutrition: Calories 281 Total Carbs 3g Protein 24g Fat 19g Sugar 0g Fiber 0g

Grilled Chicken Wraps

Preparation Time: 10 minutes

Cooking Time: 6 minutes

Servings: 4

Ingredients:

*   4 oz. chicken breasts, boneless and skinless
*   2 teaspoons oregano, crushed

*   ¼ cup mint, chopped
*   2 onion slices, peeled

What you will need from the store cupboard:

*   2 12-inch Arabic bread or Naan pieces
*   2 tablespoons of lemon juice
*   Cooking spray
*   Pepper and salt to taste

Directions:

1.   Preheat your oven to 350 ºF.

2.   Brush both sides of the chicken breasts with lemon juice.

3.   Sprinkle oregano.

4.   Apply cooking spray lightly and return to the grill.

5.   Keep the onion slices and chicken breasts on the grill.

6.   Cook each side for 3 minutes. Turn once.

7.   Cut the onion into strips.

8.   Cut the chicken into small ½ strips after it is done.

9.   Cut your Arabic bread into half. Leave the pita bread or naan whole.

10.   Now keep the onion strips and chicken at the center of the bread pieces.

11.   Sprinkle mint. Roll up.

Nutrition: Calories 328, Carbohydrates 36g, Fiber 5g, Cholesterol 82mg, Total Fat 3g, Protein 39g, Sodium 415mg

French Onion Chicken & Vegetables

Preparation Time: 10 minutes

Cooking Time: 4 hours

Servings: 10

Ingredients:

*   1 lb. chicken breasts, boneless and skinless, cut in 1-inch pieces
*   1 lb. green beans, trim
*   1 lb. red potatoes, quartered
*   ½ lb. mushrooms, halved
*   ½ cup sweet onion, sliced
*   1 tsp. lemon zest

What you'll need from store cupboard:

*   2 14 ½ oz. cans low sodium chicken broth

- 2 tbsp. onion soup mix
- 1 tbsp. sunflower oil
- 2 tsp. Worcestershire sauce
- ½ tsp. lemon pepper
- ½ tsp. salt
- ½ tsp. pepper
- ¼ tsp. garlic powder

Directions:

1. Sprinkle chicken with lemon pepper.

2. Heat oil in a large skillet over medium heat. Cook chicken 4-5 minutes or until brown on all sides.

3. Layer the green beans, potatoes, mushrooms, and onion in the crock pot.

4. In a small bowl, combine remaining Ingredients and pour over vegetables. Top with chicken.

5. Cover and cook on low heat 4-5 hours or until vegetables are tender. Serve.

Nutrition: Calories 256 Total Carbs 15g Net Carbs 12g Protein 30g Fat 8g Sugar 2g Fiber 3g

Lemon Chicken

Preparation Time: 10 minutes

Cooking Time: 10 minutes

Servings: 4

Ingredients:

- 3 large boneless, skinless chicken breasts cut into strips
- ¼ cup red bell pepper, cut into 2 inch strips
- ¼ cup green bell pepper, cut into 2 inch strips
- ¼ cup snow peas
- ¼ cup fresh lemon juice
- 1 tsp. fresh ginger, peeled and diced fine
- What you'll need from store cupboard:
- ¼ cup + 1 tbsp. low sodium soy sauce, divided
- ¼ cup low-fat, low-sodium chicken broth
- 1 tbsp. Splenda
- 1 tbsp. vegetable oil
- 2 cloves garlic, diced fine
- 2 tsp. cornstarch

Directions:

1. In a medium bowl, whisk together 1 teaspoon cornstarch and 1 tablespoon soy sauce. Add chicken, cover and chill about 10 minutes.

2. In a separate medium mixing bowl, stir together lemon juice, ¼ cup soy sauce, broth, ginger, garlic, Splenda, and remaining cornstarch until thoroughly combined.

3. Heat oil in a large skillet over med-high heat. Add chicken and cook, stirring frequently, 3-4 minutes or just until chicken is no longer pink.

4. Add sauce, peppers and peas. Cook 2 more minutes or until sauce thickens and vegetables are tender-crisp. Serve.

Nutrition: Calories 242 Total Carbs 9g Net Carbs 8g Protein 27g Fat 10g Sugar 5g Fiber 1g

Mediterranean Grilled Chicken

Preparation Time: 5 minutes

Cooking Time: 10 minutes

Servings: 4

Ingredients:

- 4 chicken breasts, boneless, skinless
- What you'll need from store cupboard:
- 6 oz. pesto
- ¼ cup olive oil
- ¼ cup lemon juice
- 2 tbsp. red wine vinegar
- 2 tsp. garlic, diced fine

Directions:

1. In a large freezer bag or a container mix together the olive oil, lemon juice, red wine vinegar, minced garlic and pesto. Add chicken and toss to coat. Place in refrigerator and marinate for 6 to 8 hours.

2. Heat grill to med-high. Cook chicken, 3-4 minutes per side, or until cooked through. Or, you can bake it in a 400 degree oven until no longer pink, about 30 minutes. Serve.

Nutrition: Calories 378 Total Carbs 2g Protein 36g Fat 25g Sugar 2g Fiber 0g

Spicy Grilled Turkey Breast

Preparation Time: 15 minutes

Cooking Time: 1 ½ hours

Servings: 14

Ingredients:

- 5 lb. turkey breast, bone in

- What you'll need from store cupboard:
- 1 cup low sodium chicken broth
- ¼ cup vinegar
- ¼ cup jalapeno pepper jelly
- 2 tbsp. Splenda brown sugar
- 2 tbsp. olive oil
- 1 tbsp. salt
- 2 tsp. cinnamon
- 1 tsp. cayenne pepper
- ½ tsp. ground mustard
- Nonstick cooking spray

Directions:

1. Heat grill to medium heat. Spray rack with cooking spray. Place a drip pan on the grill for indirect heat.

2. In a small bowl, combine Splenda brown sugar with seasonings.

3. Carefully loosen the skin on the turkey from both sides with your fingers. Spread half the spice mix on the turkey. Secure the skin to the underneath with toothpicks and spread remaining spice mix on the outside.

4. Place the turkey over the drip pan and grill 30 minutes.

5. In a small saucepan, over medium heat, combine broth, vinegar, jelly, and oil. Cook and stir 2 minutes until jelly is completely melted. Reserve ½ cup of the mixture.

6. Baste turkey with some of the jelly mixture. Cook 1-1 ½ hours, basting every 15 minutes, until done, when thermometer reaches 170 degrees.

7. Cover and let rest 10 minutes. Discard the skin. Brush with reserved jelly mixture and slice and serve.

Nutrition: Calories 314 Total Carbs 5g Protein 35g Fat 14g Sugar 5g Fiber 0g

Turkey Meatballs with Spaghetti Squash

Preparation Time: 15 minutes
Cooking Time: 35 minutes
Servings: 4

Ingredients:

- 1 lb. lean ground turkey
- 1 lb. spaghetti squash, halved and seeds removed

- 2 egg whites
- 1/3 cup green onions, diced fine
- ¼ cup onion, diced fine
- 2 ½ tbsp. flat leaf parsley, diced fine
- 1 tbsp. fresh basil, diced fine

What you'll need from store cupboard:

- 14 oz. can no-salt-added tomatoes, crushed
- 1/3 cup soft whole wheat bread crumbs
- ¼ cup low sodium chicken broth
- 1 tsp. garlic powder
- 1 tsp. thyme
- 1 tsp. oregano
- ½ tsp. red pepper flakes
- ½ tsp. whole fennel seeds

Directions:

1. In a small bowl, combine bread crumbs, onion, garlic, parsley, pepper flakes, thyme, and fennel.

2. In a large bowl, combine turkey and egg whites. Add bread crumb mixture and mix well. Cover and chill 10 minutes. Heat the oven to broil.

3. Place the squash, cut side down, in a glass baking dish. Add 3-4 tablespoons of water and microwave on high 10-12 minutes, or until fork tender.

4. Make 20 meatballs from the turkey mixture and place on a baking sheet. Broil 4-5 minutes, turn and cook 4 more minutes.

5. In a large skillet, combine tomatoes and broth and bring to a simmer over low heat. Add meatballs, oregano, basil, and green onions. Cook, stirring occasionally, 10 minutes or until heated through.

6. Use a fork to scrape the squash into "strands" and arrange on a serving platter. Top with meatballs and sauce and serve.

Nutrition: Calories 253; Total Carbs 15g; Net Carbs 13g ;Protein 27g; Fat 9g; Sugar 4g; Fiber 2g

Turkey Stuffed Peppers

Preparation Time: 10 minutes

Cooking Time: 55 minutes

Servings: 8

Ingredients:

- 1 lb. lean ground turkey
- 4 green bell peppers, halved and ribs and seeds removed
- 1 onion, diced
- 1 ½ cup mozzarella cheese
- 1 cup cauliflower, grated
- 1 cup mushrooms, diced

What you'll need from store cupboard:

- 3 cups spaghetti sauce
- 3 cloves garlic, diced fine
- 2 tbsp. olive oil

Directions:

1. Heat the oil in a large skillet over med-high heat. Add the garlic, mushrooms, and onion. Add the turkey, cook, breaking up the turkey with a spatula, until turkey is cooked through, about 10 minutes.

2. Stir in the cauliflower, and cook, stirring frequently, 3-5 minutes. Add the spaghetti sauce and 1 cup mozzarella. Stir to combine and remove from heat.

3. Heat oven to 350 degrees. Place bell peppers in a large baking dish, skin side down. Fill the insides with the turkey mixture, place any extra filling around the peppers. Top each pepper with remaining mozzarella. Bake 40-45 minutes or the peppers are tender. Serve immediately.

Nutrition: Calories 214; Total Carbs 14g; Net Carbs 10g; Protein 20g; Fat 11g; Sugar 9g; Fiber 4g

Thyme and Apple Chicken

Preparation Time: 10 minutes

Cooking Time: 20 minutes

Servings: 4

Ingredients:

- 2 chicken breasts, boneless and skinless
- 1 teaspoon thyme leaves, crushed
- 1 green apple, cored, sliced thin
- 1 shallot, minced
- Thyme sprigs for garnishing

What you will need from the store cupboard:

- ¼ cup balsamic vinegar
- Salt and pepper to taste
- Cooking spray

Directions:

1. Preheat your oven to 350 ºF. Apply cooking spray on your baking dish lightly.

2. Rinse the chicken breasts. Use paper towels to pat dry.

3. Sprinkle salt and pepper on the breasts.

4. Place on your baking dish in a single layer.

5. Keep apple slices around and over the chicken.

6. Sprinkle thyme leaves and shallot.

7. Pour the balsamic vinegar.

8. Bake for 10 minutes.

9. Keep the cooked chicken breasts on a platter.

10. Spoon the cooking juice and apples on top.

11. You can garnish with thyme.

Nutrition: Calories 163, Carbohydrates 9g, Fiber 1g, Cholesterol 66mg, Total Fat 2g, Protein 27g, Sodium 78mg

RECIPE INDEX

Beef Patty 57
Beef steaks with green asparagus 100
Beef Stew 201
Beef Stroganoff 145
Beef with Mushrooms 56
Beef with Sesame and Ginger 62
Beef-Vegetable Ragout 121
Beefy Pie 133
Beets Dijon 113
Blackberry Pulled Pork Shoulder 128
Blackened Shrimp 80
Blue Cheese Chicken Wedges 109
Blueberry Almond Tart 169
Blueberry Orange Dessert Sauce 195
Blueberry-Chia Smoothie 33
Braised Lamb with Vegetables 127
Breakfast Banana Barley 35
Breakfast Cheese Bread Cups 16
Breakfast Cod Nuggets 16
Breakfast Egg Bites 38
Broccoli and Mushroom Frittata 27
Broccoli Beef Stir-Fry 140
Broccoli Omelet 100
Broccoli with Hot Sauce 77
Broth-Braised Cabbage 112
Brownie Sundae Pie 170
Brunswick stew 207
Brussels Sprout Hash and Eggs 39
Brussels Sprout with Fried Eggs 43
Bubble and Squeak 129
Buckwheat Chocolate Cake 166
Buffalo Chicken and Cheese Meatballs 70
Buffalo-Style Chicken Salad 50
Burgoo 205
Butter milk lentil 28

C

Cajun Catfish 80
Cajun Flounder & Tomatoes 80
Cajun Shrimp & Roasted Vegetables 81
Cake with Whipped Cream Icing 180
Canadian bacon and Egg Muffin Cups 27
Cantaloupe Sorbet 188
Carribbean Chicken 63

Carrot Cake 170
Carrot Cake Oatmeal 36
Carrot Soup 208
Cauliflower & Onion Salad 225
Cauliflower and Beef Fajita 147
Cauliflower and Goat Cheese Croquettes 235
Cauliflower and Spinach Salad 77
Cauliflower avocado mash with chicken breast 94
Cauliflower Fritters 221
Cauliflower in Vegan Alfredo Sauce 53
Cauliflower Pizza Crust 193
Cheddar Bacon Burst 108
Cheese & Egg Breakfast Sandwich 17
Cheese Cake 179
Cheese Stuffed Roasted Peppers 233
Cheesy and Creamy Corn 68
Cheesy Stuffed Chicken 240
Cheesy Taco bites 154
Cheesy Tomato Chicken 64
Cherry, Chocolate, and Almond Shake 33
Cherry-Glazed Lamb Chops 144
Chia Coco Pudding 169
Chicken & Tofu 55
Chicken breast on vegetable noodles 96
Chicken Cacciatore 55
Chicken in Tomato Juice 60
Chicken Mac & Cheese 49
Chicken Marsala 240
Chicken Thighs 78
Chicken Zucchini Patties with Salsa 240
Chili Lime Salmon 214
Chili Sin Carne 219
Chilled Cantaloupe Soup 158
Chipotle Chili Pork Chops 141
Chipotle Spicy Fish Tacos 72
Choco Peppermint Cake 177
Chocolate Apple Cake 161
Chocolate Chip Cookies 172
Chocolate Fudge Nut Cake 163
Chocolate Layer Cake with Fluffy White Frosting 189
Chocolate Mousse with Raspberries 183
Chocolate Orange Soufflé 183
Chocolate Walnut Brownies 164
Chocolate-Zucchini Muffins 37

Flavors Cioppino 238
Flawless Pork Chops 130
Flax seed Crackers 155
Flourless Chocolate Cake 178
Foil-Wrapped Haddock 66
Four-Bean Field Stew 209
French Onion Chicken & Vegetables 241
Fresh Pot Pork Butt 143
Fresh Strawberry Granita 159
Fried Tofu Hotpot 219
Frozen Lemon & Blueberry 175
Fruit and Nut Muesli 188
Fruit Pizza 177
Full English breakfast 195

G

Garlic Chicken Balls 106
Garlic Egg Noodles 226
Garlic Parmesan Air Fryer Asparagus 210
Garlic Rosemary Lamb Chops 63
Garlic Shrimp with Sun Dried Tomatoes 84
Garlicky Clams 53
Garlicky Creole Shrimp 66
Ginger Blackberry Bliss Smoothie Bowl 25
Ginger Cake 227
Glass chicken salad with fruits 97
Glazed Carrots and Cauliflower 111
Glazed Ham Balls 130
Gluten-Free Carrot and Oat Pancakes 38
Goat Cheese and Avocado Toast 42
Grandma Sue's Sugar-Free Simple Mocha Chocolate Cake 183
Greek Chicken Kebabs 197
Greek Flat Iron Steaks 122
Greek Lamb Pita Pockets 196
Greek Yogurt Sundae 36
Greek-Style Green Beans 114
Greek-Style Roasted Tomatoes with Feta 235
Greek-Style Vegetable Bake 236
Green Bean Casserole 113
Green omelette with smoked salmon 96
Grilled Chicken Wraps 241
Grilled Herbed Salmon with Raspberry Sauce & Cucumber Dill Dip 50

Grilled Lamb Chops 117
Grilled Lemon Butter Salmon Kebobs 74
Grilled Peach and Coconut Yogurt Bowls 187
Grilled Tuna Steaks 85
Ground Turkey, Asparagus and Basil 75

H

Halibut with Lime and Cilantro 104
Ham and Cheese English muffin Melt 15
Ham in Cider 131
Ham-Potatoes Green Bean Casserole 131
Harvest Blackberry Quinoa Bowl 35
Healthy and Tasty Strawberry Sherbet 160
Healthy Chicken Kale Soup 199
Healthy Chocolate Ice Cream 180
Healthy Spinach Soup 200
Heart-Healthy Yogurt Parfaits 25
Hearty Pumpkin Chicken Soup 89
Herb Lamb Chops 117
Herb Tomato Soup 202
Herbed Chicken Meal 88
Herbed Meatballs 145
High-Protein Oatmeal 35
Homemade Noodles 188
Homemade Pasta 190
Homemade Turkey Breakfast Sausage 40
Honeydew Blueberry Soup 158
Honeysuckle Pineapple 157
Huevos Rancheros 23
Hummus and Salad Pita Flats 74

I

Ice Cream Brownie Cake 176
Instant Pot Cinnamon Apricot and Pears 112
Irish Lamb Stew 110
Irish Pork Roast 124
Italian Beef 126
Italian bun 30
Italian Pork Chops 90
Italian Steamed Mussels 85
Italian Tofu Scramble 114

J

Jalapeño Potato Hash 23
Jambalaya 85